McGraw-Hill Series in Nuclear Engineering

WALTER H. ZINN, *Consulting Editor*

JEROME D. LUNTZ, *Associate Consulting Editor*

CONTROL OF NUCLEAR REACTORS AND POWER PLANTS

McGraw-Hill Series in Nuclear Engineering

WALTER H. ZINN, *Consulting Editor*

JEROME D. LUNTZ, *Associate Consulting Editor*

BENEDICT AND PIGFORD · Nuclear Chemical Engineering

BONILLA · Nuclear Engineering

SCHULTZ · Control of Nuclear Reactors and Power Plants

(Other books in preparation)

Control of Nuclear Reactors and Power Plants

M. A. SCHULTZ

Physics, Instrumentation and
Control Department, Westinghouse Electric
Corporation, Pittsburgh, Pennsylvania

McGRAW-HILL BOOK COMPANY, INC.

New York   Toronto   London

1955

CONTROL OF NUCLEAR REACTORS AND POWER PLANTS

Library of Congress Catalog Card Number 55–7283

III

THE MAPLE PRESS COMPANY, YORK, PA.

PREFACE

This preface is being written as President Eisenhower waves the wand to start construction of the first commercial nuclear power plant at Shippingport, Pennsylvania. This event, symbolizing the entrance of the age of nuclear power, focuses attention on the background of nuclear-power-plant control. Historically, the early nuclear-reactor-control designers were concerned only with the similarity of the reactor to a bomb. The problems they faced were ones of safety and of complete distrust for refined control elements. The legend is told in the industry that in the first reactor, constructed under the west stands of the University of Chicago stadium, there existed, in addition to the normal pneumatic safety-rod mechanism, another safety rod suspended by a rope, with a hatchet placed conveniently nearby. The progress in nuclear control from this point to where useful power could be safely handled has been monumental. Now, in this new age, the problem is simply stated: Given a nuclear power plant, what is the best way of controlling it? The answer is presented in engineering terms similar to those used in any complex control problem. The newly developed techniques of servomechanisms are quickly brought forth as a basic design method, and now a nuclear power plant, a jet engine, or a guided missile is treated with confident engineering certainty.

This book, one record of nuclear-control progress, is therefore largely in elementary servo form and language. Some concessions are made to the nuclear physicist in recognition of the essential partnership involved between the physicist and control engineer in the design of a control system for a nuclear power plant. The entire field of reactor and power-plant control is far from covered in this book. Only one specific type of reactor, the solid-fuel heterogeneous reactor, is used for descriptive and illustrative purposes. More complication is generally involved in the design of plants containing different reactors such as circulating-fuel homogeneous reactors. However, the basic techniques for the solution of the nuclear-control problem are presented in such a manner that the design of control systems for other types of reactor plants may be obtained by extension of the methods presented.

At this point it is customary to acknowledge a few of one's coworkers in the field and to ignore the remainder as being too numerous to men-

v

tion.   Because of the pioneering efforts of the small and somewhat closed fraternity of engineers in this new industry, I should very much like to acknowledge the tremendous historic labors of my associates in this field.

First, since all the present activity in this country in the field of nuclear power plants is under the direction of the United States Atomic Energy Commission, most of the references originally came from the basic work accomplished under the commission.   Grateful acknowledgment is made to the AEC for permission to publish this material.   Second, I should like to thank the Westinghouse Electric Corporation for supplying me with the necessary educational background for this project.   I should also like to thank Westinghouse and Radiation Counter Laboratories for the use of some of the illustrations used in this book.   Finally, I must mention specifically the people at various AEC-sponsored projects who have directly or indirectly contributed.

At Westinghouse I am particularly grateful to J. N. Grace for his basic work, assistance, and criticism.   I have borrowed liberally from my friends and colleagues G. Anderson, W. Baer, R. T. Bayard, G. Conley, J. C. Connor, R. C. Cunningham, R. Durnal, F. Engel, W. Esselman, T. Fairey, J. Franz, E. F. Frisch, W. Hamilton, A. Henry, J. Kostalos, R. Leonard, H. McCreary, W. Pagels, W. Ramage, V. Shaw, J. C. Simonds, C. Single, G. Stubbs, O. Swift, S. Wallach, and J. Wolff.

At the General Electric Company's Knolls Atomic Power Laboratories the initial servomechanism concept of the reactor transfer function was achieved by J. Owens and J. Piggott.   E. Wade of this laboratory also made many contributions to reactor-control instrumentation.

I am indebted to my friend W. Pease, formerly of the Massachusetts Institute of Technology, for my initial education in the control of nuclear reactors.   He, of course, was responsible for the automatic control design of the Brookhaven reactor.

At the Argonne National Laboratory J. M. Harrer, J. Dietrich, J. Deshong, and D. Krukoff, among others, were responsible for the tremendous effort to make an engineering science of reactor control.   It was their initial work on the oscillation of a reactor that gave the servo engineer respectability in the nuclear field.

At the Oak Ridge National Laboratory T. Cole and W. Jordan were always of assistance to me on power-plant-control problems while they pioneered with their colleagues on the Materials Testing Reactor control system.

My thanks go to J. Newgard, R. Longini, and W. Brazeale for reading this book in manuscript form.

M. A. SCHULTZ

CONTENTS

vii

CHAPTER 1

INTRODUCTION

1-1. Introduction and Purpose. At present the state of nuclear power plants in this country is a fluid one, with many technical ramifications being entwined with political considerations. Nevertheless, in the fields of reactor and nuclear-plant control several ideas have been crystallized and are already regarded in terms of long-standing theory. As there is no universal agreement regarding the best type of power plant, there obviously can be no agreement as to the best type of control system. Each reactor plant that has been built thus far contains a different control system. These control systems differ radically in mechanical design, but many common theoretical problems and basic design concepts have arisen. An attempt will be made in this text to present these common points.

Another aim of this book is to present an elementary picture of reactor and nuclear-plant control for the new group of control engineers now entering this field. Historically, nuclear power plants grew from nuclear reactors, which in turn grew from basic nuclear physics. The detailed understanding of the design and synthesis of a nuclear reactor is a complex subject steeped in intricate mathematics and clothed in security. It is fortunate that the control problems of nuclear reactors can be handled by simplified conventional methods which are now familiar to those in the servomechanisms field. However, it is often necessary for the control designer to make certain assumptions and simplifications concerning nuclear reactors, which in some cases may create concern on the part of the nuclear physicists that they and the control designers are not talking about the same terms.

It is now generally recognized that the nuclear-power business is in a transition stage from the physicists to the engineers. The plants that have been constructed are as complex in their own way as are the basic physical equations upon which the reactors are founded. The engineer therefore tends to regard the reactor only as a component in a much larger system, and consequently he deals with it in conventional engineering terms which are compatible with the rest of the system. The phys-

1

icist in turn has been more concerned with the intricate details of the internal reactor structure and tends to regard the plant as an auxiliary device which is a necessary evil.

The problem of reactor control has existed since the first reactor and has been the subject of extensive study for many years. The problem of nuclear plant control is a newer one, and the answers are not as well known.

1-2. Analogy of a Nuclear Power Plant to a Direct-current-generator System. Let us consider a reactor operating by itself serving no function other than perpetuating a chain reaction. This type of operation might be compared with the open-circuit no-load operation of a d-c generator. Tying a load onto the reactor and extracting power from it would corre-

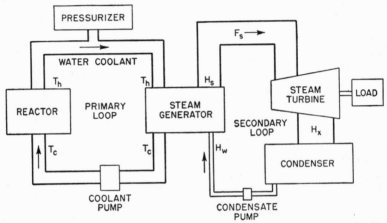

FIG. 1-1. Block diagram of elementary nuclear power plant containing pressurized water reactor and conventional steam system.

spond to tying a load onto the d-c generator. In the case of the generator it would easily be anticipated that the load would affect the generator characteristics. Historically, it was not quite so apparent that the power plant would affect the characteristics of the reactor. This reaction could occur in a complex plant from many sources. Even minor auxiliary devices could find their performances reflected back on the basic reactor performance. In order to gain a better appreciation of this problem from an over-all point of view, the reactor plant, d-c generator analogy can be pursued further by an illustrative example.

1-3. Example of Analogy of a Nuclear Power Plant to a Direct-current-generator System.[1]† Let us assume that our nuclear power plant consists of a pressurized water-cooled reactor system and a conven-

† Superior numerals in the text correspond to the numbered References at the end of each chapter.

tional steam-turbine system as shown in Fig. 1-1.   In this plant high-pressure water is used to cool the reactor and extract heat from it.   This heat is transferred to the secondary loop in a steam-generator system consisting of a boiler and a steam separator.   The output loop of the plant contains a steam turbine, condenser, and all the necessary auxiliaries.   The turbine is directly coupled to a load, in this case presumably an electric generator.   Both the primary coolant and steam systems are closed loops.

Control Program.   Many types of programs of primary and secondary parameters can be set up for a plant of this sort, depending upon the components and local specifications.   As a direct relationship exists between the water temperatures of the primary loop and the steam temperature and pressure of the secondary loop, a control program may be specified from either loop.   For the purpose of this discussion the plant operation will be specified from the primary loop in terms of the coolant temperatures at the reactor inlet and at the reactor outlet as functions of power level.   The following symbols are used:

Q = total reactor power output
T_h = coolant temperature at reactor outlet
T_c = coolant temperature at boiler outlet
T_{av} = average coolant temperature = $(T_h + T_c)/2$
T_s = steam temperature at outlet of steam generator
p_s = absolute steam pressure at outlet of steam generator
H_s = enthalpy of steam at outlet of steam generator
H_x = enthalpy of exhaust steam at turbine outlet, for isentropic expansion
H_w = enthalpy of feed water
F_s = rate of steam flow

Let us assume that our control program is such that the average temperature of the primary loop coolant is held constant regardless of the load requirements of the secondary portion of the plant.   This so-called constant-T_{av} program causes no change in primary coolant volume as the power output is changed, and a small simple water pressurizer may be used.   The flow of water created by the pump is at a fixed rate and does not change as a function of the power level.   The specific relationships between the primary and secondary temperatures of this type of plant control are shown in Fig. 1-2, for the arbitrary condition of $T_{av} = 500°F$.   It can be seen in this plant that the steam temperatures fall off very rapidly as the power output is increased.   This fall in steam temperature calls for a corresponding drop in steam pressure.

Thermodynamic Analysis.   In analyzing this plant it can be seen that the power output of the reactor is proportional to $T_h - T_c$.   The constant primary coolant flow is assumed such that, again using arbitrary numbers, at full output of the reactor $T_h - T_c = 50°F$. The power transferred from the primary-coolant water to the secondary loop is proportional to $T_{av} - T_s$. The proportionality constant depends on the power rating and on the boiler dimensions. For illustrative purposes let us again assume that at unity power $T_{av} - T_s = 60°F$, which will be designated as rated full power. The numerical values of all these tem-

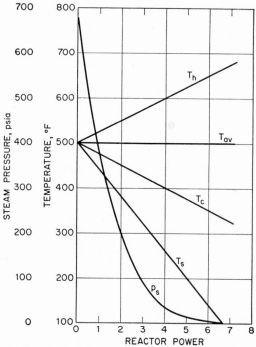

FIG. 1-2. Temperature and pressure control conditions for plant having constant-T_{av} program.

peratures are the ones given in Fig. 1-2. In this elementary plant the steam leaving the steam generator is of high quality, but it is not superheated. However, we can assume that the steam generator furnishes dry and saturated steam at all power levels. The steam pressure then depends only on the steam temperature and may be obtained from steam tables.

If we assume that the changes in potential energy and kinetic energy of the steam are negligible compared with changes in enthalpy throughout the steam loop, the power delivered to any component becomes simply $F_s \Delta H$, where F_s (lb/hr) is the steam-flow rate and ΔH (Btu/lb) is the enthalpy drop across the component. Then F_s, H_w, and H_x can be calculated, and the turbine output power may be plotted as a function of reactor power. The normalized output power and efficiencies are plotted in Fig. 1-3. The curves represent fully the over-all steady-state performance of this type of nuclear power plant.

The Electrical Analogue of the Constant-T_{av} Program. The most direct d-c generator analogue for the situation just described is to permit enthalpy drop ΔH to be represented by a voltage drop ΔV and the steam flow F_s by a current I. The product $F_s \Delta H$ represents power, as does the product $I \Delta V$. The d-c circuit that is roughly analogous to the nuclear power plant is shown as Fig. 1-4. This circuit has a source of power, a power-consuming section representing condenser loss, and a load representing shaft power. These three components are in series since the components of the steam loop are in series. The reactor and steam generator are simulated by the d-c generator. The generated voltage corresponding to $H_s - H_w$ drops about 10 percent from no load to maximum load. The condenser is represented by an opposing battery and resistor. The battery is used because the power lost in the condenser is more nearly proportional to F_s than to F_s^2. The turbine is represented by a variable resistance. The output characteristics of this analogous plant are given in Fig. 1-5, and they roughly approximate the plant characteristics shown in Fig. 1-3.

From the above analogy it can be seen that the steady-state over-all plant performance of a nuclear power plant is not too dissimilar from that of conventional systems. It can also be seen that in the particular type of plant control presented, the control is strongly related to steam-plant control and the role of reactor control is apt to be a subservient one. The nuclear-power-plant-control engineer thus finds that his education must be a mixture of nuclear physics and servomechanisms with a strong overtone of conventional thermodynamics.

1-4. Philosophy of Reactor and Plant Control. Before setting out to design a specific reactor plant, the designer of the control system must have a complete philosophy of operation in mind. Up to the present this philosophy has been the one in which the control system as well as all other auxiliary components must be supersafe. The peculiar position of nuclear power plants has been such that if one were to blow up inadvertently, the resulting publicity would severely harm the entire program of nuclear power for several years. For this reason it is to be anticipated that control-system design philosophy in the future will also be of the supersafe variety.

It should be pointed out that technically possible accidents which might occur in a nuclear power plant are not so severe as might first be imagined. It is popularly thought that the principal difference between an "atomic bomb" and a nuclear power plant is one of control—in the first case the energy is given off instantly, in the second case it is given off slowly. In the event of a failure of the control system the obvious thought is that the power plant might become a bomb. Hurwitz[2] has indicated that a con-

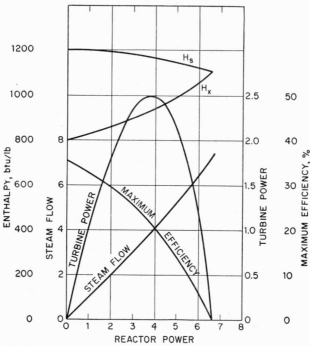

FIG. 1-3. Performance of constant-T_{av} plant as a function of reactor power output.

siderable matter of degree is involved in a nuclear-reactor accident. Roughly, the damage caused in a reactor accident would approximate the damage caused by an amount of TNT equivalent in weight to the amount of uranium in the nuclear reactor. This accident obviously creates less damage than the destruction wrought by an atomic bomb. But from a philosophical point of view, it will undoubtedly be many years before nuclear power plants are regarded by the public in the same classification as other industrial plants. Consequently, every effort must still be expended to obtain supersafe control systems.

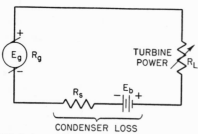

FIG. 1-4. Analogous d-c-generator system.

Conventional Power-station and Airplane Philosophies. Under this given supersafe over-all philosophy of operation, two subphilosophies of reactor shutdown are available to the control designer. These sub-philosophies may be called the conventional power-station philosophy and the airplane philosophy. In the conventional power-station philosophy, the generator and other expensive items in the circuit must, in the event of a significant component failure in any portion of the plant, be disconnected and shut down at once in order to protect the large investment involved. Other machines are easily available to take up the load, and no great harm is done by taking any one machine off the

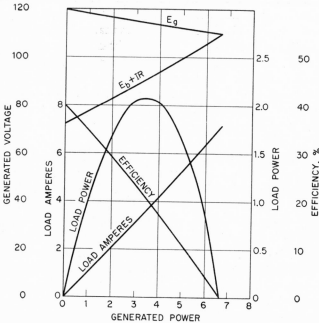

FIG. 1-5. Performance of d-c-generator system as a function of generated power.

line. In the case of a hypothetical nuclear power-generating station, under this philosophy the reactor would be shut down as fast as possible, not only for the above reason but also because if it were not shut down, it would be likely to aggravate any failure situation by continuing to pour out power.

In the airplane type of philosophy, component failures must protect themselves, and components, including reactors, must fail in such a manner as not to endanger the system. In other words, the airplane engine cannot be shut off for any external cause or the entire structure may be lost. Both these philosophies are available to present-day nuclear-power-plant designers, and the one that should be used obviously depends upon the specified operating situations of the plant. That these philosophies affect basic design is quite apparent.   In a given plant, for example, the desire to protect the reactor may be so strong that all of the reactor instrumentation might be provided in triplicate, while in the remainder of the plant only single-channel instrumentation would be used.

Automatic-control Philosophy.   Another philosophical point that must be determined quite early in the design of a reactor-power-plant control system is the degree of automatic control desired.   Here again the ultimate usage of the plant greatly affects the decision.   For example, a military plant might conceivably have less automation than a central station nuclear power plant, on the grounds that operating costs for labor are not particularly important in the military plant.   In considering over-all safety, the proposition has been advanced for extensive use of automatic control rather than manual control, on the basis that, although automatic systems have been known to fail, they can be made to fail safely.   When an automatic system is operating properly, it never makes a mistake.   The same cannot be said for the human being as a control element.

1-5. Control-system Specification.   It is interesting to note at this point that the nuclear-plant-control designer does not specify many of the basic conditions that he has to meet.   The reactor designer will specify the amount of heat that can be taken from the reactor and how much overload for how long a period of time will be permitted.   The pump designer will specify how much cooling fluid can be circulated. The boiler designer will specify given steam temperatures and pressure ranges.   The metallurgist will specify maximum temperatures throughout the plant, which must not be exceeded if excessive corrosions and strains are not to exist.

The control-system designer must tie all these factors together in individual and over-all control loops in such a manner that everyone is satisfied.   Then he conceivably has time to ask himself the inevitable question: Is it stable?   Fortunately, as will be shown later, most nuclear power plants are inherently stable, but it is well known that even the most stable basic system can be upset by improper detailed control design.

1-6. Scope of Text.   The ultimate scope of this book is to lead new nuclear-reactor-control designers to the final stage of obtaining an over-all picture of the requirements of nuclear-power-plant-control design. It is assumed that the reader has a basic knowledge of the elementary processes of reactor physics.[3]   This text will first present a review of the elementary physics of reactor control.   Engineering symbols are used in this review, and very little hint as to the complex basic physics problems involved is presented.   Rather, the reactor is regarded as a "black box" and its performance described by simple external measurements.   Once this physical picture is established, a mathematical presentation of the response of a basic reactor to various types of driving functions is presented, and the transfer function of the reactor is derived for future use as an element in a control system. A reactor control loop is then presented, and its response to transient disturbances studied. Since a particularly interesting and critical element of the reactor control loop is the actual output-control mechanism, a diversion is taken at this point to describe the reactor control requirements and to present some examples of present-day practices. The stage has now been set for a short glance at over-all plant control, and some of the basic problems of plant response and programming will be looked at.

The details of some of the special reactor components that are not familiar to the control designer will then be studied. Nuclear instrumentation is pursued and its problems are presented. The operation of a nuclear power plant is then investigated because it can be shown that certain types of operations affect the individual control-element design. Startup problems, power range operational problems, and shutdown problems are given. Finally, because it is realized that an inescapable urge often exists on the part of any designer to try out his device, Chap. 11 deals with electronic plant simulators. By means of these computing machines the hazards existing with attempts to try out a new device on an actual reactor plant may be eliminated.

REFERENCES

1. Schultz, M. A., and J. N. Grace: A Simple Analogy to a Nuclear Power Plant, *WAPD-T*-38, Westinghouse Atomic Power Division, Pittsburgh, Pa. Declassified, June, 1953.
2. Hurwitz, H., Jr.: Safeguard Considerations for Nuclear Power Plants, "Proceedings of the 1953 Conference on Nuclear Engineering," University of California Press, Berkeley, Calif., 1953.
3. Glasstone, S., and M. C. Edlund: "The Elements of Nuclear Reactor Theory," D. Van Nostrand Company, Inc., New York, 1952.

CHAPTER 2

ELEMENTARY PHYSICS OF REACTOR CONTROL

In this chapter a simplified description of reactors and reactor processes is presented in order to introduce reactor control terminology. It is presumed that some text on reactor physics or engineering[1-3] has been studied previously by the control engineer. The terminology presented is only the barest minimum required for control purposes. In instances where the control engineer is dealing superficially with a reactor, he does not need to know exact derivations of physical parameters. Consequently, some of the terminology hereby defined is loose and not to be interpreted exactly. References 1 to 3 may be used for more rigid definitions.

2-1. Description of a Reactor. The rudimentary parts of a power reactor are shown in Fig. 2-1. In the center section of the reactor is

Controls a number of
Neutrons in core

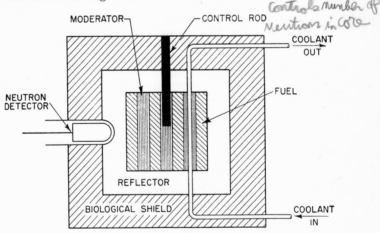

FIG. 2-1. Elementary components of a power reactor.

located the fuel, which consists of uranium, either uranium 235 or uranium 238. Either isotope may be used alone or in combination, depending upon the design of the reactor. In this book the fuel is considered to be in a fixed solid form. A description of the control of circulating-fuel reactors or others in nonsolid form will not be attempted. The fuel is in close proximity to, and intermingled with, a moderating material such as hydrogen, beryllium, or any suitable light element. The moderating material is used to slow down fission neutrons to where they possess the desired energy spectrum. The combination of fuel, moderator, and associated structural components will be called the core. Passing through the core and in intimate contact with it is a heat-transfer material. Gases, water, or liquid metals may be used as the heat-transfer material. The moderator may also be circulated through the core and serve as the heat-transfer material. Outside the core proper is a reflector which is used to conserve neutrons and "bounce" them back into the core in an optical reflector sense. Surrounding the reflector is a biological shield which serves the purpose of attenuating the radiations emanating from the core. This shield is usually a combination shield which attenuates both neutrons and gamma rays. Inside the core or the reflector are located the control rods, the basic purpose of which is to regulate the power level of the core by controlling the number of neutrons in it.

2-2. Fission Process. Inside the core there exists an initial source of neutrons from some radioactive decay process. When a neutron of a given energy is absorbed by a uranium nucleus, there is a finite probability of splitting this nucleus into two or more fragments. This process is called fission, and a large amount of energy is produced in this fission process (approximately 200 Mev per fission). In the act of fission two to three neutrons are released from the fragmentation, and these neutrons are capable of creating more fissions in other uranium nuclei under the proper conditions. The two to three neutrons that are produced in fission may take part in several reactions, all of which are competitive. A neutron may be absorbed in core material other than uranium. It may be lost to the core by leaking out of the system. In any event, for a chain reaction to take place, for each uranium nucleus capturing a neutron and undergoing fission, a minimum of one neutron on the average must be produced, which in turn creates the fission of another nucleus.

Reactor Types. A nuclear reactor, then, is a system usually consisting of a moderator, a fuel containing fissionable material, heat-removing means, and a geometric structure in which a chain reaction can be maintained. In the fission process so-called fast neutrons are produced. These fast neutrons have high energies. Inside the reactor these neutrons may suffer scattering collisions, mainly elastic, as a result of which their energy is decreased. And as mentioned, they may also be absorbed by the various materials in the system or be lost through escape from it. Depending upon the relative amounts and nature of the moderator, fuel, other substances, geometrical arrangement, and the dimensions of the system, the main portion of the neutron absorptions by uranium leading to fission will take place within a certain energy range.

If most of the fissions result from the capture of neutrons which have been slowed down to thermal energies by collisions with the moderating material, the so-called thermal neutrons, the system is referred to as a thermal reactor. When most of the fission processes are caused by the absorption of neutrons of higher energy, sometimes called intermediate neutrons, the term intermediate reactor is used. The usual range of neutron energies in an intermediate reactor is from thermal energy up to about 1,000 ev. If the main source of fissions is the capture of fast neutrons directly by the fuel without the neutrons having suffered any energy losses, the system is called a fast reactor. Power reactors in general are of thermal and intermediate types; fast reactors are usually used in weapons and will not be discussed further.

Multiplication Factor. The chain reaction condition that each uranium nucleus capturing a neutron and undergoing fission must ultimately yield a minimum of one neutron, which in turn also causes fission, leads to a definition of a multiplication factor k. The multiplication factor k may be defined as the ratio of the number of neutrons in any one generation to the number of corresponding neutrons of the immediately preceding generation. If k is equal to or slightly greater than unity, a chain reaction can take place. If k is less than unity, the chain reaction cannot persist and will ultimately die down.

For the chain reaction in the core to keep going, the production of neutrons must equal the leakage plus the absorption of the neutrons. Therefore $k = \text{production}/(\text{leakage} + \text{absorption})$. In this text the symbol k will be used to refer to the multiplication factor of the so-called infinite pile, in some texts referred to as k_{inf}. The term $k - 1$ is defined as k_{ex} (k excess) and again is usually rigorously used in conjunction with an infinite pile. The term k_{ex} represents the amount the multiplication differs from unity, and as most reactors operate around unity, k_{ex} gives a more accurate picture as to the state of the reactor.

The more common multiplication factor which is used in conjunction with specific reactors is k_{eff} (k effective), which is the effective multiplication factor for a given finite-sized reactor. Reactivity is defined for a finite specific reactor in a similar manner to k_{ex} as

$$\rho = \frac{k_{eff} - 1}{k_{eff}} \tag{2-1}$$

In this text the symbol δk will be used for reactivity, meaning the amount the multiplication factor of a specific reactor differs from unity or

$$\delta k = \rho = \frac{k_{eff} - 1}{k_{eff}} \tag{2-2}$$

From an engineering point of view these terms are generally used in the neighborhood of a multiplication factor of unity. For control problems of a general nature k and k_{eff} have been used in the past interchangeably, and k_{ex} and δk have similarly been loosely interchanged. The cause of this confusion stems from the fact that for control purposes the internal structure of the reactor and the details of the multiplication in the core are not important. The control designer obtains his information from external measurements of an over-all type. To him the reactor has a given multiplication factor. He usually does not concern himself about the size, shape, and composition of the reactor.

Neutron Lifetime. The average time between successive neutron generations in an infinite reactor is defined as the neutron lifetime l. The symbol l^* is used for the mean effective lifetime of a neutron in a finite reactor containing uranium 235. In other words, l^* is the mean time which elapses from when neutrons are produced in fission until they return again to fission or are lost to the reaction. The term l^* may be considered as

$$l^* = \frac{l}{k} \tag{2-3}$$

Again, strictly speaking, this equation is the result of a "one-group" theory calculation, or it applies rigorously only to large reactors.[1]

2-3. Neutron Level. The excess of neutrons in a finite reactor from one generation over the preceding generation is then δk. If there are initially n neutrons per cubic centimeter present in the core, the rate of increase in each generation is $n\delta k$. If l^* is the effective time between succeeding generations,

$$\frac{dn}{dt} = \frac{\delta k}{l^*} n \tag{2-4}$$

and integrating this equation yields

$$n = n_0 e^{(\delta k/l^*)t} \tag{2-5}$$

where n_0 is the number of neutrons per cubic centimeter initially and n is the number after a lapse of time t. On this basis the number of neutrons rises exponentially with time if the effective multiplication factor is greater than unity.

The number of neutrons in the core is proportional to the number of fissions occurring, and for 3×10^{10} fissions per second 1 watt of power is produced. The power output of a reactor then is proportional to the number of neutrons in the core in any given time interval, and the symbol n is used to designate neutron level, with the implication that a power level is involved.

2-4. Reactor Period. The period of a reactor can arbitrarily be defined as

$$\text{Period} = \frac{1}{(1/n)(dn/dt)} \tag{2-6}$$

with the inverse reactor period $(1/n)(dn/dt)$ being the quantity usually measured. We can solve for the period of the reactor of Eq. (2-5), where $n = n_0 e^{(\delta k/l^*)t}$, and find

$$\text{Period} = \frac{l^*}{\delta k} = T \qquad \text{sec} \tag{2-7}$$

Therefore in terms of period, Eq. (2-5) becomes $n = n_0 e^{t/T}$. An alternate definition of reactor period may now be given. The period of a reactor is that amount of time which the reactor would take to change its level by a factor of $e = 2.716$. It will be observed that the period of a reactor is a dynamic quantity. That is, when the reactor is in operation at a fixed power level, the period is infinite. Only when the reactor is changing its level is there a finite measurable period.

2-5. Reactor State. The state of a reactor at any given instant is defined by the use of the multiplication factor. When $k = 1$, the reactor is said to be critical, $k < 1$ subcritical, and $k > 1$ supercritical. It will be noted that no power level is involved in the definition of criticality. A reactor may be critical at a level of 1 watt or a megawatt.

Delayed Neutrons. In the above equations it has been assumed that all the neutrons created in the fission process were given off instantly and had a lifetime of l. Actually a small fraction of the neutrons created in fission are given off at discrete amounts of time after the actual fission process occurs. These neutrons which are produced after fissioning represent approximately 0.75 percent of the total neutrons produced and are called delayed neutrons. The heart of reactor control depends upon delayed neutrons. Table 2-1 indicates the properties of the delayed neu-

TABLE 2-1. Properties of Delayed Neutrons Given Off in U²³⁵ Fission Process by Thermal Neutrons

Mean life t_i, sec	Decay constant λ_i, sec⁻¹	Fraction of total neutrons β_i
0.071	14.0	0.00025
0.62	1.61	0.00084
2.19	0.456	0.0024
6.50	0.151	0.0021
31.7	0.0315	0.0017
80.2	0.0124	0.00026

trons which are given off in the uranium 235 fission process by thermal neutrons.[4,5,7] The delayed neutrons are given off in six distinct groups at different times and in different quantities. The symbol β is used to denote the total fraction of the delayed neutrons with β_i being the fraction of the delayed neutrons in the ith group of delayed neutrons. Similarly, λ_i represents the decay constant of the ith group of delayed neutrons. For certain problems it is convenient to treat all of the delayed neutrons as a single delayed group having a total fraction $\beta = 0.0075$ and an average decay constant $\lambda = 0.1 \text{ sec}^{-1}$.

2-6. Prompt Critical. When the effective multiplication factor of a reactor is 1.0075, the reactor is said to be prompt critical.* This statement means that the reactor would be capable of sustaining a chain reaction without the use of the delayed neutrons. If k is greater than 1.0075, extremely rapid exponential multiplication of reactor power level results. For this reason most control systems attempt to prevent k from ever becoming greater than 1.0075.

2-7. Subcritical Level Operation. Let us assume that we have a neutron-multiplying medium which has a multiplication factor $k < 1$ and a given neutron lifetime l, as shown in Fig. 2-2. A control rod which may be considered merely a device for absorbing neutrons, and thus ensuring that our multiplying medium is subcritical, may also be added. Let us insert in this medium a source of neutrons. Such sources exist in nature naturally from cosmic rays, or neutrons may be artificially provided from radio-active isotopic mixtures such as radium beryllium or polonium beryllium.

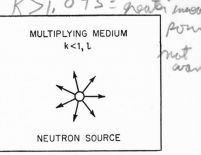

FIG. 2-2. Black-box representation of a subcritical reactor having a multiplication factor k and a mean neutron lifetime l.

Under the condition of subcriticality it can be shown simply that the number of neutrons which exist in this multiplying medium at the end of a sufficiently long interval of time is

$$n = n_0(1 + k + k^2 + \cdots + k^{m-1}) \tag{2-8}$$

or in closed form

$$\frac{n}{n_0} = \frac{1 - k^m}{1 - k} \tag{2-9}$$

At the end of a sufficiently long interval of time for $k < 1$, this equation degenerates into

$$\frac{n}{n_0} = \frac{1}{1 - k} \tag{2-10}$$

* This definition is for a thermal reactor containing U^{235} fuel.

This ratio is known as the subcritical multiplication factor, and all reactors exhibit this effect. The result of this equation is shown graphically in Fig. 2-3 for a source suddenly inserted into a multiplying medium. With a k of 0.5 in the multiplying medium, the number of neutrons consequently levels off at the end of several lifetimes l to a value of $n/n_0 = 2$. The subcritical multiplication factor of this reactor then is 2. If one were to change k to 0.9 by removing part of the control rod from the medium, the subcritical multiplication would ultimately be 10, and so on. As k approaches 1, the subcritical multiplication factor approaches infinity and the number of neutrons in the medium rises in a straight line

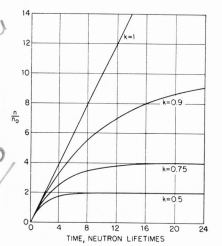

FIG. 2-3. Subcritical multiplication.

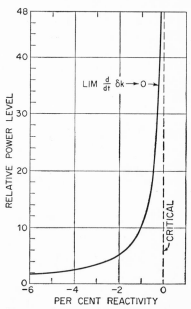

FIG. 2-4. Relative power level as a function of reactivity remaining in the reactor for infinitely slow reactivity change.

with time. It will be observed that as the subcritical multiplication factor becomes higher and higher, more time is always taken for the medium to settle out at a given level. And finally it does not settle out at all but continues to rise. This situation holds only if there is a source present. Without an actual source, the neutron level in any subcritical medium must ultimately die down to zero.

Let us now examine how the power level changes in this subcritical reactor as we increase the k of the medium slowly toward unity by removing the control rods. The simplest case is to consider pulling the rods at an infinitely slow rate, and in this case the total multiplication is always the subcritical multiplication. Because the withdrawal rate is so slow, the decay times of even the longest-lived delayed emitters are short in comparison with the time for a noticeable reactivity change. Therefore all the delayed neutrons have ample time to be emitted before the power changes appreciably. The number of neutrons present then conforms at each instant to the subcritical multiplication formula of Eq. (2-10). Figure 2-4 shows the neutron-level build-up under this condition. The curve is a true hyperbola and approaches criticality asymptotically. The curve is plotted so that when $k = 0.9$ the power level is 1.

2-8. Subcritical Period. The period that results from this very slow pulling rate can be obtained from the definition of period of Eq. (2-6). Performing the suggested differentiation on the subcritical multiplication formula results in the expression

$$\text{Period} = \frac{1 - k}{dk/dt} \tag{2-11}$$

From this expression it can be seen that if the rate of change of k is constant with time, then the period decreases directly as the reactivity remaining in the reactor becomes smaller. For our example of extremely slow rod pulling at a constant time rate of change, the period approaches zero as the medium approaches criticality.

2-9. Critical Operation. It will be recalled from the definition of criticality that $k = 1$ for this condition to exist. No mention was made of sources in this definition; consequently, although it may have been inferred that the power level of the medium was constant with $k = 1$, it is obvious from Sec. 2-7 that the source neutrons continue to add in and create a rising power level. From a practical point of view this phenomenon is noticeable only at extremely low operating levels and is useful in determining the operation of reactors in a low power condition. A reactor operating at a power level high enough to produce useful power represents at criticality a steady multiplication, by one, of billions of neutrons. The usual reactor source strength may vary from a few neutrons per second to possibly a few million neutrons per second. The number of neutrons involved in the source emission then is only a minute percentage of the number of neutrons involved in a power operation. Consequently, for all practical purposes at power operation, $k = 1$ represents a state of constant power level.

2-10. Supercritical Operation. Equation (2-5) indicates how a reactor behaves when $k > 1$ if all the neutrons were prompt. An illustrative example of the change of level under this condition may be given. Let us assume that we have a critical multiplying medium with an l^* of 10^{-3} sec. This is roughly the value of l^* for a large graphite moderated reactor. Now let us suddenly insert a reactivity change of $+\delta k = 0.003$

into the reactor.   Equation (2-5) then indicates that at the end of 3 sec
the power level will have risen by a factor of 8,000.

Let us now examine the situation when delayed neutrons are present.
Our neutron-level equation becomes of the form[6]

$$\frac{dn}{dt} = \frac{\delta k}{l^*}\, n - \frac{\beta}{l^*}\, n + \sum_{i=1}^{6} \lambda_i C_i \tag{2-12}$$

where C_i is the concentration of the delayed neutrons emitted of group i
and the other symbols have the same meanings as previously described.
C_i is defined by

$$\frac{dC_i}{dt} = \frac{\beta_i}{l^*}\, n - \lambda_i C_i \tag{2-13}$$

The rate of change of n has the contribution of the delayed neutrons
subtracted from the prompt neutrons, but of course the concentration of
delayed neutrons coming in from the past must be added to make up the
total rate of change.

Complete solutions to the above equations will be given in Chap. 3 for
various types of δk disturbances.   For comparison purposes and in order
to obtain a feeling for the effects of the delayed neutrons, it is interesting
to solve the approximate equations that result when the delayed neutrons
are assumed all to be bunched in one group which has an average value
of λ of 0.1 sec^{-1} (see Ref. 5). β_i then becomes β and C_i becomes C.
Let us also assume that δk is small so that k and k_{eff} can be used interchangeably.   Under these conditions, Eqs. (2-12) and (2-13) become

$$\frac{dn}{dt} = \frac{\delta k - \beta}{l^*}\, n + \lambda C \tag{2-14}$$

$$\frac{dC}{dt} = \frac{\beta}{l^*}\, n - \lambda C \tag{2-15}$$

The solution of these equations is a summation of two exponential terms
of the form[8]

$$\frac{n(t)}{n(0)} = \frac{b - c}{b - a}\, e^{at} + \frac{c - a}{b - a}\, e^{bt} \tag{2-16}$$

where

$$a = \frac{\delta k \lambda}{\lambda l^* + \beta - \delta k} \tag{2-17}$$

$$b = \frac{\delta k - \beta}{l^*} \tag{2-18}$$

$$c = \frac{\delta k}{l^*} \tag{2-19}$$

If the assumption is further made that, when practical numbers are used, product terms containing λ can be neglected, Eq. (2-16) becomes simply

$$\frac{n(t)}{n(0)} = \frac{\beta}{\beta - \delta k} \, e^{[\lambda \delta k/(\beta - \delta k)]t} - \frac{\delta k}{\beta - \delta k} \, e^{-[(\beta - \delta k)/l^*]t} \qquad (2\text{-}20)$$

In order to compare actual numbers with the prompt neutron example previously given, let us again insert a δk of $+0.003$ into a critical reactor having an l^* of 10^{-3} sec. Then

$$\frac{n(t)}{n(0)} = 1.67e^{0.067t} - 0.67e^{-4.5t} \qquad (2\text{-}21)$$

A plot of this result is shown in Fig. 2-5. The effect of the delayed neutrons is at once apparent. It will be recalled from Eq. (2-5) that with only prompt neutrons, the power level soared to 8,000 times the original level in 3 sec when $+0.003\delta k$ was inserted into the multiplying medium.

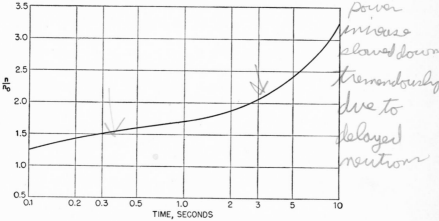

FIG. 2-5. Relative neutron level as a function of time for a step reactivity change of 0.003.

From Fig. 2-5 it can be seen that at the end of 3 sec the power level has risen by a factor of only 2.1. Thus the effect of a mere 0.75 percent of delayed neutrons is such as to make the entire problem of reactor control a simple feasible one rather than a most difficult if not impossible one.

An examination of the approximate equation (2-20) shows that the first term ultimately predominates, and after a few tenths of a second, the second term may be neglected. The second term contributes to what is called a transient period, whereas the first term creates a so-called stable reactor period. The stable period of Eq. (2-20) would then be

$$T = \frac{\beta - \delta k}{\lambda \delta k} = 15 \text{ sec} \qquad (2\text{-}22)$$

for the example just presented as against the prompt neutron period of Eq. (2-7)

$$T = \frac{l^*}{\delta k} = 0.33 \text{ sec} \qquad (2\text{-}23)$$

for the corresponding prompt neutron example.

2-11. Elementary Reactor Operation. The role of the control rods must now be examined in more detail. It will be recalled that the production of neutrons equals the leakage plus absorption for critical operation. If it is desired to change the production of neutrons, there are the two choices of manipulating either the leakage or the absorption. To change the leakage one might mechanically put a hole or a window in the reflector. Changing the multiplication by absorption is the more commonly used method, particularly for thermal reactors; and control rods of cadmium, boron steel, and other high-thermal-neutron-cross-section materials may be used to absorb neutrons from the reaction. It will be assumed that the control rods mentioned in this book are of the absorptive type and are located in the core unless otherwise specified.

Control rods may be moved in or out of the reactor singly or in banks. They are given various names according to their functions. Certain groups of rods may be designated as safety rods or shutoff rods. Other rods may be shim rods, whose function is to affect the power level in a coarse manner. A regulator rod is often used to cause fine changes in power level.

It will be recognized that a multiplication factor $k > 1$ must inherently be built into the reactor and then some reactivity removed by inserting control rods partially into the reactor in order to obtain critical operation. The total multiplication the multiplying medium possesses when the control rods are completely extracted minus one will be termed excess reactivity. One minus the total amount of reactivity in the medium when the control rods are completely inserted will be called the shutdown reactivity of the reactor.

Let us now examine the method of changing the power level in a simple reactor. Figure 2-6 illustrates the process. Assume that the reactor is initially critical at a low power level and it is desired to increase this level. The first step is to extract a control rod a small amount and change the multiplication factor k from 1 to a value slightly greater than 1. The neutron level then starts to rise, roughly in accordance with Eq. (2-20). As the power level rises and approaches the desired ultimate level, it is obvious that the control rod must then be inserted back to where $k = 1$. If no anticipation is provided in the system, it can be seen from Fig. 2-6 that the control rod must oscillate about the $k = 1$ position, but ultimately it will settle down at the original position from which it started. We have then a system in which the power level is independent of rod position, and in order to change power level one moves a control rod temporarily in or out of the medium and then returns it right back to its original position.

2-12. Depletion. The preceding reactor concept is the classic one of reactor control. It is recognized that control rods may have to be moved during the lifetime of a reactor because of fuel depletion. That is, as the uranium in the reactor is used up, the number of fissions occurring will

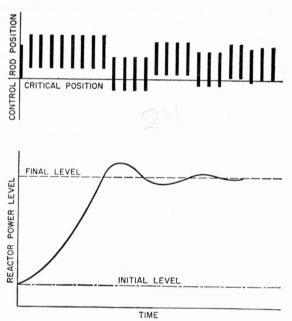

FIG. 2-6. Control-rod positions for a manual-level change.

decrease, consequently k will be reduced and control rods will have to be moved out to compensate for the reduction in k.

2-13. Elementary Reactor Operation with Negative Temperature Coefficient. Other causes exist for moving control rods, one of them being the temperature of the reactor. Most reactors have what is termed a negative temperature coefficient. This term means that as the reactor heats up, its reactivity is reduced. Reactors which have water or gas as moderators usually have large negative temperature coefficients. This temperature coefficient will later be shown to be a most important control-system parameter, but for the present let us examine the basic operation of a reactor with a negative temperature coefficient.

Assume that a reactor is critical at a low power level and consequently is effectively at room temperature. The control rods are in a given fixed position. Now, through some external means such as that of heating the normal coolant of the reactor, let us raise the average temperature of the reactor to where it might actually run as a power reactor. This process of heating will reduce the reactivity of the reactor. Consequently, the reactor is no longer critical, but probably greatly subcritical. Control rods must then be extracted to make up for this loss of reactivity. Actually it does not matter whether the heat is applied from an external source or whether the reactor power level is changed. Cold critical then refers to the position of the control rods when the reactor is critical at room temperature, and hot critical refers to the position

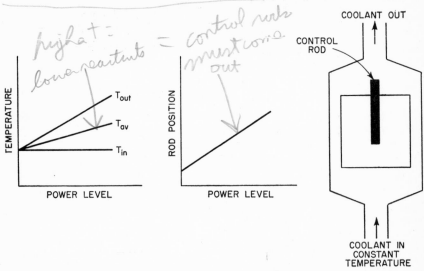

FIG. 2-7. Elementary operation of a reactor having negative temperature coefficient and constant coolant inlet temperature.

of the control rods when the reactor is critical at its normal operating temperature.

An interesting type of control-rod operation results when the inlet temperature to this type of reactor remains constant. Figure 2-7 illustrates this condition. For a simple example assume that the coolant into the reactor is supplied from a faucet or equivalent at constant temperature and the coolant out of the reactor is used in heating radiators and then dumped. If the flow from the faucet is constant, the temperature versus power level is shown in Fig. 2-7. Here, as the power output of the reactor rises, the average temperature rises, and to compensate for this rise in average temperature, control rods must be extracted from the reactor in order to keep the multiplication factor unity. Assuming then that the control rods are equally effective at all positions in the reactor, it can be seen that under this condition the *position of the control rods is directly proportional to the power output of the reactor.* In a practical situation many other types of programming can exist. The position of the control rods will rarely be either of the two simple functions of power level just described.

2-14. Fission-product Poisoning. It has been indicated that control rods, depletion, and temperature affect the multiplication factor of a reactor. Another quantity must also be introduced which plays a vital role in the operation of large thermal power-producing reactors. This quantity is fission-product poisoning. As the reactor continues to operate, fission products are created from the uranium. Many direct fission products exist, and in addition, a host of daughter nuclides are created by decaying emissions from these fission products. Some of these direct and indirect nuclides may have large cross sections for the absorption of neutrons, and therefore they can act as poisons. If these poisons are produced in appreciable amounts, they can affect the over-all multiplication of the reactor. Because some of these poisons may continue to be formed by radioactive decay even after the reactor is shut down, the concentration of the poison may increase to a maximum after reactor shutdown. It is apparent then that additional excess reactivity must be designed into a thermal reactor to take care of these poisons.

Because of their large thermal neutron absorption cross sections, two nuclides are of particular interest, xenon 135 and samarium 149. Xenon 135 is formed as a result of the decay of the direct fission product tellurium 135. Tellurium 135 actually consists of over 5 percent of the direct fission products and decays rapidly by β emission in the following manner:

$$\text{Te}^{135} \xrightarrow{1 \text{ min}} \text{I}^{135} \xrightarrow{6.7 \text{ hr}} \text{Xe}^{135} \xrightarrow{9.2 \text{ hr}} \text{Cs}^{135} \xrightarrow{2.1 \times 10^6 \text{ yr}} \text{Ba}^{135}$$

Barium 135 is stable. Xenon 135 has an absorption cross section for thermal neutrons of approximately 3.5×10^6 barns and decays to cesium with a half life of approximately 9.2 hr.

Sm^{149}, on the other hand, is the stable end product of the chain

$$\text{Nd}^{149} \xrightarrow{1.7 \text{ hr}} \text{Pm}^{149} \xrightarrow{47 \text{ hr}} \text{Sm}^{149} \text{ (stable)}$$

This reaction occurs in roughly 1.5 percent of the fissions, and the Sm^{149} has a somewhat lower cross section for thermal neutrons of approximately 5.3×10^4 barns. For these reasons it does not contribute as much to the poisoning of a reactor as does the Xe^{135} and consequently the Sm^{149} effect will be ignored in future control discussions on poisoning.

In order to introduce terminology that we shall use later in discussing reactor control, the above-described relationships can be put into mathematical form as follows.

The equation for the concentration of Xe^{135} in a reactor at any time becomes

$$\frac{dX'}{dt} = (\gamma_x \Sigma_f - \sigma_x X')\phi + \lambda_I I' - \lambda_x X' \tag{2-24}$$

where X' = number of atoms of Xe^{135} present per cubic centimeter at any time t

γ_x = fractional yield of xenon as direct fission product

σ_x = microscopic thermal-neutron absorption cross section of Xe^{135} (3.5×10^6 barns)

ϕ = thermal-neutron flux

λ_I = decay constant of I^{135}

I' = number of atoms of I^{135} present per cubic centimeter at any time t

λ_x = decay constant of Xe^{135}

Σ_f = macroscopic fission cross section of fuel in reactor

A similar equation can be written for the concentration of I^{135} at any time. Because the half life of Te^{135} is very short compared with that of I^{135} (1 min against 6.7 hr), we can make the simplifying assumption that the direct fission product is I^{135}. Then

$$\frac{dI'}{dt} = \gamma_I \Sigma_f \phi - \lambda_I I' \tag{2-25}$$

where γ_I is the fractional yield of I^{135} from the direct fission process and the other terms have the meaning just defined.

It can be seen that two kinetic effects occur which concern reactor control. The first effect is the so-called equilibrium poisoning, and the second the peak poisoning. The equilibrium poisoning occurs during reactor power operation, and the peak poisoning after shutdown of the reactor from a high power level. From Eq. (2-24), the amount of xenon present in the reactor builds up from the concentration of the iodine 135 and dies off both by the radioactive decay into cesium and from the destruction of xenon 135 by thermal-neutron absorption. It is obvious that, after long operation at a given fixed power level, an equilibrium can exist between the build-up and the two decays, so that at the end of a long period of time a steady amount of poison can exist in the reactor. Figure 2-8 shows the time scale to build up to equilibrium for such a process. The amount of poisoning involved depends upon the steady power level of the reactor and the design of the particular reactor involved. The steady-state xenon concentration may be obtained simply by setting $dX'/dt = 0$ in Eq. (2-24) and $dI'/dt = 0$ in Eq. (2-25). Then

$$X_0' = \frac{\Sigma_f(\gamma_x + \gamma_I)\phi_0}{\lambda_x + \sigma_x \phi_0} \tag{2-26}$$

Let us now shut down a thermal reactor as fast as possible from a high power level operating condition. In this instance the thermal-neutron level is reduced to effectively zero, and consequently the decay term due to thermal-neutron absorption of the xenon 135 no longer exists. Consequently, the xenon 135 concentration builds up to a maximum from the iodine 135 which has been previously formed. Ultimately the radio-

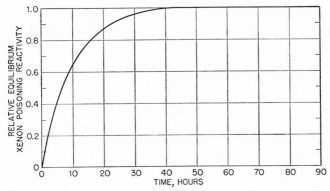

FIG. 2-8. Equilibrium xenon poisoning build-up for an enriched thermal reactor.

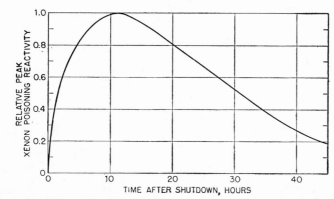

FIG. 2-9. Relative peak xenon poisoning reactivity as a function of time after shutdown for a thermal reactor.

active decay of the xenon 135 to cesium 135 takes over and the total xenon 135 concentration drops off. The time involved in this process is shown in Fig. 2-9, with a peak in xenon concentration appearing in approximately 11 hr after shutdown. The magnitude of this peak again depends upon the initial steady power level of the reactor and its specific design. However, the peak xenon poisoning may be many times the value of the equilibrium xenon 135 poisoning. It will be recognized that an entire range of poisoning conditions can exist, depending upon the magnitude of the initial power level and the extent to which the power level is shut down.

Other variables of operation can enter. After a reactor has been shut down and the xenon poison concentration partially built up, the reactor may be turned on again and subsequently burn out the xenon back to the equilibrium condition. This operation can call for a fast rate of change of reactivity from the control rods to keep the reactor critical and is one determining factor in the speed of reactor control.

From the curve on Fig. 2-9 a very appreciable amount of reactivity may be involved in the peak xenon poisoning. It is conceivable that this amount of reactivity may be so much that the reactor does not contain sufficient uranium to completely "override" this peak even when the control rods are pulled out all the way. Under these conditions, where only a fixed amount of reactivity is available, unless the reactor is started up quickly after a shutdown, a large period of time will exist in which it will be impossible to start the reactor until the xenon decays down. As an example from Fig. 2-9, let us assume that sufficient reactivity exists in a reactor that it can still be made critical up to ½ hr after shutdown from a given power level. The figure indicates that unless a startup is made within this ½ hr, it may be 40 hr before the reactor can be started up again.

2-15. Inventory of Items Affecting Reactivity. It has been shown that control rods must be moved to compensate for depletion, temperature, and poisoning. If these effects are defined in reactivity worth, control rods may also be so rated. Sufficient extra reactivity must be designed into the control rods to hold the reactor safely shut down when all rods are inserted. The amount of negative reactivity needed to keep a reactor safely shut down differs from reactor to reactor. Approximately −2 percent in reactivity is probably the minimum value used. A range of 5 to 10 percent in negative reactivity is more usual for reactor shutdown.

To form a reactivity inventory, let us again take an example. Assume that a given reactor changes its reactivity by 5 percent going from cold critical to hot critical, it has a 3 percent reactivity allowance for depletion and low cross-section poisons, and 10 percent in reactivity is needed to completely override xenon poisoning after shutdown. An excess reactivity of 17 percent is designed into the machine, and it is desired that the shutdown reactivity be 9 percent. Shutdown reactivity is defined here as the amount of negative reactivity in a new cold reactor when all the rods are fully inserted. For this particular set of conditions it can be seen that rod motion will be required to overcome 18 percent in reactivity for the depletion, temperature, and peak poisoning effects. With an excess reactivity of 17 percent, the reactor will not fully override the xenon poisoning on the last day of its rated life provided that it is started up hot. Rather, it will override the xenon completely for two-thirds of its life and in the last third it will be necessary to start up the reactor cold, to operate the reactor in such a manner that the poisons do not build up fully, or to provide for a possible waiting period. The 9 percent shutdown reactivity requires that the reactivity value or rod worth of the rods fully inserted into the cold clean reactor must be at least 26 percent.

The inventory just completed is crude, as rod worths usually change with temperature and poisoning. These effects would be taken into account in an actual reactor plant design.

Many control schemes can be conceived so that poisons are not permitted to build up beyond the capabilities of the control system. It is an interesting coincidence, however, that with normal one-shift operation of a reactor plant on an 8- to 12-hr-day basis, starting up the next morning is usually a startup made quite close to the peak of the xenon poisoning. Therefore, on occasion, even the type of working day must be considered in the design of how much reactivity shall be built into the reactor.

2-16. Control-rod Effectiveness. The above discussions have assumed that the effects of control-rod position in reactivity would be linear with

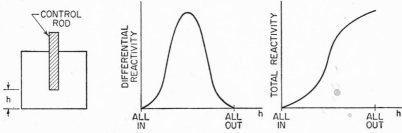

FIG. 2-10. Control-rod effectiveness as a function of rod position in a reactor.

rod position in the reactor. Actually this is not the case. Moving a control rod or a bank of control rods in a simple geometric reactor such as a cylinder normally produces a change in reactivity which varies approximately as the sine squared of the rod position. To make the matter more complex, the position of each individual rod usually can affect the reactivity worth of other nearby rods. The sine-squared approximation may generally be used for control purposes even though it is found to be incorrect at the end points. It would not be expected that the worth of a rod would have a zero slope at its end positions. Figure 2-10 indicates the differential reactivity and the total reactivity of an elementary reactor having this type of rod worth. It can be shown that the peak-to-average ratio of rod effectiveness is approximately 2:1. It will also be shown later that for safety considerations it is quite important to know at what rate of reactivity change the reactor goes through critical during a startup problem.   Consequently, the factor of 3:1 must be taken into account for safety considerations as well as the obvious nonlinear change in loop gain servo considerations.

The minimum rod effectiveness is also important in problems such as are encountered in following transient xenon poisoning by means of control rods.   An attempt should be made to design the reactor control-rod positions so that minimum rod worth does not occur when the xenon transient is decaying down at its maximum rate and consequently is inserting reactivity into the reactor at its maximum rate.   For this condition the control rods must put in reactivity fast enough to override the xenon poisoning.

REFERENCES

1. Glasstone, S., and M. C. Edlund: "The Elements of Nuclear Reactor Theory," D. Van Nostrand Company, Inc., New York, 1952.
2. Stephenson, R.: "Introduction to Nuclear Engineering," McGraw-Hill Book Company, Inc., New York, 1954.
3. Murray, R. L.: "Introduction to Nuclear Engineering," Prentice-Hall, Inc., New York, 1954.
4. Hughes, D. J., J. Dabbs, A. Cahn, and D. Hall: Delayed Neutrons from Fission of U^{235}, *Phys. Rev.*, vol. 73, no. 2, p. 111, 1948.
5. Blizard, E. P., and F. S. Maienschein: Sources of Radiation, *ORNL*-56-6-120, 1952.
6. Soodak, H., and E. C. Campbell: "Elementary Pile Theory," John Wiley & Sons, Inc., New York, 1950.
7. Sun, K. H., et al.: Delayed Neutrons from U^{238} and Th^{232} Fission, *Phys. Rev.*, vol. 79, no. 1, p. 3, July 1, 1950.
8. Phillips, H. B.: "Differential Equations," John Wiley & Sons, Inc., New York, 1939.

CHAPTER 3

REACTOR KINETICS

The first two chapters have provided background from which we can start to examine design problems and operating problems of reactor control. Later the complex problems of controlling reactors associated with power plants will be discussed. Before the control of reactors and plants can be investigated, more must be known about the kinetic characteristics of the reactor. In servo language, before synthesizing the control of the reactor as a servo component, it is necessary to know its open-loop responses. In later operating problems, responses to step functions, ramp functions, and sine waves all fit into specific parts of reactor operation. It is the analytic solutions of the reactor response to these driving functions which will be examined in this chapter.

3-1. Introduction. These responses will be studied from a black-box type of approach; i.e., the only significant reactor constants that are present are δk, l^*, and n in a multiplying medium. The temperature coefficient will be presumed to be zero. Measurements of these quantities can be made external to the reactor, and its performance calculated. It is well known, of course, that spatial effects inside the reactor can cause changes in reactivity and output. However, the one-point black-box type of treatment usually yields kinetic answers that are consistent with experimental accuracy.[1]

The response of the reactor to step changes in δk will first be developed. Then solutions will be provided for ramp functions in δk. Finally the reactor will be treated by methods of servo theory, whereby a sinusoidal input in δk is compared with a sinusoidal output in power level. In this way the transfer function will be derived for future use in control circuits.

3-2. Solution of Kinetic Equations for Step-function Input in δk. The kinetic equations of a chain-reacting pile have been derived in the literature many times.[2-4] We shall use the form previously developed in Chap. 2.

$$\frac{dn}{dt} = \frac{\delta k - \beta}{l^*} n + \sum_{i=1}^{6} \lambda_i C_i \qquad (3\text{-}1)$$

$$\frac{dC_i}{dt} = \frac{\beta_i}{l^*} n - \lambda_i C_i \qquad (3\text{-}2)$$

where the symbols have the meanings previously defined. The nature of the solutions of Eqs. (3-1) and (3-2) for step function inputs is also well known.[5,6] These kinetic equations can be combined to form a

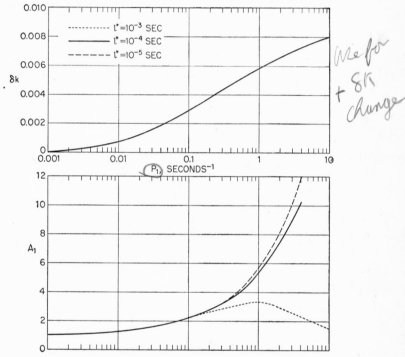

FIG. 3-1. Chart for response of reactors to a step change in reactivity, positive step only.

single differential equation of the seventh order in n. For a step input in δk the solution will take the form

$$n(t) = n_0 \sum_{j=1}^{7} A_j e^{P_j t} \qquad (3\text{-}3)$$

where the first exponent P_1 has the same sign as δk, the input disturbance, and where the other six exponents are negative.

Equations (3-1) and (3-2) are a family of linear differential equations with constant coefficients, and there is a definite relationship among the values of A_j, P_j, and δk. This relationship can be shown graphically

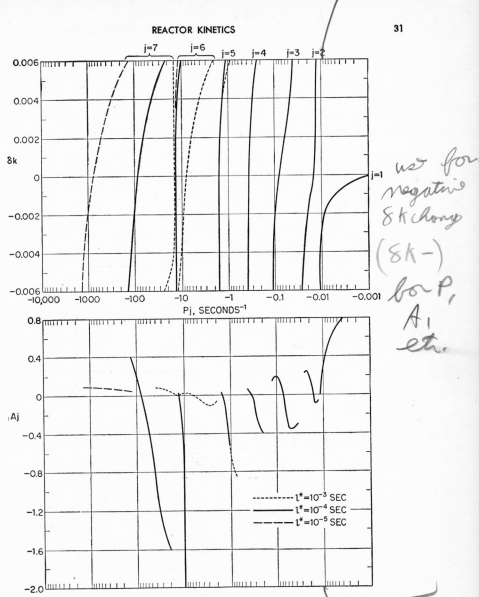

FIG. 3-2. Chart for response of reactors to a step change in reactivity.

and is presented for reactors of $l^* = 10^{-3}$ sec, 10^{-4} sec, and 10^{-5} sec in Figs. 3-1 and 3-2.   Figures 3-1 and 3-2 are used when a positive δk step is involved, and Fig. 3-2 only is needed for negative δk steps.

These curves are used in the following manner: The size of the δk step is selected and the value of the exponent P_1 is read from the top graph of Fig. 3-1 or the farthest curve to the right top of Fig. 3-2.   Then reading vertically down from that value of P_1 to the bottom graph, the corresponding coefficient A_1 may be read.   In a similar manner, one continues across the top curves of Fig. 3-2, from right to left, locates the value of P_j opposite the ordinate of the selected δk, and then reads down to the corresponding coefficient A_j.

Using these charts in an example, one might derive the equation for the response of a reactor having an $l^* = 10^{-4}$ sec when a δk step of

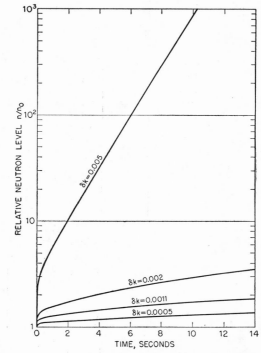

FIG. 3-3. Relative neutron level versus time for positive step function reactivity changes, $l^* = 10^{-4}$ sec.

$-0.003\,\delta k$ is inserted into the reactor.   Reading across and down for each exponent and coefficient, the equation for $n(t)$ can be found as

$$n(t) = n_0(0.19e^{-0.012t} + 0.24e^{-0.022t} + 0.19e^{-0.11t} + 0.01e^{-0.38t}$$
$$+ 0.02e^{-1.6t} + 0.005e^{-13t} + 0.28e^{-110t}) \quad (3\text{-}4)$$

It can be seen from Figs. 3-1 and 3-2 that the positive exponent P_1 increases rapidly with increasing δk and the coefficient A_1 also increases very rapidly.   These rapid rises take place at values close to prompt critical.

Figure 3-3 shows the neutron-level response of a reactor having an l^* of 10^{-4} sec for various step δk inputs.   The value of l^*, as noted from

Figs. 3-1 and 3-2, principally affects the front edge of the rise. After an initial rise caused mostly by the prompt neutrons, the reactor settles down to a steady period created by the delayed neutrons. Figure 3-4 indicates the response of this reactor for longer periods of time, and it can be seen that for step reactivities in the neighborhood of $\delta k = 0.005$ or greater, extremely rapid and long rises occur.

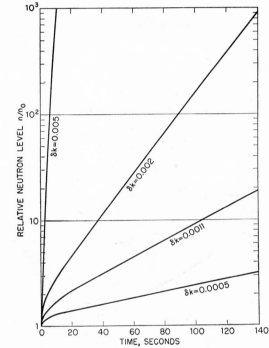

FIG. 3-4. Relative neutron level versus time for positive step reactivity changes, $l^* = 10^{-4}$ sec, large time scale.

Figures 3-5 and 3-6 illustrate the performance of a reactor having an l^* of 10^{-4} sec, for negative δk step inputs. Here it will again be noted that after an initial drop, the rate of drop is determined by the delayed emitters and the ultimate rate by the longest-lived delayed emitter, which, from Table 2-1, has a time constant of approximately 80 sec. These effects can be seen mathematically by examination of Eq. (3-4). It can be seen that the last term of this equation is the predominant one for very short periods of time. However, the two terms preceding the last term in Eq. (3-4) have comparatively small coefficients. The first four terms have small exponents. Therefore, after the large initial drop, the neutron concentration changes slowly and behaves ultimately as indicated by the first term of Eq. (3-4).

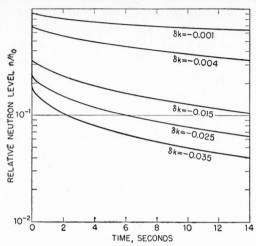

FIG. 3-5. Relative neutron level versus time for negative step function reactivity changes, $l^* = 10^{-4}$ sec.

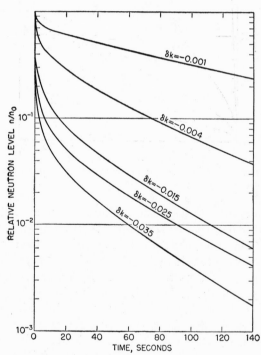

FIG. 3-6. Relative neutron level versus time for negative step function reactivity changes, $l^* = 10^{-4}$ sec, large time scale.

After the first dropoff, the reactor level cannot fall off at a rate faster than an 80-sec period. Figure 3-7 illustrates this condition. It will be noted that this period determines the maximum rate of neutron shutdown of a reactor. Some reactors are capable of being shut down by 10 decades. To reach such a shutdown level would require a minimum of 30 min.

Approximate Solution for Initial Response.[7] The shape of the initial response of a reactor to a step change in δk can usually be analyzed by an approximation method. During an initial time interval of the order of $\frac{1}{10}$ sec, the delayed-neutron emitters can be considered a constant source of neutrons. If the reactor is in equilibrium, the delayed-neutron emitters yield β neutrons for each neutron produced. That is, they are acting as a constant source of strength $(\beta/l^*)n_0$. Hence the initial

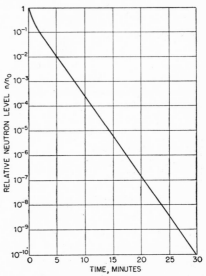

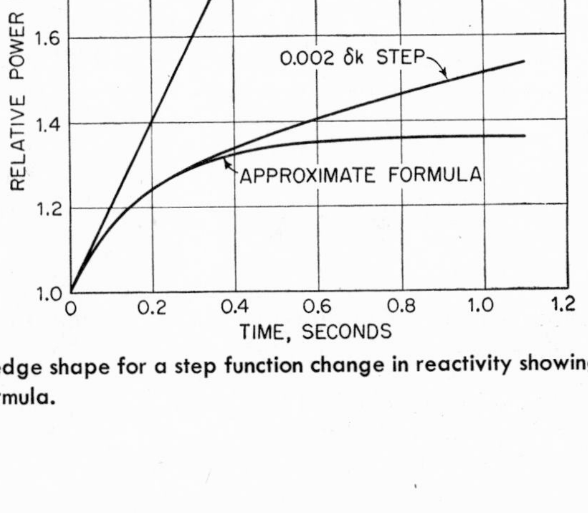

FIG. 3-7. Relative neutron level after shutdown.

FIG. 3-8. Front edge shape for a step function change in reactivity showing results of using approximate formula.

response of the reactor is described by

$$\frac{dn}{dt} = \frac{\delta k - \beta}{l^*} n + \frac{\beta}{l^*} n_0 \tag{3-5}$$

The solution of Eq. (3-5) is

$$\frac{n(t)}{n(0)} = -\frac{\beta}{\delta k - \beta} + \frac{\delta k}{\delta k - \beta} e^{[(\delta k - \beta)/l^*]t} \tag{3-6}$$

The neutron density in this expression approaches the asymptotic value of $-\beta/(\delta k - \beta)$. How close the approximate expression matches the actual case can be seen in Fig. 3-8. Here the initial rise created by the insertion of a $0.002\delta k$ step into a reactor having an l^* of 10^{-3} sec is compared with the approximate expression. The front edges are alike for the first few tenths of a second.

3-3. Solution of Kinetic Equations for Ramp Function.

Injecting a ramp function of the form $\delta k = \alpha + \gamma t$ into the black box produces useful information, as this is an approximation of what happens when a control rod is pulled out of a reactor. It will be recalled that control-rod effectiveness is usually such that the reactivity does not change linearly as a function of rod position. Nevertheless, useful information can be obtained by considering linear rates of reactivity change and modifying the slope of these linear reactivity rates of change in discrete intervals if desired.

The exact solution of the reactor kinetic equations for this type of ramp input is a complex one, tedious to calculate, and will only be outlined below.† Where many solutions are required, the use of a reactor kinetic simulator, as described in Chap. 11, is usually preferred to the direct analytical method.

The analytical method follows these steps: the basic kinetic equations (3-1) and (3-2) are first presumed to consist of only one group of delayed neutrons having a single value of λ and β. It can be shown that the solution is not particularly affected when several groups of delayed neutrons are used. Then Eqs. (3-1) and (3-2) become

$$\frac{dn}{dt} = \frac{\delta k - \beta}{l^*} n + \lambda C + S \tag{3-7}$$

$$\frac{dC}{dt} = \frac{\beta}{l^*} n - \lambda C \tag{3-8}$$

These equations are then combined to form a second-order differential equation in n whereby

† This solution was originally obtained by Sylvan Wallach, and the presentation here closely follows his method with his permission.

$$\frac{d^2n}{dt^2} + \frac{\beta + \lambda l^* - \delta k}{l^*}\frac{dn}{dt} - \frac{\delta k\lambda + d\delta k/dt}{l^*}n = \lambda S \qquad (3\text{-}9)$$

and as $\delta k = \alpha + \gamma t$, Eq. (3-9) can be written in the form

$$\frac{d^2n}{dt^2} + (At + B)\frac{dn}{dt} + (Ct + D)n = \lambda S \qquad (3\text{-}10)$$

The solution of this equation is represented as an integral expression similar to a Laplace transform, whereby

$$n = \int_{\mathcal{L}} e^{xt}R(x)\,dx \qquad (3\text{-}11)$$

$R(x)$ is defined as

$$R(x) = \frac{1}{Q(x)}\exp\left[\int\frac{P(x)}{Q(x)}\,dx\right] \qquad (3\text{-}12)$$

and $P(x)$ and $Q(x)$ are the polynomials

$$P(x) = x^2 + Bx + D \qquad (3\text{-}13)$$
and
$$Q(x) = Ax + C \qquad (3\text{-}14)$$

Equation (3-11) is a proper solution of Eq. (3-10), provided that a suitable integration path $\mathcal{L}$ is selected in the complex x plane. We can now substitute Eq. (3-11) into Eq. (3-10) and find that

$$\int_{\mathcal{L}} e^{xt}R(x)[t(Ax + C) + (x^2 + Bx + D)]\,dx = \lambda S \qquad (3\text{-}15)$$

Substituting the definitions of Eqs. (3-13) and (3-14) into Eq. (3-15)

$$\int_{\mathcal{L}} e^{xt}R(x)[Q(x)t + P(x)]\,dx = \lambda S \qquad (3\text{-}16)$$

The suggested integration of Eq. (3-16) is then performed, first integrating by parts as follows:

$$\int_{\mathcal{L}} e^{xt}R(x)Q(x)t\,dx = \int_{\mathcal{L}} U\,dV \qquad (3\text{-}17)$$
where
$$U = R(x)Q(x) \qquad (3\text{-}18)$$
and
$$dV = te^{xt}\,dx \qquad (3\text{-}19)$$

The expression for λS is then found to reduce to

$$\lambda S = [R(x)Q(x)e^{xt}]_{x_1}^{x_2} \qquad (3\text{-}20)$$

where x_1 and x_2 are the end points of the path of integration $\mathcal{L}$. $R(x)$ may be found by substituting Eqs. (3-13) and (3-14) into Eq. (3-12)

$$R(x) = \sigma \left(x + \frac{C}{A} \right)^{\mu-1} \exp \left\{ \frac{1}{A} \int \left[x + \left(B - \frac{C}{A} \right) \right] dx \right\} \qquad (3\text{-}21)$$

where
$$\mu = \frac{D - (C/A)[B - (C/A)]}{A} \qquad (3\text{-}22)$$

and σ is an arbitrary constant of integration depending upon the limits of integration imposed by each problem.

The final solution in terms of the original parameters becomes

$$n(t) = \sigma \int_{\mathcal{L}} e^{x(\delta k - \beta)/\gamma - x^2 l^*/2\gamma} (x + \lambda)^{\beta\lambda/\gamma} \, dx \qquad (3\text{-}23)$$

The constant σ and the path $\mathcal{L}$ remain to be determined. The complete solution of Eq. (3-10) is given by two linearly independent solutions of the homogeneous equation ($S = 0$) and by any solution of the inhomogeneous equation. Accordingly, three paths of integration are required. Along these paths Eq. (3-11) must converge and Eq. (3-20) must be satisfied with appropriate values for S.

For the case encountered in reactor startup problems, the path of integration $\mathcal{L}$ can be taken as the positive real axis from zero to infinity. As δk is continually increasing, γ is positive. Then the x^2 term in the exponential of Eq. (3-23) is always negative. The x term is negative when δk is below prompt critical, zero at prompt critical, and positive when the reactivity exceeds prompt critical. Hence it is clear that as the reactivity increases with time, the neutron density begins to grow very rapidly at prompt critical, but below prompt critical the growth is comparatively small.

For simple computational purposes σ may be evaluated as that multiplication factor which brings $n(0)$ to a value of $S/1 - k$ at $t = 0$. Figure 3-9 presents a solution to the ramp function input problem for

$$\delta k = -0.333 + 7 \times 10^{-4} t \qquad (3\text{-}24)$$

and $l^* = 10^{-4}$ sec.[8]

As can be seen from Eq. (3-23), the neutron-level response is not particularly sensitive to l^*. It will be noted that below critical the form of the response is that of the subcritical multiplication curve (Fig. 2-4) and above prompt critical the reactor literally "takes off."

The effect of different linear reactivity change rates may be seen from Fig. 3-10.[8] The curves are plotted as a function of the reactivity remaining in the reactor. Here the subcritical multiplication curve is furnished as a reference curve, being the case of infinitely slow reactivity change. It can be seen that as reactivity is inserted into the reactor at higher and higher rates, the critical point comes at lower and lower neutron levels.

Of interest also is the reactor period as a function of linear reactivity rates of change. Figure 3-11 indicates the periods that result as the multiplication factor of the reactor comes closer and closer to unity at linear rates of change. It is of interest to note that at high reactivity change rates, a short period, easily detectable by measuring instruments,

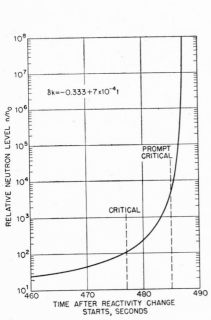

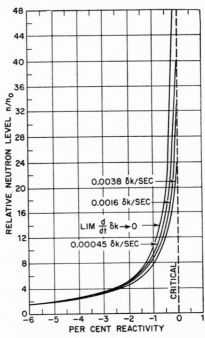

FIG. 3-9. Relative neutron level versus time for ramp function input.

FIG. 3-10. Relative neutron levels versus reactivity remaining in a reactor for various ramp function reactivity changes.

is available at quite low multiplication factors. Whereas if the rate of change of reactivity is small, the multiplication factor must be very nearly unity before a period in the neighborhood of 20 sec results. Figure 3-11 is somewhat deceptive in that it might possibly be interpreted as meaning that one should, in an actual startup operation of a reactor, extract the rods rapidly in order to see quickly a measurable period. Figure 3-12 is a plot of the same information as a function of time, and here it can be seen that one actually has a somewhat more gradual operating approach to a given period if the reactivity is inserted at a slower rate. Startup rates of reactivity change are discussed in detail in Chap. 8.

3-4. Approximate Solution of Kinetic Equations for a Ramp Function for a Critical Reactor.

A problem that arises quite frequently in theoretical reactor operation is one in which the reactor is critical and reactivity is steadily increased because of malfunctioning of a control rod. The following assumptions are made: First, the reactor is operating at

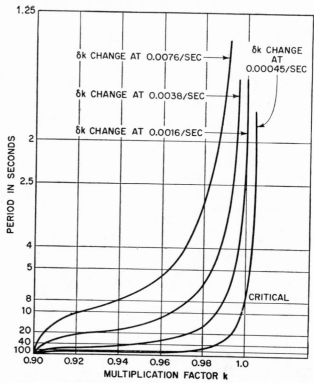

FIG. 3-11. Reactor period versus multiplication factor for various ramp function reactivity change rates.

a steady state before the application of the disturbance. Second, the disturbance starting at time zero has the form of $\delta k = At$.

On the basis of these assumptions, for short-time intervals we can develop this solution.

Equation (3-1) takes the same form as approximate equation (3-5)

$$\frac{dn}{dt} = \frac{\delta k - \beta}{l^*} n + \frac{\beta}{l^*} n_0 \qquad (3\text{-}25)$$

now, however,
$$\delta k = At \qquad (3\text{-}26)$$

Therefore
$$\frac{dn}{dt} - \frac{At - \beta}{l^*} n = \frac{\beta}{l^*} n_0 \qquad (3\text{-}27)$$

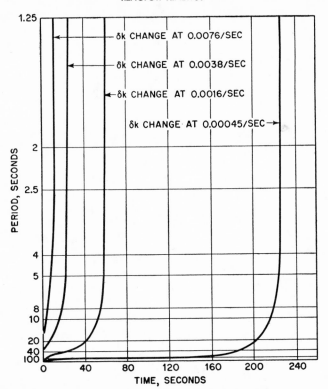

FIG. 3-12. Reactor period versus time for various ramp function reactivity change rates.

The solution for this equation is of the form

$$n = [\exp(\int - P\, dt)]\{\int[\exp(\int P\, dt)]Q\, dt + C\} \qquad (3\text{-}28)$$

where
$$P = \frac{-At + \beta}{l^*} \qquad Q = \frac{\beta n_0}{l^*} \qquad (3\text{-}29)$$

Then

$$\frac{n}{n_0} = \frac{\beta}{l^*} e^{(At^2 - 2\beta t)/2l^*} \left(\int_0^t e^{-(At^2 - 2\beta t)/2l^*}\, dt + \frac{C}{n_0} \right) \qquad (3\text{-}30)$$

Since at $t = 0$, $n/n_0 = 1$, C/n_0 must equal l^*/β, the integral term in Eq. (3-30) may be rewritten in the form

$$e^{\frac{\beta^2}{2Al^*}} \int_0^t e^{-(\alpha t + \gamma)^2}\, dt$$

where
$$\alpha = \sqrt{\frac{A}{2l^*}} \quad \text{and} \quad \gamma = -\frac{\beta}{\sqrt{2Al^*}} \qquad (3\text{-}31)$$

Substituting $\alpha t + \gamma = \mu$, we get

$$\int_0^t e^{-(\alpha t + \gamma)^2} dt = \frac{1}{\alpha} \int_\gamma^{\alpha t + \gamma} e^{-\mu^2} d\mu$$

$$= \frac{\sqrt{\pi}}{2\alpha} \left(\frac{2}{\sqrt{\pi}} \int_0^{\alpha t + \gamma} e^{-\mu^2} d\mu - \frac{2}{\sqrt{\pi}} \int_0^\gamma e^{-\mu^2} d\mu \right) \quad (3\text{-}32)$$

This form is that of the probability integral whose values are available in mathematical tables.[9] The complete solution then becomes

$$\frac{n}{n_0} = \frac{\beta}{l^*} e^{\mu^2} \left[\frac{\sqrt{\pi}}{2\alpha} \left(\frac{2}{\sqrt{\pi}} \int_0^{\alpha t + \gamma} e^{-\mu^2} d\mu - \frac{2}{\sqrt{\pi}} \int_0^\gamma e^{-\mu^2} d\mu \right) + \frac{l^*}{\beta} e^{-\beta^2/2Al^*} \right]$$

$$(3\text{-}33)$$

Plotted from this equation, Fig. 3-13 shows the results of suddenly applying rates of change of δk to a critical reactor. It is easily seen that put-

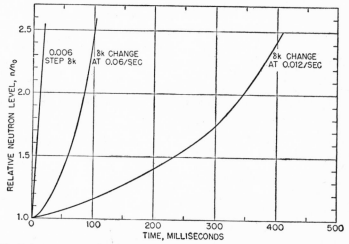

FIG. 3-13. Relative neutron level versus time for various ramp function reactivity change rates, using approximate formula.

ing in reactivity at finite rates into a reactor, instead of in step function fashion, results in considerably slower rates of initial rise of neutron level. This type of calculation has been presented in some detail, as it is useful in operational problems involving study of accidents.

3-5. Solution of Kinetic Equations for Sinusoidal Input in δk.[14] In the dynamic analysis of any system it is often necessary to determine the frequency response or transfer function[10,11] of each of the elements of the system. The concept of a transfer function for a reactor implies a sinusoidal variation of δk. Consequently, the set of linear differential equations (3-1) and (3-2) is no longer a set with constant coefficients, a necessary condition for developing a transfer function. However, if we assume sufficiently small excursions of n, these equations can be approximated by a set with constant coefficients.

Let n be composed of two parts: n_0, a steady-state value, and δn, a small excursion. Similarly, let C_i be composed of a steady-state C_{i0} and an excursion δC_i. Equations (3-1) and (3-2) can be rewritten first by combining Eq. (3-2) with Eq. (3-1)

$$\frac{dn}{dt} = \frac{\delta k}{l^*} n - \sum_{i=1}^{6} \frac{dC_i}{dt} \tag{3-34}$$

because $\sum_{i=1}^{6} \beta_i = \beta$. Then

$$\frac{dn}{dt} = \frac{d\delta n}{dt} = \frac{\delta k}{l^*} n_0 + \frac{\delta k \delta n}{l^*} - \sum_{i=1}^{6} \frac{d\delta C_i}{dt} \tag{3-35}$$

$\delta k \delta n / l^*$ may be neglected in comparison with $(\delta k / l^*) n_0$ and

$$\frac{dC_i}{dt} = \frac{d\delta C_i}{dt} = \frac{\beta_i}{l^*}(n_0 + \delta n) - \lambda_i(C_{i0} + \delta C_i) \tag{3-36}$$

as in the steady state

$$\frac{dC_{i0}}{dt} = 0 = \frac{\beta_i}{l^*} n_0 - \lambda_i C_{i0} \tag{3-37}$$

Equation (3-36) becomes

$$\frac{d\delta C_i}{dt} = \frac{\beta_i}{l^*} \delta n - \lambda_i \delta C_i \tag{3-38}$$

Reducing Eqs. (3-35) and (3-38) to Laplace-transform operational form gives

$$s\delta n(s) = \frac{n_0}{l^*} \delta k(s) - s \sum_{i=1}^{6} \delta C_i(s) \tag{3-39}$$

$$s\delta C_i(s) = \frac{\beta_i}{l^*} \delta n(s) - \lambda_i \delta C_i(s) \tag{3-40}$$

where the initial condition transforms have been dropped. This is permissible since we define a transfer function in terms of the steady-state response. Combining Eqs. (3-39) and (3-40) gives

$$\frac{\delta n(s)}{\delta k(s)} = \frac{n_0}{l^*} \frac{1}{s\left[1 + \sum_{i=1}^{6} \frac{\beta_i}{l^*(s + \lambda_i)}\right]} \tag{3-41}$$

or
$$\frac{\delta n(s)}{\delta k(s)} = \frac{n_0}{l^*} \frac{\displaystyle\prod_{i=1}^{6} (s + \lambda_i)}{\displaystyle s \prod_{i=1}^{6} (s + r_i)}$$
(3-42)

At this point it is necessary to evaluate the roots of the sixth-degree equation formed by expanding the denominator in Eq. (3-42) and equat-

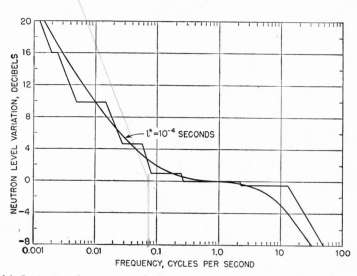

FIG. 3-14. Derivation of reactor transfer function amplitude using break frequency method

ing it to zero. The method is outlined in Refs. 11 and 12. For an example of $l^* = 10^{-4}$ sec, the roots are found to be

$$r_1 = 77.6 \qquad r_4 = 0.336$$
$$r_2 = 13.38 \qquad r_5 = 0.0805$$
$$r_3 = 1.43 \qquad r_6 = 0.0147$$

The resulting complete transfer function for $l^* = 10^{-4}$ sec is

$$\frac{\delta n(s)}{\delta k(s)} = \frac{n_0}{l^*}$$
$$\frac{(s + 14)(s + 1.61)(s + 0.456)(s + 0.151)(s + 0.0315)(s + 0.0124)}{s(s + 77)(s + 13.38)(s + 1.43)(s + 0.336)(s + 0.0805)(s + 0.0147)}$$
(3-43)

The complex fractional term is now the normalized frequency response plotted in Fig. 3-14.

From this data it is now possible to plot the frequency response characteristic (Bode diagram)[13] of the pile, replacing s by $j\omega$. This is shown in Fig. 3-14, using the break frequency method.[10]

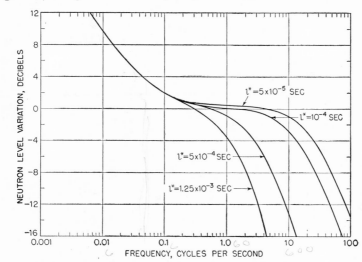

FIG. 3-15. Amplitude of reactor transfer function.

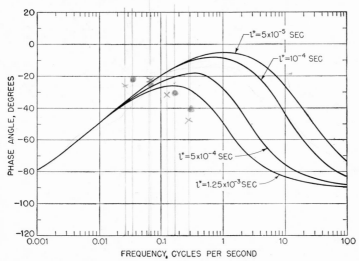

FIG. 3-16. Phase shift of reactor transfer function.

It can be seen from the foregoing analysis that a change in l^* changes the gain and the roots. Figure 3-15 gives the amplitude response of the reactor for various values of l^*. Figure 3-16 shows the phase shift under similar conditions. The $l^* = 10^{-4}$-sec curve is arbitrarily normalized so that 0 db falls at 1 cycle/sec. This requires the multiplication of the gain factor n_0/l^* by the gain of the frequency dependent portion,

$$\frac{\prod_{i=1}^{6} (s + \lambda_i)}{s \prod_{i=1}^{6} (s + r_i)} \text{ at 1 cycle}$$

For many engineering purposes the expression of Eq. (3-43) can be simplified by expressing the parentheses in the numerator as a single lead term and those of the denominator as a single lag term. Thus

$$\frac{\delta n(s)}{\delta k(s)} = \frac{n_0}{l^*} A_1 \frac{(s + \bar{\lambda})}{A_1 s(s + \bar{r})} \tag{3-44}$$

The choice of values of $\bar{\lambda}$ and $\bar{r}$, the average delayed-neutron-decay time and average root, is a matter of engineering judgment. One choice for Eq. (3-43) might be $\bar{\lambda} = 0.075 \text{ sec}^{-1}$, and $\bar{r} = 50 \text{ sec}^{-1}$. The corresponding value of A_1 would then be 0.021.

The principal feature to be noticed from the transfer function derived above as Eq. (3-41) is the nonlinearity of this transfer function. That is, the small signal sinusoidal gain of the reactor as a circuit element depends upon the level at which it is operating. This situation is an intolerable one for a reactor control loop, and the dependence upon level must be removed before satisfactory automatic control of a reactor can be achieved. This problem is discussed in Chap. 4.

The use of this type of transfer function to describe a reactor as a control-loop element has been justified on the basis of a classic experiment performed by Harrer, Boyer, and Krucoff on the CP-2 reactor.[1] Here a sinusoidal disturbance in δk was produced by oscillating a control rod sinusoidally over a small amplitude, and the neutron output of the reactor measured as a function of the input disturbance frequency. The results obtained were so convincing that reactor transfer functions are used with as much confidence in present-day control design as is the transfer function of a conventional amplifier.

REFERENCES

1. Harrer, J. M., R. E. Boyer, and D. Krucoff: Transfer Function of Argonne CP-2 Reactor, *Nucleonics*, vol. 10, no. 8, p. 32, 1952.
2. Glasstone, S., and M. C. Edlund: "The Elements of Nuclear Reactor Theory," D. Van Nostrand Company, Inc., New York, 1952.
3. Soodak, H., and E. C. Campbell: "Elementary Pile Theory," John Wiley & Sons, Inc., New York, 1950.
4. Goodman, C.: "The Science and Engineering of Nuclear Power," vol. 142, Addison-Wesley Publishing Company, Cambridge, Mass., 1947.

5. Isbin, H. S., and J. W. Gorman: Applications of Pile-kinetic Equations, *Nucleonics*, vol. 10, no. 11, p. 68, November, 1952.

6. Hurwitz, H.: Derivation and Integration of the Pile-kinetic Equations, *Nucleonics*, vol. 5, no. 1, p. 61, July, 1949.

7. Lundby, Arne: Kinetic Behavior of a Thermal Heavy Water Reactor, "Proceedings of the 1953 Conference on Nuclear Engineering," University of California Press, Berkeley, Calif., 1953.

8. Schultz, M. A.: "Automatic Control of Power Reactors," *AECD*-3163, 1950.

9. Lowan, A. N.: "Tables of Probability Functions," Federal Works Agency of the WPA, National Bureau of Standards, Washington, 1941.

10. Brown, G. S., and D. P. Campbell: "Principles of Servomechanisms," John Wiley & Sons, Inc., New York, 1951.

11. Chestnut, H., and R. W. Mayer: "Servomechanisms and Regulating System Design," John Wiley & Sons, Inc., New York, 1951.

12. Franz, J. P.: Pile Transfer Functions, *AECD* 3260, 1949.

13. Bode, H. W.: "Network Analysis and Feedback Amplifier Design," D. Van Nostrand Company, Inc., New York, 1945.

14. Bowen, J. H.: Automatic Control Characteristics of Thermal Neutron Reactors, *Proc. Inst. Elec. Engrs. (London)*, vol. 100, pt. 1, p. 102, 1953.

CHAPTER 4

AUTOMATIC REACTOR CONTROL

The response of the reactor to various types of driving functions having been determined, it is necessary to review again basic reactor operation before attempting to use the reactor as an element in a control loop. In this chapter we shall first examine the reactor more closely as a control component. How the elementary reactor can be considered using servo-mechanisms technique and how it is modified by temperature coefficient and poisoning will be shown. When the various forms of the reactor transfer function have been indicated, control loops will be tied around the reactor and the system examined for stability and transient response. In this chapter only automatic reactor control in the power-level range will be discussed. Startup and shutdown problems will be presented later.

4-1. Elementary Reactor As a Control Device. Let us now examine the reactor as a control element. Figures 3-15 and 3-16, in conjunction with Eq. (3-41) defining the reactor transfer function, completely describe an elementary reactor for control purposes. It will be noted that from a transfer function point of view, Eq. (3-41), the break point of highest frequency is determined by the largest root s_1, which, in turn, depends upon the value of β/l^*. It is the value of this root which determines the time behavior that distinguishes a thermal reactor from an intermediate or fast reactor. In a fast reactor the value of l^* is so small that the last break s_1 occurs at a very high frequency, usually above 100 cycles. If an attempt is made to devise a control in this frequency range, difficult component problems arise. Fortunately it is not necessary to devise a control system operating clear out through the last break in the frequency response. From a physical point of view, controlling out to this last break represents control on prompt neutrons.

From another point of view, one can examine the open-loop transient response of a reactor to a step function such as is given in Figs. 3-3 and 3-4. It will be noted that an attempt can be made to contain the initial steep front edge of the rise by means of a control system. This initial front edge is also dependent upon β/l^*. However, if slower control can be tolerated, one can design a control system that ignores this front edge and operates on the flatter portion of the open-loop response which occurs a second or two following the front edge.

In a thermal reactor, however, the break s_1 occurs within the frequency range of many conventional servo systems. It appears from this simple viewpoint that a thermal reactor in which the break point is less than 10 cycles/sec can be controlled, if desired, on prompt neutrons. Stability problems exist, and they will be discussed later in this chapter.

4-2. Reactor Representation with Temperature Coefficient and Poisoning Feedback Loops. The representation we have been using for a reactor transfer function is a somewhat naïve one in that it ignores some of the fundamental processes that must go on within a reactor and a plant. These processes can be considered in the form of feedback loops which modify the elementary reactor transfer function. When feedback of any type is present, the problem of stability exists.

There are two distinct types of feedback loops which must be considered. These are external loops and internal loops. The external and internal feedback loops can be considered to behave independently and are represented block-wise in Fig. 4-1. The external feedback loop is a loop which is associated with an external reactor plant. It is related to the circulation of the primary coolant through the reactor. In a nuclear power plant an external coolant is circulated through a reactor, some heat is removed from this coolant, and the same coolant at a new temperature is reinjected into the reactor. A discrete amount of time is involved in the process of circulating the coolant from the reactor through the heat exchanger and back into the reactor. A given amount of attenuation is also involved in this path, and the combination of this gain and phase shift in conjunction with the transfer function of the reactor determines the stability of a nuclear power plant. We shall examine this external feedback loop in detail in

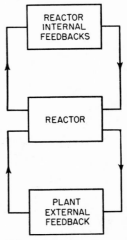

FIG. 4-1. Block diagram of nuclear reactor showing normal feedback paths.

Chap. 6 and for the present shall confine ourselves to two internal or local feedback loops of the reactor.

The internal loops are caused by temperature coefficient and by poisoning. The internal loops appear as indicated in Fig. 4-2, and each effect can be assigned a transfer function. We shall call the local temperature feedback transfer function $K_{TC}G_{TC}(s)$ and the poisoning feedback transfer function $K_xG_x(s)$.

As mentioned in Sec. 2-13, the negative temperature coefficient operates primarily because of a decrease in density of the moderator and reflector as the temperature within a reactor is raised.   Other items such as changes of cross section and changes in leakage are involved within the internal geometry of the reactor.   It is difficult to consider the reactor as a single lumped network and properly take care of all the detailed spatial changes that occur inside a reactor as a function of temperature.   In order to handle the problem completely it is necessary to treat the reactor as a distributed network and determine the effects of temperature upon reactivity in each portion of the network.   This method has been developed in the classified literature but is too complex to be useful here.   Instead, we shall continue the simplified black-box analysis and propose a simple point-type mechanism for a temperature feedback transfer function.   The reactor transfer function, as it is modified by the local temperature coefficient feedback loop, will then be examined.

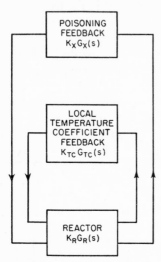

FIG. 4-2. Reactor internal feedback paths.

Poisoning acts in a similar manner as indicated in Sec. 2-14.   Xenon 135 atoms are created both directly and indirectly in the fission process, and these atoms change the reactivity of the reactor in a complex manner with time.   The effect of the local temperature coefficient feedback loop upon the reactor transfer function will be developed first.   Then the effect of the poisoning feedback loop upon the performance of this combination will be shown.

4-3. Negative Temperature Coefficient Feedback.   From a servo point of view we can combine parallel transfer functions and examine the over-all stability of the combination.   First, considering the temperature coefficient situation, the elementary transfer function we have been using for the reactor indicates that the reactor by itself is unstable. That is, at zero frequency the reactor has infinite gain.   Physically, when a small amount of positive reactivity is inserted into the reactor, its power level rises indefinitely.   It can be felt instinctively that the negative temperature coefficient effect is a stabilizing one in that, as the reactor power rises, the temperature rises, the reactivity is reduced, and conceivably the power-level rise is halted at some point.   To examine this process we shall consider the block diagram of Fig. 4-3 and shall use the well-known relationship for parallel transfer functions.[1,2]   This relationship says that

$$K_{RTC}G_{RTC}(s) = \frac{K_R G_R(s)}{1 + K_R G_R(s) K_{TC} G_{TC}(s)} \qquad (4\text{-}1)$$

where $K_{RTC}G_{RTC}(s)$ is the new combined over-all transfer function and $K_{TC}G_{TC}(s)$ is the transfer function of the local temperature coefficient effect. It is now necessary to examine the form of $K_{TC}G_{TC}(s)$. The process to be used is as follows: It is first assumed that the reactor is generating enough power so that it can change the temperature of the

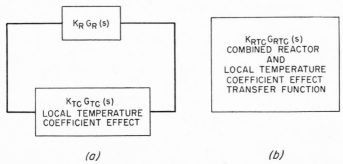

(a) (b)

FIG. 4-3. Combination of reactor transfer function with local temperature coefficient feedback transfer function. (a) Individual transfer functions. (b) Combination transfer function.

moderator in a short space of time. No plant is attached to the reactor to remove this power. However, if it is desirable to suppose that a reactor coolant is also present in the reactor, this coolant would be fixed and not circulating.

Then small variations in neutron level are presumed to occur in a sinusoidal manner. The neutron-level change affects the reactor fuel temperature level. The heat from the fuel then causes a change in the moderator-temperature level and this temperature change in turn may be represented as reactivity change. If, over a small range, these effects are assumed to be linear, an elementary form of transfer function may then be derived. Let

$$T_m = A\,\delta n \qquad (4\text{-}2)$$

where T_m = fuel temperature change
   δn = neutron-level change
   A = a constant depending upon power level, moderator, and coolant.

We can now relate the fuel temperature to the moderator temperature T_w, in the form of a simple exponential lag. This approximation will describe the elementary heat flow from the fuel to the moderator. In

Laplace notation

$$T_w(s) = \frac{T_m(s)}{\tau s + 1} \tag{4-3}$$

where τ is the time constant of the exponential heat transfer lag.[12]

$\delta k(s)$, however, is proportional to T_w via the temperature coefficient. That is,

$$\delta k(s) = (TC)T_w(s) \tag{4-4}$$

where (TC) is the temperature coefficient. The transfer function $K_{TC}G_{TC}(s)$ then becomes

$$K_{TC}G_{TC}(s) = \frac{\delta k(s)}{\delta n(s)} = \frac{A(TC)}{\tau s + 1} \tag{4-5}$$

The gain term of the transfer function may be lumped into a new gain constant K_{TC} and the transfer function becomes

$$K_{TC}G_{TC}(s) = \frac{\delta k(s)}{\delta n(s)} = \frac{K_{TC}}{\tau s + 1} \tag{4-6}$$

We now perform the suggested combination of the transfer functions given in Eq. (4-1) and

$$K_{RTC}G_{RTC}(s) = \frac{K_R G_R(s)}{1 + K_R G_R(s)[K_{TC}/(1 + \tau s)]} \tag{4-7}$$

The temperature coefficient transfer function may be plotted for given values of τ and K_{TC}, and the combination of this transfer function with the reactor transfer function can be accomplished graphically quite easily by use of Nichols charts[3] or the equivalent. Such a combination is shown in Figs. 4-4 and 4-5 for a reactor having an l^* of 10^{-4} sec, $\tau = 0.159$ sec, and several values of the temperature coefficient gain factor K_{TC}. The amplitude curves of Fig. 4-4 indicate that at very low frequencies the characteristic of the over-all combined transfer function is determined solely by the temperature coefficient effect feedback. The gain is no longer infinite at zero frequency, but a finite value of gain equal to $1/K_{TC}$ results from the combination. At very high frequencies the combined transfer function takes on the shape of the reactor curve which depends principally on l^*. We can generalize to the extent that if the break frequency caused by the time delay τ is low compared with the highest natural break frequency of the reactor set by β/l^*, the high-frequency response of $K_{RTC}G_{RTC}(s)$ is not affected by the temperature coefficient.

Figure 4-5 indicates that at low frequencies the phase shift approaches zero for reactors with negative temperature coefficients, instead of $-90°$ as in the case of the elementary reactor alone. At high frequencies,

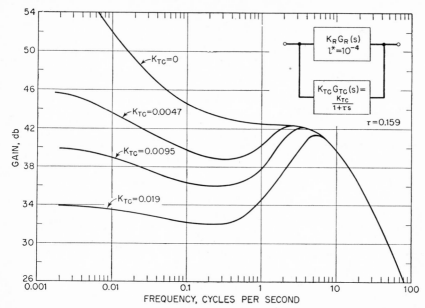

FIG. 4-4. Amplitude response of combination reactor and temperature coefficient feedback transfer functions for several temperature coefficient gains.

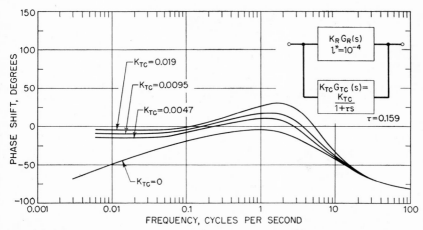

FIG. 4-5. Phase shift response of combination reactor and temperature coefficient feedback transfer functions for several temperature coefficient gains.

again, the phase shift of the combination approaches the phase shift of the reactor. Interestingly enough, some phase lead may result from the combination, and the position and magnitude of this lead depend upon τ.

It will be recalled that the reactor gain is a function of level and consequently the decibel scale for the amplitude in Fig. 4-4 is relative to some power level. The gain of the temperature feedback loop actually is proportional to power level through the constant A. As power level is reduced, the feedback effect gradually vanishes. A reactor that is naturally stable at high power levels is more difficult to control at low levels. For this reason one might limit the range of automatic control to 1 or 2 decades of power level. For automatic control, then, the reactor should not be shut down below 1 percent of full power. For analytical purposes $K_R G_R(s)$ may be defined in terms of $(\delta n/n)/\delta k$. In this form it is independent of level.

From the example of Figs. 4-4 and 4-5, it is evident that this simple representation of the combination of the two transfer functions is quite stable. Other methods can be used for determining the stability of more complex reactor negative temperature coefficient feedback systems. Weinberg and Ergen[15] have presented a method for homogeneous reactors, and Lipkin[16] has extended their method to treat heterogeneous reactors. However, the servo engineer will prefer to obtain equivalent results by refining the above analysis and adding more terms to the feedback transfer function. These more complex system representations have a real possibility of being unstable, but fortunately in practical reactor design and operation the oscillatory condition is not a common one.

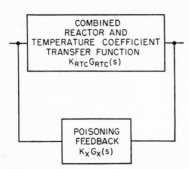

FIG. 4-6. Elementary block diagram poisoning feedback.

4-4. Poisoning Feedback. Having established the method of determining the stability of a reactor combined with a local negative temperature coefficient effect, we can continue by a similar process and examine the poison feedback loop. As all reactors have a temperature coefficient of some sort, we can start with the representation of the reactor transfer function as $K_{RTC}G_{RTC}(s)$ rather than $K_R G_R(s)$, and the poisoning feedback loop can then be tied around this combined system. Figure 4-6 shows the block diagram of the network that will be analyzed. It is now necessary to develop the form for $K_x G_x(s)$.

Repeating Eqs. (2-24) and (2-25) for convenience we have

$$\frac{dX'}{dt} = \lambda_I I' + (\gamma_x \Sigma_f - \sigma_x X')\phi - \lambda_x X' \qquad (4\text{-}8)$$

$$\frac{dI'}{dt} = -\lambda_I I' + \gamma_I \Sigma_f \phi \qquad (4\text{-}9)$$

In order to keep the solutions of these equations general, we now can divide Eqs. (4-8) and (4-9) by Σ_f since the value of Σ_f is not the same for

all reactors.   Thus, in generalized form the basic poisoning equations
become

$$\frac{dX}{dt} = \lambda_I I + (\gamma_x - \sigma_x X)\phi - \lambda_x X \tag{4-10}$$

$$\frac{dI}{dt} = -\lambda_I I + \gamma_I \phi \tag{4-11}$$

Using a similar technique to the method of deriving the reactor transfer
function (Sec. 3-4), let us divide the variables into steady-state parts and
incremental variations about this steady state such that

$$X = X_0 + \delta X \qquad \phi = \phi_0 + \delta\phi \qquad I = I_0 + \delta I \tag{4-12}$$

then Eq. (4-10) becomes

$$\frac{d}{dt}(X_0 + \delta X) = \lambda_I I_0 + (\gamma_x - \sigma_x X_0)\phi_0 - \lambda_x X_0 + \lambda_I \delta I$$
$$+ (\gamma_x - \sigma_x X_0)\delta\phi - (\sigma_x \phi_0 + \lambda_x)\delta X \tag{4-13}$$

where $(\delta\phi\delta X\sigma_x)$ has been neglected.   In the steady state

$$\frac{dX_0}{dt} = 0 = \lambda_I I_0 + (\gamma_x - \sigma_x X_0)\phi_0 - \lambda_x X_0 \tag{4-14}$$

$$\frac{d\delta X}{dt} = \lambda_I \delta I + (\gamma_x - \sigma_x X_0)\delta\phi - (\sigma_x \phi_0 + \lambda_x)\delta X \tag{4-15}$$

Similarly, Eq. (4-11) becomes

$$\frac{d}{dt}(I_0 + \delta I) = -\lambda_I I_0 + \gamma_I \phi_0 - \lambda_I \delta I + \gamma_I \delta\phi \tag{4-16}$$

In the steady state

$$\frac{dI_0}{dt} = 0 = -\lambda_I I_0 + \gamma_I \phi_0 \tag{4-17}$$

and

$$\frac{d\delta I}{dt} = -\lambda_I \delta I + \gamma_I \delta\phi \tag{4-18}$$

Transforming Eqs. (4-15) and (4-18) to Laplace notation

$$s\delta X(s) = \lambda_I \delta I(s) + (\gamma_x - \sigma_x X_0)\delta\phi(s) - (\sigma_x \phi_0 + \lambda_x)\delta X(s) \tag{4-19}$$
$$s\delta I(s) = -\lambda_I \delta I(s) + \gamma_I \delta\phi(s) \tag{4-20}$$
$$\delta I(s) = \frac{\gamma_I \delta\phi(s)}{s + \lambda_I} \tag{4-21}$$

Substituting Eq. (4-21) into Eq. (4-19)

$$s\delta X(s) = \frac{\lambda_I \gamma_I \delta\phi(s)}{s + \lambda_I} + (\gamma_x - \sigma_x X_0)\delta\phi(s) - (\sigma_x \phi_0 + \lambda_x)\delta X(s) \tag{4-22}$$

$$\frac{\delta X(s)}{\delta \phi(s)} = \frac{\lambda_I \gamma_I + (s + \lambda_I)(\gamma_x - \sigma_x X_0)}{(s + \lambda_I)(s + \sigma_x \phi_0 + \lambda_x)} \tag{4-23}$$

$$= \frac{(\gamma_x - \sigma_x X_0)\left(s + \dfrac{\lambda_I \gamma_I}{\gamma_x - \sigma_x X_0} + \lambda_I\right)}{(s + \lambda_I)(s + \sigma_x \phi_0 + \lambda_x)} \tag{4-24}$$

Equation (4-24), then, is the desired small signal transfer function. It can be seen from this equation that $\delta X(s)/\delta \phi(s)$ is a peculiar transfer function with its amplitude and phase shift very dependent on X_0 which, in turn, depends on ϕ_0. The symbols ϕ and n are being used interchangeably in this section. The physicist generally uses ϕ; the servo engineer uses n.

We may examine the transfer function of Eq. (4-24) numerically by setting in the following constants from Stephenson:[4]

$$\lambda_I = 2.9 \times 10^{-5}$$
$$\lambda_x = 2.1 \times 10^{-5}$$
$$\gamma_I = 0.056$$
$$\gamma_x = 0.003$$
$$\sigma_x = 3.5 \times 10^{-18}$$

First, the relationship between X_0 and ϕ_0 is determined from Eq. (2-26) in generalized form

$$X_0 = \frac{(\gamma_x + \gamma_I)\phi_0}{\lambda_x + \sigma_x \phi_0} \tag{4-25}$$

Fig. 4-7a shows this relationship of the xenon concentration as a function of neutron flux level. It can be seen that the poisoning rises linearly with flux until a flux level of approximately 10^{12} is reached. At higher flux levels the xenon concentration rises more slowly until at flux levels of approximately 10^{14} and higher there is no further increase in poison concentration.

From a transfer function point of view there are two flux levels which should be examined carefully. From Eq. (4-24) it can be seen that when $(\gamma_x - \sigma_x X_0) = 0$, corresponding to a flux level of $\phi_0 = 3 \times 10^{11}$, the phase of the transfer function shifts its ultimate end point with frequency. That is, at high frequencies when $\phi_0 < 3 \times 10^{11}$, there is a total phase shift in the xenon feedback path of $-90°$. When $\phi_0 > 3 \times 10^{11}$, there is an ultimate $-270°$ phase shift in the transfer function. This condition lasts until the point where $\lambda_I \gamma_I/(\gamma_x - \sigma_x X_0) + \lambda_I = 0$. The transfer function gain at zero frequency when $\gamma_x - \sigma_x X_0 = 0$ can easily be determined to be $\gamma_I/(\sigma_x \phi_0 + \lambda_x)$, and there is no discontinuity in gain as a function of ϕ_0.

It would appear that another point of interest might be when

$$\frac{\lambda_I \gamma_I}{(\gamma_x - \sigma_x X_0)} + \lambda_I = 0$$

as here the sign in the parentheses in the numerator of Eq. (4-24) would again be positive. This condition stipulates that

$$X_0 = \frac{\gamma_I + \gamma_x}{\sigma_x} \tag{4-26}$$

But from Eq. (4-25) this cannot happen without infinite flux. Therefore, at high flux levels above $\phi_0 = 3 \times 10^{11}$, $\lambda_I \gamma_I / (\gamma_x - \sigma_x X_0) + \lambda_I$ will always

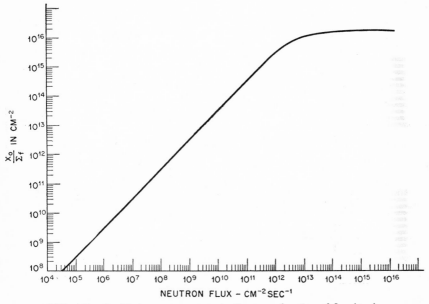

FIG. 4-7a. Equilibrium xenon concentration as a function of flux level.

be negative. Let us now examine numerically the transfer function at flux levels above and below 3×10^{11}.

Figures 4-7 and 4-8 show the relative response of the xenon concentration to small oscillations in flux normalized in gain about the $\varphi_0 = 10^{14}$ case. The absolute level for this curve is $+19.1$ db. It will be noted from the phase curves that for ϕ_0 below 3×10^{11}, the total phase lag at high frequencies is $90°$ whereas at higher flux levels the total phase lag is $270°$, as previously indicated.

The gain at zero frequency is a constant for fluxes roughly below $\phi_0 = 10^{10}$. At higher levels the gain steadily decreases with flux. This fact could have been presumed from the saturation effect of Fig. 4-7a.

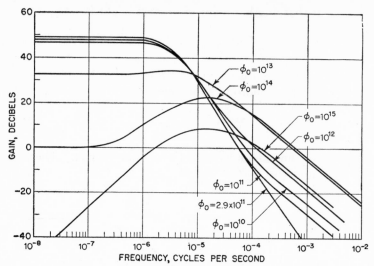

FIG. 4-7. Amplitude of transfer function of xenon feedback factor $\delta X(s)/\delta\phi(s)$.

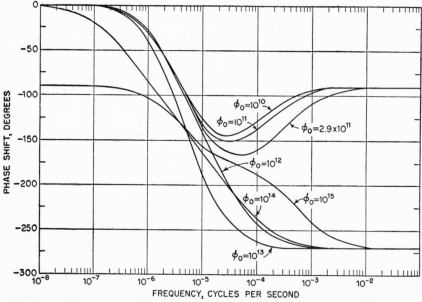

FIG. 4-8. Phase shift of transfer function of xenon feedback factor $\delta X(s)/\delta\phi(s)$.

Stability with Xenon Feedback. It has been shown that any elementary reactor containing a negative temperature coefficient of reactivity is stable no matter how small the negative temperature coefficient. A consideration of the xenon feedback loop now will require modification of this statement. Let us tie a xenon feedback loop around a reactor containing a negative temperature coefficient. The block diagram will be that of Fig. 4-9a. From Fig. 4-8 the xenon transfer function shows 180° phase lag in the neighborhood of 10^{-5} cycle/sec, and it is this frequency range which is of interest. For frequencies below 10^{-3} cycle/sec the reactor transfer function with negative temperature coefficient

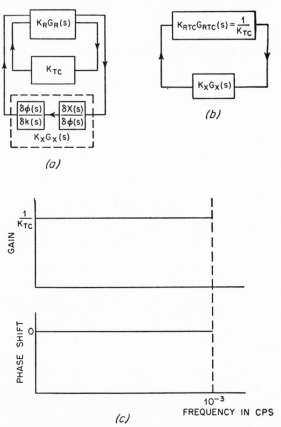

FIG. 4-9. Elementary block diagram of xenon feedback loop stability considerations. (a) Individual transfer functions. (b) Combined transfer functions. (c) Approximation to the response of $K_{RTC}G_{RTC}(s)$ for frequencies below 10^{-3} cps.

$K_{RTC}G_{RTC}(s)$ becomes a straight line having a gain of $1/K_{TC}$ and a phase shift of 0°. This condition comes about because the time constant of the negative temperature coefficient is presumed to be fast (see Figs. 4-4 and 4-5). This situation is shown in Fig. 4-9b and c, and for this analysis we shall assume that none of the frequencies above 10^{-3} cycles is important.

The transfer functions for the xenon concentration shown in Figs. 4-7 and 4-8 represent only $\delta X(s)/\delta \phi(s)$. It is now necessary to multiply this transfer function by a gain term which will, in general, be a constant.

This gain term contains Σ_f and a term depending upon operating level of the reactor. This multiplier will be denoted by $\delta\phi(s)/\delta k(s)$ as indicated in Fig. 4-9a.

The product of $[\delta X(s)/\delta\phi(s)][\delta\phi(s)/\delta k(s)]$ will be called $K_x G_x(s)$. The open-loop stability of this combination will now be examined. It can be seen that for stability the magnitude of the open-loop gain $(1/K_{TC})[K_x G_x(s)]$ must be less than unity when the total phase lag is 180°. Therefore for every flux level corresponding to given values of $K_x G_x(s)$, there exists a value of K_{TC}, or negative temperature coefficient, above which the combination is stable and below which it is unstable. Figure 4-10 indicates this situation. For values of fluxes below 3×10^{11}

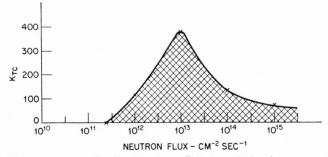

FIG. 4-10. Minimum negative feedback gain coefficient needed to keep xenon feedback loop stable. Crosshatched area unstable.

it is quite evident that no negative temperature coefficient is needed to keep the over-all loop stable. On the other hand, if the value of flux is increased, the magnitude of K_{TC} necessary to keep the system stable increases and peaks at a flux of approximately 10^{13}. At high flux levels, the amplitude of $K_x G_x(s)$ decreases, and here only a small negative temperature coefficient is needed for stability.

Although this analysis shows that instability is possible if the negative temperature coefficient is not large enough, this is not a serious situation. An unstable xenon feedback loop will oscillate continuously but with limited amplitude because of the nonlinearities in the xenon and reactor equations. This fact precludes any necessity for having large margins of stability. Instability may also be tolerable because of the extremely low frequency involved. That is, from Fig. 4-8 the oscillations would occur at a rate of only 1 to 2 cycles/day. Because of these low frequencies, future stability discussions will ignore the effect of xenon, as control-rod motions can easily take care of eliminating the poison reactivity tending to cause the oscillation.

4-5. General Requirements for Automatic Power-level Control. Having seen the kinetic behavior of a reactor with its own internal feedback loops, we are now in a position to attempt to control a reactor with an external control loop. We shall first examine broad operational requirements. To change the power level in a reactor requires the movement of a control rod or rods in such a manner that the multiplication factor of the reactor is first caused to deviate from unity. The rods are later moved to return the multiplication factor to unity. In changing power level two conditions must ultimately be satisfied by any control system: The power output level of the reactor must be the demanded power level within a given error, and the multiplication factor must ultimately be 1.

A given reactor may contain many control rods. These control rods may be operated individually or in groups or banks. Large groups of rods are moved quite slowly and usually function in control work as a coarse shimming system. These ganged rods are therefore sometimes called shim rods and may be worth several percent in reactivity. Because of the obvious hazard involved in making large reactivity changes quickly, the purpose of shim rods is usually to take care of slow changes such as depletion and poisoning. Shim-rod motion is therefore quite slow, and rates of change of reactivity between $10^{-5}\delta k$/sec and $10^{-3}\delta k$/sec are in common usage.

To take care of the routine power changes required in a reactor plant and to handle intermittent transients which may occur, one rod may be designated as a regulator rod. This regulator rod can be positioned automatically. Regulator rods may move quite quickly, but to ensure safety, the maximum worth of a regulator rod is usually kept below 0.006 in reactivity. In this manner the regulator rod can never inject as much as prompt critical reactivity into the reactor. In the event that more reactivity than 0.006 is needed for a particular operation, the shim rods may be connected to follow up the regulator rod position. That is, after the regulator rod has run out of reactivity, the shim rods can be called upon to move in the same direction as the regulator rod and thus slowly provide the necessary reactivity.

We have seen from Sec. 2-11 that manual control of a reactor is apt to be a tedious process requiring great alertness and training on the part of the operator. In changing power level, skill and anticipation will be required to prevent power-level overshoot. Poisoning and temperature fluctuations create the need for periodic control-rod manipulation. It is somewhat obvious that an automatic-control system can do a better job than a human being.

The above discussion presupposes the need for an external reactor control system. Some reactors having large negative temperature coefficients may not require an external regulating system. The criteria involved are presented later in this chapter.

An automatic-control system usually consists of a control loop around the regulator rod or a shim-rod group and can be operated as either a proportional regulating system or a discontinuous regulating system. A proportional regulating system is one in which the position of the control rod or rods is changed in proportion to and in phase opposition with any error created either by a power demand change or by an internal system transient. A discontinuous regulating system is one in which no control is attained unless an error, which is some fixed percentage away from a demanded set of conditions, is set up in the control loop. When sufficient deviation occurs from the demanded conditions, the control-rod position is usually changed at a fixed velocity. Discontinuous regulating systems can be designed to hold reactor power level to within 0.5 percent. Better accuracy can be obtained with a proportional type of control. A discontinuous system offers the advantage that it is less sensitive to noise, which may originate in detecting elements. In high-flux reactors, however, noise is usually not a serious problem, and for many purposes the increased accuracy warrants the use of the proportional system.

4-6. General Description of a Reactor Automatic-control System. Figure 4-11 shows a broad block diagram of the type of control system

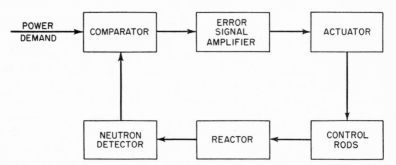

FIG. 4-11. Block diagram of the essential elements of a reactor automatic-control loop.

generally used to control a reactor in the power-level range. The reactor multiplication is changed by movement of the control rods. For this discussion we may first consider that we are using a regulator rod in a proportional system. The output of the reactor, in terms of power output or neutron level, is measured by a neutron detector, usually an ionization chamber. This reactor output is then compared with the desired power demand in the comparator, and any error between the actual output and the demanded output is noted and amplified in the error-signal amplifier. This amplifier finally controls an actuator which moves the rods the proper amount and in the proper direction to eliminate the error. The comparator, error-signal amplifier, and actuator may be of any suitable type. Pneumatic, hydraulic, electrical, and mechanical devices have all been used, and some will be described in Chap. 5. A brief description now follows of each of the components in the loop from a control-system point of view.

Reactor. The principal feature of the reactor to be noted in this control loop is its nonlinearity. As mentioned in Sec. 3-4, the reactor gain is proportional to the level at which the reactor is operating. This is a completely intolerable situation, as most control loops can operate in a stable manner only over a limited range in gain. Means to eliminate gain dependence upon level must be added to the control loop.

Comparator. The function of the comparator is twofold. First, it provides that the error signal is essentially the subtraction between the output of the neutron-detector signal and a power demand signal. Second, it is also used to compensate for the embarrassing nonlinearity of the reactor. The form of the output signal from the comparator should be error/level.

A simple comparator circuit is shown in Fig. 4-12. Here V_n is the signal from the neutron detector proportional to the power output of the reactor, V_e is the output error signal, and the power demand reference voltage V_0 is defined arbitrarily as $V_0 = E_b/K$. Then

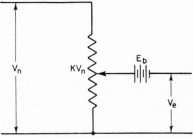

FIG. 4-12. Elementary form of comparator circuit.

$$V_e = KV_n - E_b \qquad (4\text{-}27)$$

$$= \frac{E_b V_n}{V_0} - E_b \qquad (4\text{-}28)$$

$$= E_b\left(\frac{V_n}{V_0} - 1\right) \quad \text{or} \quad E_b\left(\frac{n}{n_0} - 1\right) \qquad (4\text{-}29)$$

Letting an error signal $\delta n = n - n_0$

$$V_e = E_b\left(\frac{n - n_0}{n_0}\right) = \frac{\delta n}{n_0} E_b \qquad (4\text{-}30)$$

which is of the proper form so that the output of the comparator is inversely proportional to the neutron-demand level. Hence, the effect on the control loop of the reactor gain dependence on level is essentially canceled when the comparator is connected to the reactor. Actually, a signal inversely proportional to n rather than n_0 would be more desirable. That is, if the reactor power level changes, for complete cancellation of the nonlinearity during the transient, the comparator should divide by the actual level existing at any moment in the reactor. The difference between the actual level n and the demanded steady-state level n_0 is usually quite small, as the control system rapidly acts to make the two quantities the same. In practice it is much easier to obtain the term n_0 than n for use in a practical comparator circuit. It will be noted that the symbol n_0 is used here to denote demand level in the steady-state condition. This symbol has also been used in Chaps. 2 and 3 to denote the actual operating level of the reactor.

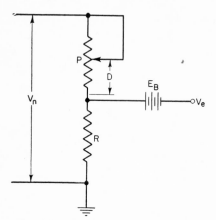

FIG. 4-13. Elementary form of comparator circuit in which the demand signal is directly proportional to the potentiometer arm rotation.

Comparators having perfect cancellation over an infinite range cannot be constructed practically, but good cancellation can take place over a limited range of about 100 to 1. Figure 4-13 shows a usable comparator circuit in which the demand signal is linearly proportional to the displacement D of the potentiometer P. When no current is taken from V_e

$$V_e = \frac{R}{R + DP} V_n - E_b \qquad (4\text{-}31)$$

where $0 \leq D \leq 1$.

Assume that when

$$V_n = V_0 \qquad V_e = 0 \qquad (4\text{-}32)$$

where V_0 is the demand voltage proportional to n_0. At $V_e = 0$

$$E_b = \frac{R}{R + DP} V_0 \qquad V_0 = E_b \left(1 + \frac{DP}{R}\right) \qquad (4\text{-}33)$$

From these expressions V_0 is linear with D. The error signal then becomes

$$V_e = \frac{R}{R + DP} (V_n - V_0) \qquad (4\text{-}34)$$

but

$$\frac{R}{R + DP} = \frac{E_b}{V_0} \qquad (4\text{-}35)$$

so

$$V_e = E_b \left(\frac{V_n - V_0}{V_0}\right) \qquad (4\text{-}36)$$

which again is of the desired form.

To ensure that no current is taken from V_e, computing techniques may be used and an operational amplifier connected, as indicated in Fig. 4-14. Here R' and R'', in parallel, have the same resistance as the original R of Fig. 4-13. The bias voltage of the amplifier also becomes the equivalent of the battery E_b.

Magnetic-amplifier Comparator. For many applications it is undesirable to use vacuum tubes in a comparator circuit and, consequently,

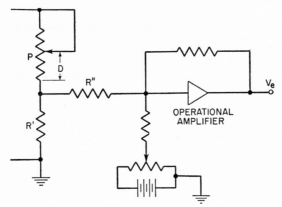

FIG. 4-14. Nonloading comparator circuit.

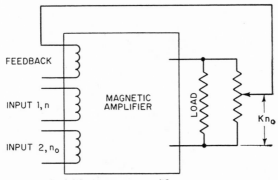

FIG. 4-15. Magnetic-amplifier comparator.

magnetic amplifiers have been used. In a magnetic amplifier an output current proportional to the difference between two control signals is generally obtained by using the control windings in opposition. Thus, one control signal tends to saturate the core while the other tends to unsaturate it. In this manner good linearity can also be obtained. Figure 4-15 indicates a schematic block diagram of a magnetic-amplifier comparator system. The output current I_L of this sort of device can be of the form $I_L = A(n - n_0)$ where A is the effective gain of the magnetic amplifier and n and n_0 are input currents proportional to the neutron level and the neutron-demand level. Magnetic amplifiers are usually operated using feedback, and feedback windings can easily be provided. Negative feedback may be used in the amplifier as well as the more customary positive feedback, and the familiar expression for the gain of an amplifier having negative feedback may be stated as

$$I_L = \frac{A(n - n_0)}{1 + AB} \tag{4-37}$$

where B is the feedback factor. If AB is now made large compared with 1,

$$I_L = \frac{n - n_0}{B} \tag{4-38}$$

It now becomes necessary only to make B proportional to n or n_0. Again, in practical circuits, it is easier to obtain n_0 than n, and a shaft rotation might be used to generate n_0 and also to connect a potentiometer into the feedback circuit. Therefore, the final output load current becomes

$$I_L = \frac{n - n_0}{n_0} \tag{4-39}$$

Error-signal Amplifier. The error-signal amplifier may be a conventional vacuum tube or magnetic amplifier. It usually amplifies the error-signal level from a few milliwatts to a few watts in order to control the actuating device. If an attempt is made to control the actuator motor directly, such as would be done if the control motor were a two-phase a-c servomotor, a few kilowatts might even be required from the amplifier. The frequency response of the amplifier usually presents no problem in comparison with that of the rest of the system. The amplifier may therefore be regarded as pure gain in a servo concept.

Rod Drive Mechanism and Actuator. As mentioned previously, almost any physical form of actuator and mechanism may be used. The actuator mechanism usually is called upon to perform a dual function. That is, in the case of shutdown of a nuclear reactor, a rapid action may be required, whereas for startup and power-level control, only a comparatively slow motion is needed. The actuator frequency response may range from a few cycles per minute to a few cycles per second. The actuator usually contains a power amplifier, and the output from the error-signal amplifier may be used to supply such conventional devices as hydraulic spool valves or torque motors. In some instances, if a d-c motor is the output actuating prime mover, control may be obtained by feeding the field voltage on an amplidyne or a Ward Leonard system motor generator set. The actuator is then coupled to a control rod whose weight, in present-day reactors, may be up to several hundred pounds. A detailed discussion of actuator requirements is given in Chap. 5.

Neutron Detectors. The neutron detector in a control system is usually an ionization chamber. This device will be treated more thoroughly in Chap. 7. For present purposes it may be stated that the ionization chamber is a device which gives out a current proportional to the number of neutrons per second which enter it. No frequency-response problems in conventional control circuits exist, as the frequency response of the chamber is not affected by operations up to a few hundred cycles per second. For analysis purposes the ionization chamber may be considered to behave as a current source similar to a pentode, as indicated in Fig. 4-16. The amount of current which is put out at saturation is a function of the amount of radiation present. The parameter which corresponds to grid voltage in a vacuum tube is radiation level in an ionization chamber.

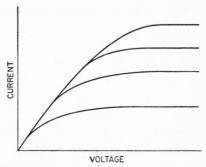

FIG. 4-16. Characteristic saturation curves of an ionization chamber.

4-7. Control-loop Response. Having examined the basic characteristics of the components of a reactor control loop, we may fittingly ask the question: What do we expect from this loop? The first requirement is that the loop be unconditionally stable. That is, under no condition of conceivable practical reactor operation are sustained oscillations to be permitted. The second requirement is that the loop shall respond satisfactorily under transient conditions. The transients to be considered are generally of two types: a change in the power demand level or a change in the reactivity of the reactor.

Control-loop Stability. The absolute stability of a reactor control system can be determined by servo synthesis techniques once the transfer functions of all the components in a loop are known. Elementary stability considerations can be accomplished by studying simplified servo systems involving the reactor. Both proportional and on-off type systems will be examined. We shall first consider proportional systems.

In an example we can combine the transfer functions of the error-signal amplifier, the actuator, and the control-rod mechanism into a single transfer function $K_B G_B(s)$, as indicated in Fig. 4-17. The reactor transfer function $K_R G_R(s)$ may be considered as given in Eq. 3-23 without any temperature coefficient feedback. If a temperature coefficient were present, $K_{RTC} G_{RTC}(s)$ would be used instead of $K_R G_R(s)$. We can now examine the over-all loop response as a function of some of the characteristics of $K_B G_B(s)$, as it is quite obvious that the stability of the loop shown in Fig. 4-17 depends upon the characteristics of $K_B G_B(s)$. Let us first consider that we can represent $K_B G_B(s)$ by an elementary quadratic

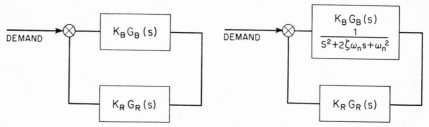

FIG. 4-17. Block diagram elementary reactor control loop, with lumped external transfer functions.

FIG. 4-18. Elementary reactor control-loop transfer functions for simplified control system.

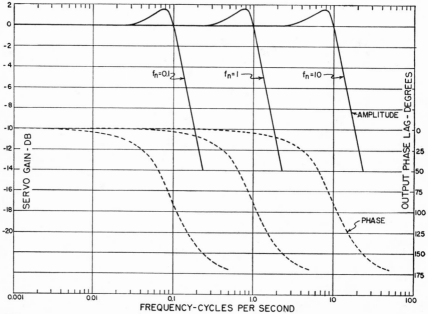

FIG. 4-19. Normalized transfer functions of external reactor control circuit for three values of external system natural frequency.

form of transfer function. Physically this might correspond to having a motor driving a control rod.

$$G_B(s) = \frac{1}{s^2 + 2\zeta\omega_n s + \omega_n^2} \tag{4-40}$$

would be the form of the frequency variant portion of the transfer function. We shall examine the insertion of various amounts of gain later. It is then desired to determine the stability of a control loop containing this form of control transfer function over a range of natural frequencies $f_n = \omega_n/2\pi$. For simplification let us assume that the damping coefficient ζ is fixed at $\zeta = 0.5$ and that we are using a reactor having the transfer function given for an l^* of 10^{-4} sec. Our simple block diagram becomes as shown in Fig. 4-18. The normalized transfer function of $K_B G_B(s)$ is shown in Fig. 4-19 for three values of f_n. These values of f_n are approximately 0.1 cycle/sec, 1 cycle/sec, and 10 cycles/sec. For stability purposes we may now examine the open-loop gain $K_R G_R(s)$ $K_B G_B(s)$. The indicated multiplication can be accomplished graphically, and the Nyquist plots[14] giving the loci of the open-loop gain points may

be examined in Fig. 4-20. It is obvious from the form of the reactor transfer function that at zero frequency the gain is infinite at an angle of $-90°$. As the possibility also exists that a total of $270°$ phase shift can be attained by the open-loop combination, oscillations can occur in this loop as a function of gain. The Nyquist plot of Fig. 4-20 for an arbitrary fixed gain shows that as the natural frequency is made higher, the possibility of oscillation becomes better, and, indeed, for the case of $f_n = 10$ cycles, the $(-1,0)$ point is encircled and oscillations would occur. In other words, in the design of an elementary reactor control system of this

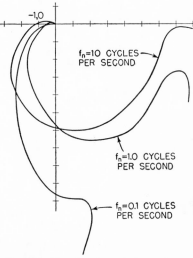

FIG. 4-20. Nyquist plots of elementary reactor control system for arbitrary gain.

type, the placement of the natural frequency of the control system is important if some arbitrary gain must be furnished for transient performance.

Phase shift compensation, of course, can be provided to permit higher gain, and most reactor control systems contain compensating networks. The common types of network that have been used in reactor control systems are given in Fig. 4-21. It must be emphasized again that this analysis was for a reactor with zero temperature coefficient. The method of analysis would be the same for a reactor with a negative temperature coefficient.

4-8. On-Off-type Reactor Control System. Until now we have been discussing proportional types of control systems. The more common system is the simple on-off type of control. Here, when the difference in signal between n and n_0 reaches a preset amount, a motor is started and caused to run at constant velocity until the error signal is reduced to another predetermined value. This discontinuous-type system has a dead zone in its control and is inherently incapable of the same accuracy

as the proportional system.   Other advantages exist, however.   The
dead-zone principle succeeds in making control-rod positioning simple in
that mechanical brakes, gearing, and other forms of friction may be used
to keep a control rod in a given position within the dead zone.   In the

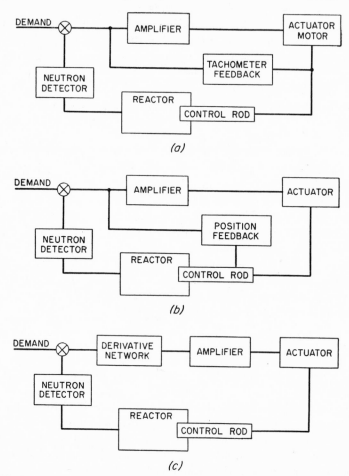

FIG. 4-21. Types of compensation networks commonly used in reactor automatic control
loops. (a) Tachometer feedback. (b) Position feedback. (c) Derivative network.

proportional system a control rod is held in place through the torque
developed by the control-drive motor and thus the complete system power
must be available to keep the proportional system control rod in a fixed
position.   As previously mentioned, another advantage of the on-off-
type system is that it is less susceptible to noise because of its dead zone.
    The on-off-type control system is at present quite common for large
experimental reactors, and the control system for the CP-3 reactor has

been described by Harrer.[5]   The method of analysis to be presented here is a general one developed by Grace,[6] and a fictitious reactor system will be presented as an illustration of the method.

The stability of an on-off system can be analyzed in the following manner: It can be felt intuitively that in order to use the on-off-type reactor control system, the reactor should have a negative temperature coefficient.   If the reactor system by itself is inherently unstable, the presence of the dead zone in the on-off system may well cause the control system to be in continuous oscillation.   Although it is quite possible to keep the reactor under control with a continuously oscillating system, prudence dictates that the wear on the control-system components should be minimized.   Consequently, we shall assume that the reactors under discussion in this section have negative temperature coefficients so that we can use $K_{RTC}G_{RTC}(s)$ as the transfer function.   After the control-system analysis is developed, we shall examine the effect of the magnitude of the temperature coefficient.

The reactors using discontinuous-type control systems, such as the CP-3, are reactors that in general merely maintain a fixed power level. These reactors usually have large values of l^*, and reactivity is changed only at very slow rates.   The design of all auxiliary systems about the reactor is such that nothing is capable of moving fast and consequently no fast transients can occur.   Therefore, in the study of the design of the control system for such reactors, the important factor becomes stability rather than fast transient response.

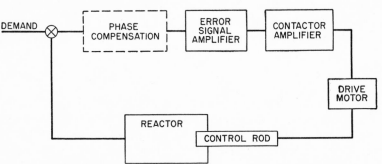

FIG. 4-22. Block diagram of discontinuous-type servo reactor control loop.

Figure 4-22 is a block diagram of the type of system under consideration.   The reactor of this block diagram may be the type of reactor described in Sec. 4-3.   The reactor and its temperature coefficient will be treated as having a combined transfer function $K_{RTC}G_{RTC}(s)$, as also given in Sec. 4-3.   A compensating network is shown in the loop to provide phase shift compensation.   The analysis will first be shown without this compensating network, and the network later added to increase the dynamic stability of the system.   The contactor amplifier indicated in the block diagram may be considered as a simple relay or relays, which close a set of contacts when the error-signal level reaches a fixed amount, then open these contacts when the error-signal level drops below another fixed value.   A corresponding set of contacts is opened and closed in a similar manner when the sign of the error signal reverses.   These contacts cause a motor to rotate in one direction or the other and to be stopped when the signal level is too small to keep either set of contacts closed.   The drive motor will be considered as running at constant velocity after an initial time lag in getting started.   A control rod is assumed to be geared to the motor, and the control-rod motion will therefore be characterized by being able to change reactivity at a fixed rate in $\delta k/\text{sec}$.

Analysis Procedure.   The type of system presented in Fig. 4-22 is a nonlinear system, the nonlinearity being caused by the contactor.   This nonlinearity may be expressed simply in that the output of the contactor is not a linear function of its input but rather a discontinuous function. The gain of a closed loop consisting of linear components is a function only of frequency.   Any nonlinearity in a system, such as the on-off feature in this reactor control loop, causes the loop gain to be a function of both frequency and amplitude.   When the amplitude-dependent transfer functions in the system can be separated from those which depend upon frequency, the loop gain can be expressed as a product. This product is loop gain = $BKAG$, where A is a complex function of amplitude independent of frequency, G is a complex function of frequency independent of amplitude, K is a constant gain factor, and B is the feedback factor which equals -1 in this reactor control loop.   The over-all transfer function of a system with $B = -1$ is the familiar expression

$$\frac{\text{Output}}{\text{Input}} = \frac{KAG}{1 + KAG} = \frac{KA}{G^{-1} + KA} \tag{4-41}$$

Expressing the over-all transfer function in the form given in Eq. (4-41) indicates that the stability of the system can be obtained by comparing G^{-1} and $-KA$.   The conventional method of performing this comparison is from a polar plot of G^{-1} and $-KA$.   The value of G^{-1} can be plotted for all values of frequency, and the value of $-KA$ can be plotted for all values of amplitude.   If the two loci intersect, that is, if $G^{-1} = -KA$, the system is capable of sustaining an oscillation.   The frequency of the oscillation would be the frequency corresponding to the point of intersection on the G^{-1} locus, and the amplitude can be found from the $-KA$ locus.

In the analysis of the block diagram of Fig. 4-22, the loop gain of the reactor control loop can be divided into an over-all frequency function G and an amplitude varying function A in the manner just described.   The function G is the product of the transfer functions of the reactor, the error-signal amplifier, and the drive motor. The function A comes from the contactor amplifier alone and describes the effects of the relays. The method of determining the transfer function of the relays will be based on the development of Kochenburger[7] and essentially depends upon the assumption that only the fundamental component of the square wave signal of rod velocity coming out of the relay is significant. Higher harmonics are more attenuated by the system, particularly by the motor, and consequently may be ignored.

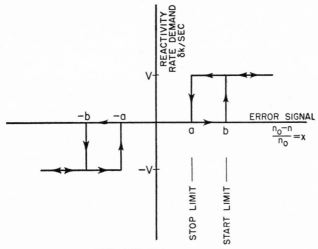

FIG. 4-23. Relay program.

Figure 4-23 illustrates the relay cycle and the terminology that will be used. The error signal into the relays is proportional to $(n_0 - n)/n_0$. As the error signal increases, it reaches the point b, which closes the relay starting the drive motor and creating the reactivity rate demand signal V. Once the control rods are started moving in the direction to reduce the error signal, the hysteresis of the relay causes the contacts in the relay to remain closed until the point a is reached and the drive motor is turned off. It is assumed that the contactor amplifier is symmetrical for negative signals, with $-b$ being the negative start limit and $-a$ being the negative stop limit. Let us now assume that the output of the error-signal amplifier is $x = |x| \sin \omega t$. Figure 4-24 indicates the phase relationships between the input signal x and the fundamental component v of the output signal. The terms which are of consequence in the analysis are the ratios b/a, V/b, and $|x|/b$. From this figure it can be seen that if $b/a = 1$, the output of v is in phase with the input x. When b/a is greater than 1, phase shift occurs between x and v, with the output phase lagging the input phase. The worst case is when $a = 0$, and at this point a 45° phase shift occurs for $|x|/b = 1$. When $|x|/b$ is very large, it can also be seen that the phase shift between output and input approaches zero.

The magnitude of the fundamental component of the contactor square wave output is also a function of b/a and $|x|/b$. It is obvious that the

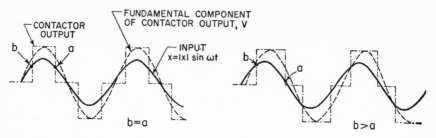

WHEN b=a, NO PHASE SHIFT
WHEN b>a, FUNDAMENTAL OF SQUARE WAVE OUTPUT LAGS INPUT
WORST CASE WHEN a=0, 45° PHASE SHIFT FOR $\frac{|x|}{b}=1$
WHEN $\frac{|x|}{b}$ IS LARGE, PHASE SHIFT APPROACHES ZERO

FIG. 4-24. Contactor input and output phase considerations.

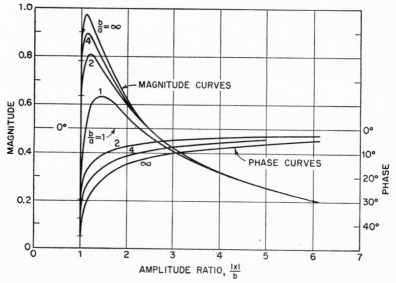

FIG. 4-25. Relationships of $A_{b/a}(|x|/b)$ as functions of $|x|/b$.

gain of the contactor, that is, its output/input ratio, falls off as $|x|$ is increased. The ratio V/b appears directly as a gain factor in the contactor amplifier, making the complete transfer function of the nonlinear section $(V/b)A_{b/a}(|x|/b)$. The transfer relationship $A_{b/a}(|x|/b)$ without the fixed gain multiplier V/b is plotted in Fig. 4-25 for various values of

b/a. It can be seen from this curve that the locus terminates abruptly at $|x|/b = 1$. Obviously, for all amplitudes of x less than the start limit b, the system does not respond. Figure 4-25 also indicates clearly that the maximum value of phase shift can be only 45°.

In anticipation of our comparing the nonlinear complex amplitude function $-A_{b/a}(|x|/b)$ with the frequency-dependent function G^{-1}, we may replot the results of Fig. 4-25 in polar coordinates as Fig. 4-26. In this figure we have also reversed the sign to obtain $-A_{b/a}(|x|/b)$. The

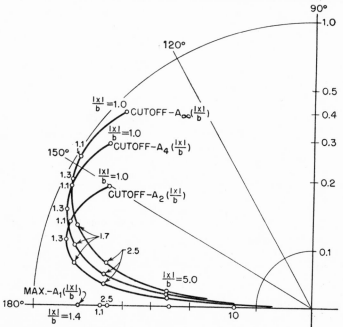

FIG. 4-26. Relationships of $-A_{b/a}(|x|/b)$ as functions of $|x|/b$ in polar coordinates.

abrupt stop at $|x|/b = 1$ and the maximum phase shift of 45° are again emphasized. These curves are presented again for various values of b/a without the constant multiplying factor V/b. It is evident that as the fixed gain portion of the contactor amplifier is increased in magnitude, the curves of Fig. 4-26 will all be moved out radially.

Example of On-Off-type Reactor-control-system Operation. We are now in a position to try the above approach. First, we can select a specific control-loop configuration specifying transfer functions and gains for all the components of the loop. Figure 4-27 indicates a block diagram of a specific loop. The transfer function form of the contactor has just been derived. The actual reactivity rate into the reactor is the contactor output v delayed by the lag in the drive motor, which has the form $1/(1 + \tau s)$.

Since the motor delay depends on frequency, it may be conveniently lumped in with the reactor transfer function. The demanded reactivity rate v would then be input to the combined transfer functions of the reactor and motor. For this example we may choose a specific value for $\tau = 0.5$ sec. This is a reasonable value which many actual motors can exceed.

For the transfer function of the reactor we shall select the combined reactor temperature coefficient transfer functions $K_{RTC}G_{RTC}(s)$ of Figs. 4-4 and 4-5 and carry through the analysis for different values of K_{TC}. It will be noted that our input to the reactor is now not a change in reactivity but a change in rate of change of reactivity. Consequently, our

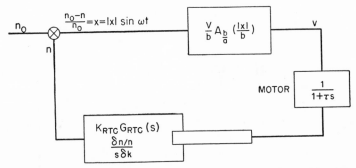

FIG. 4-27. Servo block diagram of discontinuous reactor control loop indicating transfer functions of principal components.

output will be a change in level as a function of a change in reactivity input rate. That is, the transfer function is of the form $(\delta n/n)/s\delta k$. The $1/s$ term will modify the transfer function representation of Fig. 4-4 and effectively make the amplitude changes more pronounced as a function of frequency.

We may now combine all of the frequency dependent portions of the transfer function $G(s)$, invert this function, and plot it on a polar diagram as shown in Fig. 4-28. It can be seen from this that the larger the temperature coefficient, the more open is the locus. Consequently, there is a greater area for stable operation. With no temperature coefficient, the smaller enclosed area drastically limits the range of V/b which can be permitted for a stable system. The shape of these curves will, of course, be modified by any specific motor time delay constant τ.

Let us now go back to the comparison of the amplitude function and the frequency function by combining the curves of Fig. 4-26 and Fig. 4-28 to the same scale. This combination is shown in Fig. 4-29. Under these conditions it will be recalled that $V/b = 1$ and it is obvious that the system will oscillate for all but the very largest of the temperature coefficient gain time constants. Even for the case where $K_{TC} = 0.019$, the phase margin is so small that the system is apt to be unsatisfactory.

This situation can be corrected by reducing V/b, and it is fortunate that safety considerations usually require this ratio to be considerably less than 1. Current practice in reactor operations limits V to a range of 10^{-3} to 10^{-6} $\delta k/\text{sec}$. The start limit b depends upon the accuracy to which it is desired to hold the power level, as b effectively represents an

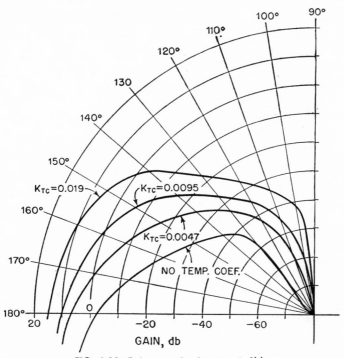

FIG. 4-28. Polar transfer function $G^{-1}(s)$.

indeterminate dead zone. A value of b of the order of 0.1 might be a reasonable number. Consequently, V/b might range from 10^{-2} to 10^{-5}. It will be noted that as V/b is reduced, the control system containing no temperature coefficient becomes conditionally stable; that is, a range of V/b exists whereby, if its value were larger than a given amount or smaller than another amount, the system could oscillate. For reactors having negative temperature coefficients of sufficient magnitude this condition does not exist. The only problem is to maintain V/b below a given amount. Gain margins and phase margins here are determined by experience. In linear servo practice a phase margin of 35° and a gain margin of 8 db are typical values for satisfactory stability and transient response. In the nonlinear case it is likely that smaller phase margins might be used, as the amplitude of any oscillation would be limited by the output of the contactor.

Phase Shift Compensation. The safety considerations in limiting V/b may provide a control system that does not oscillate but nevertheless does not have suitable phase margin for a desired transient response. The situation may be corrected by providing proper phase compensation as indicated in the block diagram of Fig. 4-22. As an example, let us

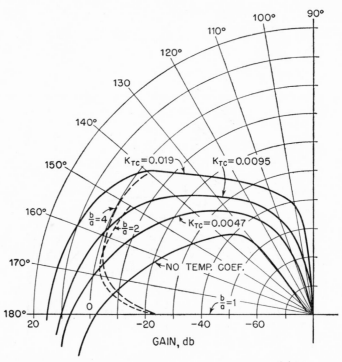

FIG. 4-29. Comparison at unity gain of amplitude function $-A_{b/a}(|x|/b)$ with frequency function $G^{-1}(s)$.

consider the case just presented where $b/a = 4$, $V = 10^{-3}\delta k/\text{sec}$, $b = 0.1$, and $K_{TC} = 0.0047$. This situation is shown in Fig. 4-30. It can be seen that although adequate gain margin exists, the phase margin is only 22°, which may be small when one considers that this elementary analysis did not take into account any of the second-order effects which must exist in a practical physical system. Phase compensation may then be used and a G^{-1} curve modified, as shown by the dotted line in Fig. 4-30. Here adequate phase margin is provided. Some type of phase compensation is generally used in practical systems.

4-9. Transient Response of Control Loop. The assumption is usually made that an optimum steady-state response leads to a reasonable transient response, but these qualifications depend upon the reactor usage and its safety factors. A transient overshoot of 2:1 probably is not damaging to most reactors providing it does not last too long. However, under certain high-power operating conditions, transient overshoots of this magnitude could conceivably cause damage to a specific reactor. Rather than attempting to set down absolute permissible magnitudes of transient response, it is more fitting to examine now the form of the

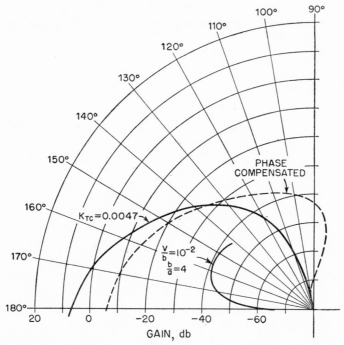

FIG. 4-30. Stability of discontinuous control-loop example with and without phase compensation.

response to given transients and to let the suitability of this response be determined from an over-all picture.

The transient response to a change in power-level demand is usually unimportant compared with the response to a change in reactivity. The power demand change rate can be limited externally to any desired value, but the internal rate of change of reactivity may, on occasion, be beyond the control of the design engineer. Consequently, this is the type of transient that is apt to be more disturbing to the system. We shall consider the system response to a severe disturbance which will be a sudden step change in reactivity. Physically, the problem becomes: Given a specific control loop, how does the reactor output power level change if the reactor is suddenly subjected to a step change in reactivity from any cause? Controlwise, the problem resolves into: Given the transfer functions of all the control-system components, what is the time variation of the output power signal $V_n(t)$ for a step-function input of reactivity?

In order to approach the form of the output response, let us again simplify the block diagram of Fig. 4-11 into the servo block diagram of Fig. 4-31. Here again the reactor transfer function has been indicated as $K_R G_R(s)$ and the error-signal amplifier, the actuator, and control-rod mechanism have been lumped together into the common transfer function $K_B G_B(s)$. The comparator is indicated as the summation device between V_0 and V_n, and the neutron detector is indicated as having only

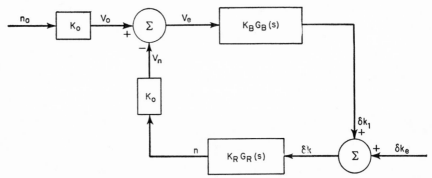

FIG. 4-31. Servo block diagram of reactor control loop used for transient analysis.

pure gain K_0 independent of frequency. In order to inject steps of reactivity conveniently, means have been provided to insert the disturbance δk_e. It will be noted from this block diagram that no phase compensation has been added and, for simplicity, the temperature coefficient of reactivity has been ignored. From the block diagram of Fig. 4-31 we can solve for the Laplace transform $V_n(s)$ in terms of the transfer functions of the system components and the reactivity. We can then take the inverse transform to obtain finally $V_n(t)$. From Fig. 4-31 we can see the following equivalents using Laplace notation:

$$V_e(s) = V_0(s) - V_n(s) \tag{4-42}$$
$$\delta k_1(s) = K_B G_B(s) V_e(s) \tag{4-43}$$
$$\delta k(s) = \delta k_1(s) + \delta k_e(s) \tag{4-44}$$
$$V_n(s) = K_0 n(s) \tag{4-45}$$

It will be recalled from the determination of the transfer function of the reactor given in Sec. 3-4 that only oscillations about a steady-state level were considered in deriving the transfer function. This simplification enabled us to remove the steady-state power-level term from the analysis. To consider the effect of transient changes of reactivity on the system as a whole, however, it is necessary to reintroduce the steady-state term. From this statement it follows that

$$n(s) = n_0(s) + \delta n(s) \tag{4-46}$$

$$\delta n(s) = K_R G_R(s) \delta k(s) \tag{4-47}$$

Now combining Eqs. (4-42) to (4-47) we have

$$V_n(s) = K_0 n_0(s) + K_0 \delta n(s) \tag{4-48}$$

$$= V_0(s) + K_0 K_R G_R(s) \delta k(s) \tag{4-49}$$

$$-V_e(s) = V_n(s) - V_0(s) = K_0 K_R G_R(s)[\delta k_1(s) + \delta k_e(s)] \tag{4-50}$$

$$= K_0 K_R G_R(s)[K_B G_B V_e(s) + \delta k_e(s)] \tag{4-51}$$

$$= \frac{K_0 K_R G_R(s) \delta k_e(s)}{1 + K_0 K_R K_B G_R(s) G_B(s)} \tag{4-52}$$

$$V_n(s) = V_0(s) + \frac{K_0 K_R G_R(s) \delta k_e(s)}{1 + K_0 K_R K_B G_R(s) G_B(s)} \tag{4-53}$$

We can assume that during the reactivity change, the power-level demand does not change, so that $V_0(t)$ is a constant.

In order to determine the inverse transform of $V_n(s)$ we must know the actual transfer functions of the components in the control loop. For the components indicated in Fig. 4-31 we must stipulate a transfer function form for $K_R G_R(s)$ and $K_B G_B(s)$. Elementary approximations will again be used to indicate the form of solution. Let us assume that we are going to attempt to control our reactor with a fast control system of such a speed that we do not have to consider delayed neutrons but rather are effectively controlling on prompt neutrons. We shall also assume that the response of the control system is so fast that we can ignore the integrating effect of the reactor. For a solution of this type we can approximate the reactor transfer function by

$$K_R G_R(s) = \frac{K_R}{Ts + 1} \tag{4-54}$$

We can similarly approximate the transfer function of the driving system, which consists of the amplifier and the actuator mechanism. An illustrative form of transfer function for a hydraulic mechanism might be given by

$$K_B G_B(s) = \frac{K_B}{s[(s/\omega)^2 + 2\zeta(s/\omega) + 1]} \tag{4-55}$$

We are now ready to substitute the expressions for the transfer functions into Eq. (4-53), which yields

$$V_n(s) = V_0(s) + \frac{K_0 K_R s(s^2 + 2\zeta\omega s + \omega^2)}{s(Ts + 1)(s^2 + 2\zeta\omega + \omega^2) + K_0 K_R K_B \omega^2} \delta k_e(s) \tag{4-56}$$

The Laplace transform of a unit step function is $1/s$, so that

$$\delta k_e(s) = \frac{\Delta k}{s} \tag{4-57}$$

where Δk represents the magnitude of the step change.   Equation (4-56) then reduces to the form

$$V_n(s) = V_0(s) + \frac{K_0 K_R}{T} \frac{s^2 + a_1 s + a_0}{s^4 + b_3 s^3 + b_2 s^2 + b_1 s + b_0} \Delta k \tag{4-58}$$

where

$$a_0 = \omega^2$$

$$a_1 = 2\zeta\omega$$

$$b_1 = \frac{\omega^2}{T}$$

$$b_2 = \omega^2 + \frac{2\zeta\omega}{T}$$

$$b_3 = 2\zeta\omega + \frac{1}{T}$$

The inverse transform of this equation can be found to be of the form[8]

$$V_n(t) = V_0 + A V_0 \delta k [e^{-\alpha t} - B e^{-\beta t} + C e^{-\gamma t} \cos (xt + \phi)] \tag{4-59}$$

The form of these results, of course, depends on the specific values of the constants used.   For illustration, Eq. (4-59) can be solved for the case

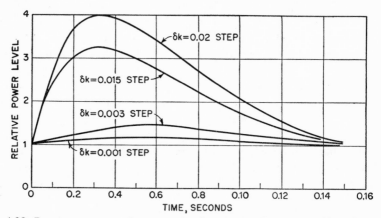

FIG. 4-32. Transient response of an example of proportional-type control loop for various step reactivity inputs.

of a reactor having an l^* of 4×10^{-4} sec, controlled by a fast hydraulic servo loop having constants $\zeta = 0.5$, $\omega = 26$ radians/sec, $T = 0.069$ sec, $K_0 K_e = 120 V_0$, and $K_0 K_e K_B = 1.62$.   Figure 4-32 shows the response of this system to step reactivity changes.

It can be seen in this approximate solution that the peak heights of the transient response are a direct function of the input δk step amplitude and that the time for the transient to return to its steady point is approximately constant. It must be remembered, however, that the transfer function of the reactor was derived for small oscillations. Consequently, the response, as determined in this manner, will be correct only for relatively small values of δk steps.

Elementary Control System for Reactor with Negative Temperature Coefficient. Approximate solutions for the stability and transient response of a proportional-type reactor control loop in which the reactor has a negative temperature coefficient are accomplished in a similar manner to that just presented. In the stability considerations the block diagram of Fig. 4-33 may be used and the open-loop gain obtained and examined. It will usually be found that greater gain can be permitted for the control loop with the negative temperature coefficient. The transient analysis becomes much more complex, and another method of handling this will be presented in Sec. 4-10.

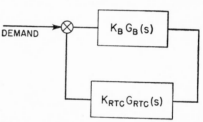

FIG. 4-33. Elementary block diagram for transient analysis of reactor control loop considering temperature coefficient.

4-10. Determination of Control-loop Performance by Simulation Technique. In order to eliminate many of the approximations we have just made in the transient analysis of an actual system, we can resort to a change in technique and attempt to find more exact solutions to the transient problem using analogue-computing methods. First, however, it becomes necessary to define in more detail the problem of what is required from an over-all reactor control system. It has been seen, from the elementary transient analysis just performed, that many parameters are involved. Each one of these parameters can conceivably be optimized one against another, provided that a set of standards are laid down. Although some reactors possess no significant temperature coefficient, the majority of the reactors in use at present have substantially large negative temperature coefficients. The magnitude and the effective time constant of this temperature coefficient must be taken into account, and many items added to our elementary control-loop block diagram.

In general, a system of this sort may be examined by four criteria:

1. Absolute stability—this criterion means no exponentially increasing oscillations can exist.

2. Relative stability—what is the number of oscillations before a transient has essentially died out?

3. Maximum power-level excursion—the peak power reached by the reactor for a fixed-shape input disturbance.

4. The restoring time of the system—the time for the transient to die out essentially.

It is apparent, then, that various systems and components may be compared by means of these criteria and decisions made on an over-all basis as to what is the best control configuration for a given problem.

Specific Example.   In order to grasp the magnitude of this problem, let us follow through this examination procedure for a specific example. Assume that a control system has a block diagram such as is given in Fig. 4-34.   In this block diagram we have a reactor that, for the sake of

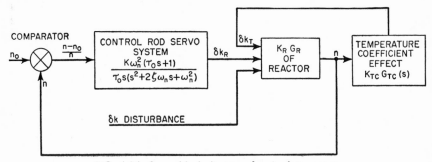

FIG. 4-34. Servo block diagram for simulator setup.

example, has a mean neutron lifetime of 10^{-4} sec and, consequently, the transfer function given in Figs. 3-15 and 3-16.   The reactor also has a negative temperature coefficient, and this negative temperature coefficient will be treated as a separate servo system around the reactor as indicated in Sec. 4-3.   Consequently, it will have a given time constant, or bandwidth, that depends upon the type of reactor construction.

The heat-transfer coefficient from the fuel of the reactor to the moderator will principally determine the time constant of the temperature coefficient effect.   Actually, in a practical plant, as mentioned in Sec. 4-3, there will be two time constants involved.   The temperature coefficient is one of the most important variables in the plant, and it is desired to study its effect upon the control system from ranges of $K_{TC} = 0$ to approximately $0.04 \delta k/(n/n - n_0)$.

Control-rod Servo System.   The control-rod servo system transfer function to be examined in this example is

$$\frac{\delta k/(n - n_0)}{n_0} = \frac{K\omega_n{}^2(\tau_0 s + 1)}{\tau_0 s(s^2 + 2\zeta\omega_n s + \omega_n{}^2)} \tag{4-60}$$

where K = gain in reactivity per unit error, $\dfrac{\delta k/(n - n_0)}{n_0}$

$f_n = \omega_n/2\pi$ = undamped natural resonant frequency of the control-rod servo system, cycles/sec

ζ = damping ratio of the servo system

$f_0 = 1/2\pi\tau_0$ = an integrating break frequency, cycles/sec

The choice of this form of the transfer function of the control-rod system is made for several reasons. First, it is an excellent approximation to some of the practical servo systems now in use in reactor control systems. Second, a quadratic form of this sort should closely approximate the behavior of almost any type of physical equipment which might be chosen to drive a control rod. That is, an electric motor or hydraulic system should be essentially of this form. The $(\tau_0 s + 1)/\tau_0 s$ portion of this transfer function is used principally to eliminate the steady-state error between n and n_0. It will be recognized from an examination of the block diagram of Fig. 4-34 that an error can exist between n and n_0 and yet the reactivity requirements that $k = 1$ for steady state of the reactor be completely satisfied by the temperature coefficient effect system alone. The integration thus provided by this transfer function eliminates a steady-state error, but for many control systems this portion of the transfer function might not be used.

It can now be seen that to study this given reactor control system completely requires an understanding of the effects and optimization of the following seven variables:

1. The magnitude of the temperature coefficient
2. The time constant of the temperature coefficient
3. K, the system gain
4. f_n, the natural frequency of the control system
5. ζ, the damping ratio
6. f_0, the integrating break frequency
7. The shape of the transient disturbance

It is possible to examine the stability and the transient response by the methods outlined in Secs. 4-7, 4-8, and 4-9. To determine the stability and to solve for the transient responses for a range of values of all the various parameters within reason for a system of this sort by means of these methods is a long and tedious procedure. With this large number of variables, an empirical approach may be tried and methods of analogue computation and simulation are quite attractive. Chapter 11 outlines the means of designing simulation apparatus. We shall assume that a specific simulator has been designed for the example of Fig. 4-34 and that all of the seven above-mentioned parameters may be varied.

Let us now carry through this specific problem. The method to be used will be to set up the simulated plant, inject given types of disturbances, and study the effects of changing the parameters one at a time. It would be anticipated that the form of the transient output disturbance would be essentially that of Fig. 4-32. The particular local conditions we can select for this study are that the reactor is operating at full power, the power demand n_0 fixed at full power, and no manipulation is to be permitted to the coolant flow through the reactor. A positive reactivity disturbance will then be inserted into the reactor, and the form of the power output transient will be examined.

Input Disturbance. The input disturbance to be used will be, as before, one in which the reactivity into the reactor is changed in a prescribed manner. Since one of the evaluation criteria of the performance of the servo system is based upon its response to this transient disturbance, it is clear that the transient disturbance must be specified accurately. The form of the disturbance to be used is a first-order time delay of the form $\delta k = 0.003(1 - e^{-t/\tau})$. This type of disturbance is chosen because, by selection of the proper value of the parameter τ, an input is obtained that is reasonably typical of the form of transients to be expected in actual physical systems. The value of $\tau = 0$ denoted a $0.003\delta k$ step function which is obviously physical fiction. Nevertheless, responses to this type of input are of interest because the analytical calculations for this type of response are comparatively simple. In addition, a step input gives the worst transient response in most physical systems, and thus an upper limit is established on the system performance. The use of a constant amplitude of reactivity change of $0.003\delta k$ is quite severe and probably represents a worse case condition in that reactivity changes of 0.003 in δk are very unlikely in most reactors operating at a constant power level.

Temperature Coefficient. It will be recognized from Fig. 4-34 that the effect of the negative temperature coefficient is an inherently stabilizing one in the over-all reactor control system. In fact, for many types of reactors there is no need to have an external servo system for transient protection when the negative temperature coefficient is of sufficient magnitude. However, with analogue computational techniques it is just as simple to examine the effect of the negative temperature coefficient acting alone or acting in conjunction with an external servo system, and this is the procedure that will be used. The temperature coefficient magnitude will be defined by the use of $K_{TC} = ATC$, as indicated in Sec. 4-3.

Procedure. We can first optimize the constants of the external control-rod servo system. It will be found in this type of problem that the damping factor, the gain, and the integrating break frequency can all be set by cut-and-try methods on the analogue simulator to effective optima. These optimum constants can then be used while the natural frequency response of the servo loop is examined. For these optimum conditions the control-rod servo system may be specified by one parameter alone, that is, the natural frequency of the control servo, f_n.

Damping. We can now proceed with the optimization process. Figure 4-35 shows the effect of varying ζ from 0.5 to 1.5, when a $0.003\delta k$ step transient is inserted into a system having a temperature coefficient gain of $K_{TC} = 0.039$, a natural frequency of 0.3 cycle/sec, and an integrating break frequency of 0.032 cycle/sec. It can be seen that the overdamped servo provides the best of the three damping coefficients considered. This figure also shows that a higher gain is permissible for the same stability in the overdamped condition. The time to reach a steady state following the transient differs little between the cases shown in

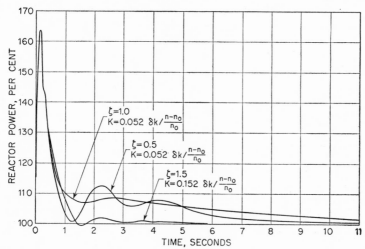

FIG. 4-35. Control-system transient response to $0.003\delta k$ step function as damping coefficient is varied.

Fig. 4-35 in that the damping ratio affects principally the extent of the oscillation following the transient. Although these results are indicated for only one value of f_n and temperature coefficient, the performance of the system as a function of damping constant would be found to be similar for other natural frequencies and temperature coefficients.

Gain. As Fig. 4-35 indicates that $\zeta = 1.5$ gives the best system response, only data taken from $\zeta = 1.5$ need be considered from here on. The next parameter to optimize is the loop gain K. The effects of varying K are indicated in Fig. 4-36. This figure illustrates that the loop gain is not a critical adjustment within limits. A factor of 10 in gain reduction from a stable maximum does not cause extreme differences in transient shape. The primary effect of higher gain is to reduce the amplitude of the tail of the transient without seriously affecting its slope. If the gain is increased higher and higher, however, instability ultimately

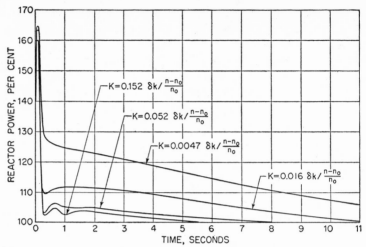

FIG. 4-36. Control-system transient response to $0.003\delta k$ step function as loop gain is varied.

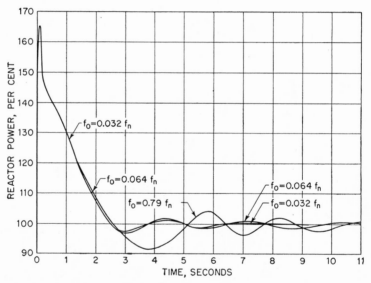

FIG. 4-37. Control-system transient response to $0.003\delta k$ step function as ratio of integrating break frequency to natural frequency is varied.

will result. As indicated from Fig. 4-36, gains of $K = 0.152 \dfrac{\delta k}{(n - n_0)/n_0}$ might be permitted.

Integrating Break Frequency. We have just seen that the gain and the damping may be set empirically to optimum values in that neither is particularly critical. The integrating break frequency f_0 can next be varied.   The function of this low-frequency integration is to restore the controlled variable to the control point as quickly as possible once the disturbance has been counteracted and to reduce steady-state control errors to zero.   Again, the effect of varying f_0 is to reduce the tail of the transient.   The integrating break frequency f_0 is related to f_n, the natural frequency of the system.   In general, a value of $f_0 = 0.1f_n$ is found to be quite satisfactory.   Figure 4-37 indicates the response to the same step transient as f_0 is varied with respect to f_n.

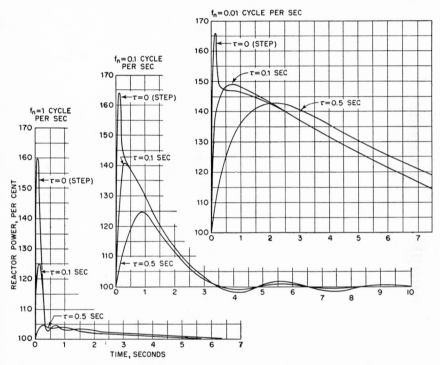

FIG. 4-38. Transient response of optimized control system for given types of transients at three natural frequencies when $K_{TC} = 0.039$.

Control-rod Servo Frequency Response.   The parameter of major importance in the transient response of the control system is the undamped natural frequency of the control servo.   Basically, the servo problem concerns a control system which has two feedback paths in parallel, each of which serves to modify the output of the controlled device in response to a particular input.   One of the feedback loops is the effect of the negative temperature coefficient, whereas the other is the control-rod servo system.   We have just seen that all of the parameters associated directly with the servo except one, the natural frequency, may be optimized, so that the reactor control servo can be classified by a single parameter, namely, its undamped natural frequency.

The negative temperature coefficient, similarly, is a feedback loop which behaves very much like the control loop, except that it lacks low-frequency integration. Around a given power level for a specific reactor, the servo behavior of the negative temperature coefficient loop can also be described in terms of a single number, the value of the temperature coefficient itself, provided its time constant is considered fixed by reactor

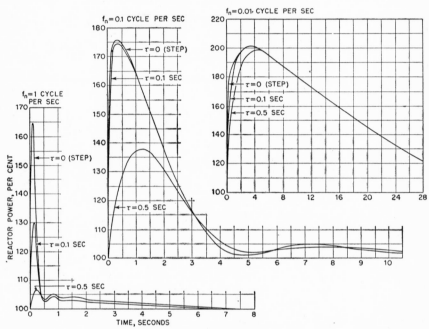

FIG. 4-39. Transient response of optimized control system for given types of transients at three natural frequencies when $K_{TC} = 0.009$.

geometry. Finally, to describe the input functions employed in this sort of study, a single number of the nature of a time constant is sufficient to describe each input function. Therefore, a complete transient-response investigation can now be described in terms of three parameters in place of the original seven. These are the temperature coefficient, the natural frequency of the control-system servo, and the time constant of the input disturbance. Figures 4-38, 4-39, and 4-40 indicate the type of response that can be obtained from a given system by varying these parameters. Figure 4-38 shows a group of curves obtained for a temperature coefficient such that $K_{TC} = 0.039$ for various types of input functions at given servo natural frequencies. It can be seen that the front edge of each of these transients is effectively limited in amplitude by the temperature coefficient effect, whereas the rear edge of the transient assumes the time constant of the control-system servo.

Figure 4-39 indicates a weaker temperature coefficient of $K_{TC} = 0.009$, and here combinations of both the temperature coefficient and the control servo come into play, particularly at the low natural frequency. Figure 4-40 shows the same group of transients in a system which has no temperature coefficient, and here the entire control rests upon the control-rod servo system. A comparison of Figs. 4-38 and 4-40 gives a true picture as

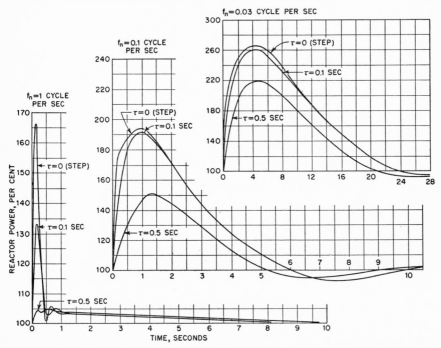

FIG. 4-40. Transient response of optimized control system for given types of transients at three natural frequencies when $K_{TC} = 0$.

to the relative difference between controlling transients on a strong negative temperature coefficient and controlling by external system with no temperature coefficient.

In order to compare the temperature coefficient effectiveness as a servo system in limiting peak power attained during transients, the information attained in Figs. 4-38, 4-39, and 4-40 can be cross-plotted as given in Fig. 4-41. Here the peak power attained during a step transient is plotted against the natural frequency of the control-rod servo system for various values of the temperature coefficient. In this figure the curve for zero temperature coefficient is the measure of the performance of the control servo alone. The measure of the servo performance of the temperature coefficient alone can be obtained by extrapolating the curves containing temperature coefficients to the left to a zero value of f_n, which effectively corresponds to the elimination of the control servo. If the peak power values thus obtained are projected horizontally to the right, the intercepts with the zero temperature coefficient curve give the equivalent control-system performance natural frequency. For example, the temperature coefficient gain of $K_{TC} = 0.009$ has the equivalent servo natural frequency of 0.08 cycle/sec. The temperature coefficient effect of $K_{TC} = 0.039$ has the equivalent servo frequency of 0.4 cycle/sec.

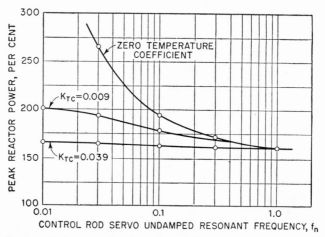

FIG. 4-41. Reactor peak power level reached as a function of natural frequency and temperature coefficient in optimized control system with 0.003 step input.

4-11. Peak Limiting by Negative Temperature Coefficient. Before attempting to evaluate the usefulness of these curves for design purposes, an examination of the information just supplied by analogue-computer studies indicates that the negative temperature coefficient alone is capable of limiting the peak power output value which a reactor can attain under the condition of step input transients. This answer can also be obtained analytically. Let us consider a bare reactor having no control system, and let us mathematically ignore its temperature coefficient for the moment, except to state that it is a strong one. For the case of a step input we can again write the familiar kinetic equations

$$\frac{dn}{dt} = \frac{\delta k - \beta}{l^*} n + \sum_{i=1}^{6} \lambda_i C_i \tag{4-61}$$

$$\frac{dC_i}{dt} = \frac{\beta_i}{l^*} n - \lambda_i C_i \tag{4-62}$$

Initially in the steady-state condition

$$\frac{dn}{dt} = 0 \qquad \delta k = 0 \qquad \sum_{i=1}^{6} \lambda_i C_i = \frac{\beta}{l^*} n_0 \qquad (4\text{-}63)$$

If we now inject a step δk into the reactor, we can isolate the steady-state and variable portion of n as before into

$$n = n_0 + \delta n \qquad (4\text{-}64)$$

Let us assume that following an input step of reactivity, the delayed-emitter concentration remains the same for a short interval of time. Then

$$\frac{d(\delta n)}{dt} = \left(\frac{\delta k - \beta}{l^*}\right)(n_0 + \delta n) + \frac{\beta}{l^*} n_0 \qquad (4\text{-}65)$$

$$= \frac{\delta k}{l^*} n_0 - \frac{\beta - \delta k}{l^*} \delta n$$

The solution for δn then becomes

$$\delta n = \frac{\delta k}{\beta - \delta k} n_0 (1 - e^{[(\delta k - \beta)/l^*] t}) \qquad (4\text{-}66)$$

and the maximum initial value that δn can obtain for positive steps in δk without the contributions of the delayed emitters becomes

$$\delta n_{\max} = \frac{\delta k}{\beta - \delta k} n_0 \qquad (4\text{-}67)$$

In a reactor with a negative temperature coefficient the reactivity change created by the rise in power level is in the opposite direction to the step in reactivity. Therefore, it tends to cut back the peak δn as given in Eq. (4-67). The time constants are the important factors here. If in a reactor having a strong temperature coefficient the time constant of this temperature coefficient is in the order of a few tenths of a second, then the peak in δn can never rise above the value given in Eq. (4-67). As an example, let us insert a step δk of 0.003 into a reactor having an l^* of 10^{-4} sec. The time constant for the initial rise $l^*/(\beta - \delta k)$ becomes 22 milliseconds (msec). As the effects of the delayed neutrons do not become apparent in most practical reactors for approximately 0.3 sec (see Sec. 3-2), reactors having fast temperature coefficient time constants are effectively protected by themselves against large δk step transients. Figure 4-42 plots Eq. (4-67) and indicates the peak powers that can be attained by reactors having strong, fast negative temperature coefficients under the influence of step input reactivity transients.

An examination of the peak levels involved in Figs. 4-38 and 4-39 indicates that the temperature coefficient of Fig. 4-38 is effectively limiting the peak power to the value indicated for a $0.003\delta k$ step in Fig. 4-42. The curves of Fig. 4-39, however, indicate that the temperature coefficient corresponding to a K_{TC} of 0.009 is not quite strong enough to contain the initial δn to the values of Fig. 4-42.

4-12. Evaluation of Transient Response. Although we have established four criteria in Sec. 4-10 for comparing reactor control systems, we have not as yet determined how these criteria are involved in the over-all picture of reactor and plant operation. The question of philosophy of control, coupled with many other problems such as mechanical

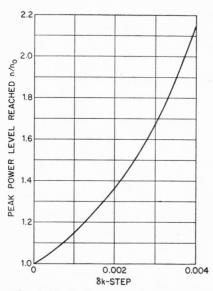

FIG. 4-42. Maximum possible transient peak power level for a reactor with a strong negative temperature coefficient as a function of input reactivity step.

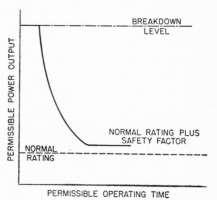

FIG. 4-43. Permissible power output from any type of generating apparatus as a function of permissible operating time.

damage to the reactor, metallurgical difficulties, and plant limitations, must be considered.

The first problem concerns itself with the question: What are the limitations of the reactor that the control system must protect? Basically, a reactor is no different from any other power-producing device insofar as its ability to handle an overload is concerned. Figure 4-43 illustrates the form of the permissible amount of power that may be taken from any piece of generating apparatus as a function of time. For example, if the apparatus under consideration is an electrical generator, the generator is designed to operate continuously at a fixed rated power output. Actually, in a practical design a small safety factor is usually permitted. Therefore, the generator may operate continuously at some rating slightly above its normal full power rating. If one now considers operation for short times, that is, times of the order of the time constant of the thermal heating of the generator, a slightly greater output from the machine may be obtained. If the generator will not reach its normal internal temperature ratings for 5 min at full power, then conceivably one might take more than full power from the generator for a time shorter than 5 min. This relationship is presumably hyperbolic up to the point where some other factor, such as insulation breakdown, occurs. That is, if full power might be drawn from the machine for 5 min, one could conceivably take twice full power from the machine for $2\frac{1}{2}$ min or four times full power for $1\frac{1}{4}$ min. At some power level breakdown would occur regardless of how short the interval of time was made.

In the case of a reactor the ultimate limitation may be the destruction of the reactor structure or melting down of the fuel. In addition, power reactors may be of such a size that they effectively possess comparatively little heat capacity. This means that the time scale on Fig. 4-43 might be shifted so that the continuous rating plus the safety factor must be carried down into times comparable to 0.1 sec. If this is the case, for times shorter than 0.1 sec it is indeed possible to run power reactors at higher power level than their rated level up to the point where something distorts or melts. Actually, it is the integrated area under a curve similar to that of Fig. 4-43 which is of importance. The number of watt seconds of energy available is what will ultimately cause damage. For examining control-system transients most breakdown phenomena can be translated into power level for use with our four basic criteria. For example, the initial indication of a failure might be the melting of the moderator. This melting can be translated into a power level.

Let us now go back to our example as illustrated by the transient-response curves in Figs. 4-38, 4-39, and 4-40. Two sets of information are at once apparent. The first is that under some conditions no external control system is needed to restrain severe transients. The temperature coefficient by itself is quite capable of handling a wide range of input disturbances. The output transients and power level encountered with modest input transients and no control system would not appear to be too severe for many types of reactor plants. The second obvious information that may be derived from these curves is that if one does use an external control system, the higher the natural frequency the better; or the faster the control system acts, the smaller will be the over-all transient disturbance.

The question then arises: Why not build extremely fast control systems which have natural frequencies in the order of 100 cycles/sec? Here over-all safety philosophy dictates against such systems. First, the components which are used in these fast systems are not at the moment as reliable as those used in slower systems. Second, a failure in a fast-acting system can in itself inject a fast transient disturbance. The faster the capabilities of the system, the more severe the transient. Therefore, the argument may be used that if nothing about the reactor control system is capable of changing at a fast rate, no fast accidents can occur. From a safety point of view one should then design any needed control system to be as slow as possible and still satisfy the overall performance requirements.

It will be realized that reactors must have an external control system of one sort or another for purposes other than transient-disturbance control. That is, means must be provided to extract control rods for startup processes, for poison compensation, and for temperature control. Control-rod mechanisms will be needed to shut down the reactor for normal operation or emergencies. Consequently, some combination of basic control-loop elements that are capable of being connected together either manually or automatically in a control circuit will exist around a reactor.

4-13. Procedure for the Selection of Control-system Constants. Granting that a reactor control system is needed, the following procedure may be used as a guide to determining the control-system constants:

1. Determine the temperature coefficient magnitude and time constant or the ranges that the temperature coefficient might have during the reactor lifetime.

2. Determine the integrated or peak energy permitted from the reactor as a function of time.

3. Decide the form of the control-system mechanisms, and derive the transfer functions.

4. Determine the adequacy of existing components of the type chosen as a function of the natural frequency of the control loop.

5. Consider the performance of the reactor control system by simulation techniques or others, and evaluate by means of the four criteria given in Sec. 4-10 for the type of desired response.

6. Choose the slowest, safest system that fits all the above conditions.

REFERENCES

1. Brown, G. S., and D. P. Campbell: "Principles of Servomechanisms," John Wiley & Sons, Inc., New York, 1951.
2. Chestnut, H., and R. W. Mayer: "Servomechanisms and Regulating System Design," John Wiley & Sons, Inc., New York, 1951.
3. James, H. M., N. B. Nichols, and R. S. Phillips: "Theory of Servomechanisms," McGraw-Hill Book Company, Inc., New York, 1947.
4. Stephenson, R.: "Introduction to Nuclear Engineering," McGraw-Hill Book Company, Inc., New York, 1954.

5. Harrer, J. M., and J. A. Deshong, Jr.: Discontinuous Servo for Control of Power Reactors, *Nucleonics*, vol. 12, no. 1, p. 44, 1954.
6. Grace, J. N.: Synthesis of Control Systems for Nuclear Power Plants, "Convention Record of the IRE 1954 National Convention," pt. 9, "Medical and Nuclear Electronics," Institute of Radio Engineers, New York, 1954.
7. Kochenburger, R. J.: A Frequency Response Method for Analyzing and Synthesizing Contactor Servomechanisms, *Trans. AIEE*, vol. 69, pt. 1, pp. 270–284, 1950.
8. Churchill, R. V.: "Modern Operational Mathematics in Engineering," McGraw-Hill Book Company, Inc., New York, 1944.
9. MacColl, L. A.: "Fundamental Theory of Servomechanisms," D. Van Nostrand Company, Inc., New York, 1945.
10. Bode, H. W.: "Network Analysis and Feedback Amplifier Design," D. Van Nostrand Company, Inc., New York, 1945.
11. Lauer, H., R. Lesnick, and L. E. Matson: "Servomechanism Fundamentals," McGraw-Hill Book Company, Inc., New York, 1947.
12. Moore, R. V.: The Control of a Thermal Neutron Reactor, *Proc. Inst. Elec. Engrs. (London)*, vol. 100, pt. 1, p. 90, 1953.
13. Bowen, J. H.: Automatic Control Characteristics of Thermal Neutron Reactors, *Proc. Inst. Elec. Engrs. (London)*, vol. 100, pt. 1, p. 102, 1953.
14. Nyquist, H.: Regeneration Theory, *Bell System Tech. J.*, vol. 11, p. 126, January, 1932.
15. Weinberg, A. M., and W. K. Ergen: Some Aspects of Non-Linear Kinetics, *Proc. Kjeller Conference on Heavy Water Reactors, JENER*, 1953.
16. Lipkin, H. J.: A Study of the Non-Linear Kinetics of the Chatillon Reactor, *J. Nuclear Energy*, vol. 1, pp. 203–213, 1955.

CHAPTER 5

REACTOR CONTROL MECHANISMS

In Chap. 4 reactor control loops were examined and it was shown that the output of the control system was usually a control-rod motion which changed reactivity. Before going on to plant control, it is of interest to examine some of the actual types of mechanisms that may be used to actuate these control rods. Of course, moving control rods is not the only way of changing reactivity in a control sense. For example, neutron-absorbing chemicals might be inserted into a reactor and change its reactivity with no physical rod motion involved. In this chapter, however, we are going to consider only the motions of neutron-absorbing types of control rods. That is, we are not going to consider forms of reflector control or other schemes that change the leakage of the reactor, but the assumption will be made in all cases that moving a control rod into the reactor structure reduces the reactivity and tends to turn the reactor off.

Physically, there have been as many different types of control rods as there have been reactors built. The only requirement for the absorptive type of rod is that the rod be black or at least "dark gray" to thermal neutrons. Many shapes of control rods have also been used. Some have been round, some square, some hollow, and some solid, all depending upon the design of the individual reactors. For thermal reactors, boron and cadmium are the most commonly used absorbing materials, and these materials may be alloyed into some other metal or may be clad by another material. In this chapter we shall consider some of the mechanical requirements of the mechanisms that move these rods in and out of the reactor. Brief descriptions will be given of the features of the simpler typical systems.

5-1. General Requirements of Control-rod Mechanisms. The control rods themselves may be classified in three groups according to function: safety rods, shim rods, or regulator rods. Each function may call for a specific speed of motion. As we have seen in Chap. 4, the purpose of the regulator rod is to maintain a constant desired power level in the face of transient reactivity changes and to assist in making a change in this power level. The control aspects and speed requirements of the regulator rod were shown to be variable, but in general the speed was to be as slow as good transient performance would permit. Movement of the regulator rod was usually automatic, but manual operation could be permitted.

As has been previously indicated, shim rods are used either for automatic follow-up of the regulator rod or for the slow movement of larger amounts of reactivity than can be handled by the regulator rod. Shim rods are particularly concerned with the startup process, and as will be shown later, their required motion is generally quite slow.

Safety rods, on the other hand, are for scramming or rapid shutdown action, and their motion inward is quite fast. Details of the speed requirements of safety rods will also be given later.

It is obvious then that different mechanical motion requirements may exist for each of these three functions. In some reactors these functions will be separated, and in others they may be combined. That is, during startup a shim rod may be operated at its normal slow speed, but as soon as it is extracted from the reactor, it conceivably may have its function changed so that it becomes a safety rod. The usual situation in most reactors is that regardless of the normal function of the control rod, it will also have provision for some form of fast insertion into the reactor.

For many purposes it is also desirable to move more than one rod at a time; consequently, mechanisms must be designed which permit either mechanical or electrical ganging. The electrical ganging systems are usually more flexible in that it is easier to change the number of rods in any given bank. It can be seen that these functional requirements dictate the possible forms of mechanical configuration that a control-rod mechanism may take.

Environmental Conditions. The type of reactor also affects the design of the control-rod mechanism in that the reactor purpose and operation create different types of environmental conditions. Most reactors can be divided into two environmental classifications: nonpressurized and pressurized. The nonpressurized reactors at present are a group of experimental or research reactors which sit at room temperature and room pressure ambient. Thus they can have their mechanisms out in the open where they are easily accessible and where lubricants can be applied to given portions of the mechanisms.

The AEC has announced that the first commercial central station power reactor will be a pressurized water reactor. Many of the other conceivable power reactors are also of the pressurized type. The coolant or the combination moderator coolant may be some substance such as water or gas, and this substance is kept at a high pressure in order to increase the thermal efficiency of the plant. Implying that a reactor is pressurized, however, means that either part of the mechanism must be inside a pressure shell or some complex means used to control the reactor from the outside of the pressure shell.

For the pressurized type of reactor the mechanism may be buried completely inside a large pressure vessel type of tank or, as is more common, some form of thimble may be used in which the mechanism can operate. Figure 5-1a indicates an internal thimble configuration, and Fig. 5-1b an external thimble setup. In Fig. 5-1a the entire mechanism

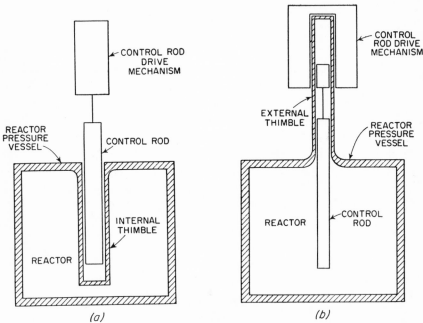

FIG. 5-1. Pressurized reactor thimbles. (a) Internal thimble. (b) External thimble.

and control rod are actually outside the reactor pressure vessel, but the pressure vessel wall is extended down to where it is a part of the reactor structure. In the external type of thimble the control rod alone extends into the reactor but the thimble contains a part of the drive mechanism. Some form of coupling then must be arranged through the thimble wall to the basic control-rod drive. It can also be seen that the portion of the mechanism inside the reactor pressure vessel enclosure must operate without any maintenance and in high-power reactors without the benefit of lubricants because of the deleterious effects of gamma radiation. On the other hand, the internal thimble configuration requires more fissionable material to compensate for additional neutron-absorptive loss in the thimble shell. It is also more difficult mechanically to fabricate and assemble the pressure vessel and reactor structure for the internal thimble system when there are many rods used in the reactor.

Other Mechanical Requirements. In addition to the environmental requirements and to the speed of motion requirements imposed upon a control-rod mechanism, there are other factors which also must be considered in the design of these mechanisms. One basic problem which always exists is that of providing some form of energy storage either in the mechanism itself or in the control system feeding the mechanism. The purpose of this energy storage is simply that in the event of a power failure it is most desirable still to be able to have a means of inserting the rods completely into the reactor. Many forms of energy storage, such as gravity, springs, or inertia, may be used, and these will be discussed later.

Also involved in the design of the mechanism is the problem of the expected life of the reactor and the mechanism. Because of the difficulty of servicing a reactor and its associated parts, the mechanisms usually must be designed for perfect operation for a long time. This problem is complicated by the fact that the scramming operation often is a violent one involving large mechanical forces. Severe damage may be done to the mechanism or the reactor structure if a reactor is scrammed too often. Means for softening these forces are usually provided in most mechanism designs.

Another requirement which is usually built into the mechanism is the requirement of rod position indication. For neutron physics reasons, such as reactivity measurements, or for control information, such as to provide position feedback, it is desirable to know the position of a control rod quite accurately. In nonpressurized reactors this poses no problem, but in the case of a pressurized reactor system, accurate determination of the position of a control rod inside a pressure vessel may be a difficult design limitation.

Operational requirements may also interpose special design requirements. In reactors used in military plants it is conceivable that the control mechanism might have to operate under external shock and vibration conditions. Conflicting limitations may arise because of this requirement. For example, take the case of scramming the control rod. From a safety point of view it might be desirable to have a mechanism of the so-called hair-trigger type, with which just a very small motion will cause the rod to scram, but this type of mechanism could also cause a scram in the event of shock. If a different mechanism were designed such that it did not unlatch easily under shock for its normal operation, it might take too long in releasing the rod for a scramming operation.

5-2. Motors and Mechanisms for Control Rods: Nonpressurized Systems. The motors and mechanisms that may be used for control-rod drives can be arbitrarily divided into two groups: those mechanisms used for nonpressurized reactors and those used for pressurized reactors. Actually, all the pressurized systems may be used for nonpressurized reactors. However, some of these drives are particularly well adapted to pressurized conditions and consequently will be treated separately here.

Electric motors are generally used in the basic power arrangement for the control-rod drive. The simplest cases are those whereby only a constant speed is required of the motor. The motor is then geared down through the rod-driving mechanism to set the rod speed at the desired value. Three-phase induction motors are common for this application.

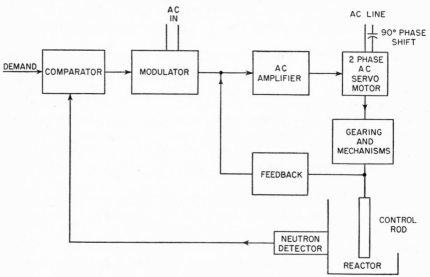

FIG. 5-2. Control loop for two-phase a-c servomotor drive system.

Single-phase induction motors are probably better in that the loss of a phase in a three-phase motor causes the motor to lose its ability to change the direction of travel of the control rod. A-c induction motors are preferred over d-c motors in that no accident can cause them to operate faster than synchronous speed. Also, their maintenance is smaller. The a-c motor, however, must be reversible.

Two-phase induction motors are easily reversed and have the advantage that certain designs may be used directly as servo control motors. Figure 5-2 indicates a control loop such as might have been used in Chap. 4 for a regulator-rod drive, using a two-phase a-c servomotor. In this diagram it will be noted that the d-c output of the neutron detector must be converted into alternating current to provide a signal to drive one of the phases of the servomotor. Switching arrangements may be supplied as desired to operate manually or reverse the direction of the motor drive.

For nonpressurized reactors gearing arrangements are the simplest forms of mechanisms used following the drive motor. Rack-and-pinion drives and screw-type drives are quite common. Figure 5-3 indicates the simple rack and pinion, whereby a drive motor of any type drives a pinion through a gearbox and a clutch. The clutch provides a convenient means of slip at the ends of the rod travel and also provides one means of

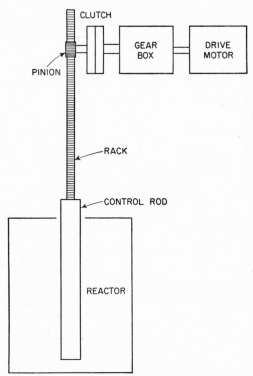

FIG. 5-3. Elementary rack-and-pinion drive for control rod.

direct gravity scram by releasing the control rod from the gearbox. This type of mechanism is particularly adapted to low-cost research reactors.

Two screw-and-nut arrangements are indicated in Fig. 5-4. Figure 5-4a shows the conventional movable nut arrangement, whereas Fig. 5-4b indicates the movable screw arrangement. Figure 5-4b can be used with a conventional motor, or if it is desired to save height in the mechanism structure, hollow-shafted drive motors may be used. Unless the shape of the control rod is round, some form of keyway is usually provided to prevent the control rod from turning.

For discontinuous motions, magnetically operated screw jacks have also been suggested. These drives are similar to the conventional automobile jack and can be made to cause the control rod to move in very small increments.

5-3. Pressurized Control-rod Drive Systems. We shall consider at this point the external thimble type of pressurized system only, as the internal thimble system may obviously use any of the drive systems mentioned above.

Magnetic Feed-through System. The simplest type of pressurized system is the one shown in Fig. 5-5, which is a magnetic feed-through system.

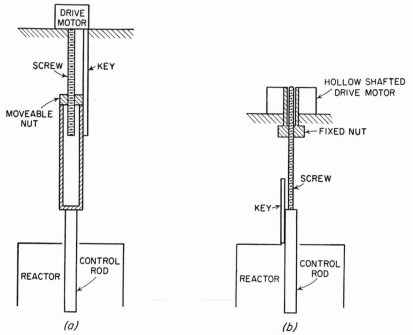

FIG. 5-4. Screw-and-nut control-rod drives. (a) Fixed screw. (b) Fixed nut.

Here the control rod is mounted on a magnetic slug, either a permanent magnet or some material such as soft iron, and an electromagnet is mounted as close as possible to the slug but outside the pressure shell. The wall of the pressure shell is reduced to the minimum amount permitted by the system pressure so as to reduce the effective air gap in the magnet. When current is applied to the electromagnet, the magnetic slug tends to position itself in the center of the magnetic field. Raising or lowering the electromagnet physically causes the slug to follow the position of the external magnet. It will also be noted that removing the current from the electromagnet would release the slug, thus causing a gravity scram. The drive system indicated in Fig. 5-5 is a winch-and-cable arrangement, but any of the other means may be used.   The necessary bearings and supports are not indicated in Fig. 5-5.

Synchronous Reluctance Motor Drives.   For cases where extremely slow rotary motion is required inside a pressure shell, special types of motors have been developed.[1]   One such type is the so-called canned synchronous reluctance motor.   This device is inherently capable of operating

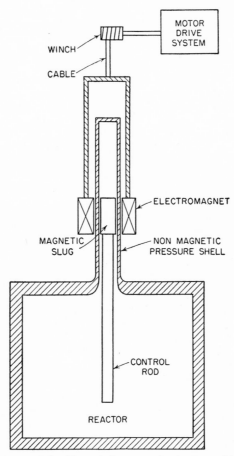

FIG. 5-5. Magnetic feedthrough for pressurized reactor drive system.

at very slow speeds, and the amount of gearing that must be used can be kept to a minimum.   For nonlubricated systems this is a distinct advantage.

The operating principle of the reluctance motor is indicated in Fig. 5-6. Here three-phase windings are shown, and we can first consider the case where the windings are supplied from a d-c bus.   The armature can be considered to be a solid piece of magnetic material, indicated as a two-pole bar in Fig. 5-6. If the windings are fed as shown with winding A and winding B placed across the d-c line and winding C being left open, a fixed field configuration will be set up inside the motor and the bar will

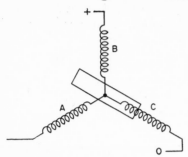

FIG. 5-6. Three-phase synchronous reluctance motor connection.

align itself in a given position in this field. If, now, by means of mechanical switching, windings A and C are fed from the line and winding B left open, a different field configuration will be set up and the bar armature will swing around to a displacement of 120° from its former position. In the event that some stepdown gearing is involved in the subsequent drive mechanism, step rotary motion of this sort may be tolerated.

By feeding full current through one phase winding and half current through the other phases, 60° steps may be obtained. Figure 5-7 shows a commutator switching arrangement of this sort. Motions of 60° in

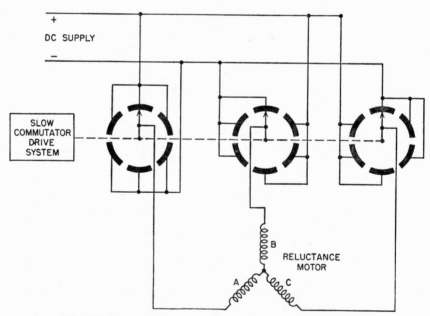

FIG. 5-7. Stepped drive system for synchronous reluctance motor.

magnitude are feasible for many applications. It will be noted that the windings are energized in the following sequence:

A connected to $+$ lead	B and C connected to $-$ lead
A and B connected to $+$ lead	C connected to $-$ lead
B connected to $+$ lead	A and C connected to $-$ lead
B and C connected to $+$ lead	A connected to $-$ lead
etc.	etc.

Of course commutators can be built with finer segments, and this system can be carried as far as desirable. If more uniform motor motions are required, continuous schemes can also be designed to feed this type of

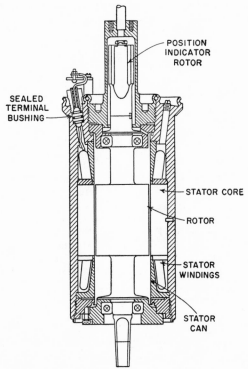

FIG. 5-8. Pressurized synchronous reluctance motor. (*Courtesy of Westinghouse Electric Corporation.*)

motor. Sine wave potentiometers plus amplifiers have been used in this application.[1] The slow commutator drive system indicated in Fig. 5-7 may be the output of any conventional servo loop. Consequently, power output regulation may be had quite easily with this sort of drive.

An actual motor designed to operate in a high-temperature, high-pressure water system has been described[1] and is shown in Fig. 5-8. This motor is capable of effectively operating completely submerged in water, as a thin-shelled can completely protects the stator. That is, in the motor air gap there is a 0.02-in. Inconel can which protects the stator windings and punchings from the water and also acts as the pressure wall. The can is, of course, backed up to take the actual pressure by the stator core. The leads of the stator windings are brought out from the top of the frame through high-pressure Kovar glass terminal insulators. The outside frame, which is made of stainless steel, acts as a pressure backup again for the stator and prevents release of any contaminated water to the outside atmosphere in case a leak develops in the can. The rotor and the shaft are made of a magnetic stainless steel. The bearings, as indicated, are of conventional ball-bearing design, except that they are made of special materials to operate at rated temperatures. To illustrate the performance of the motor of Fig. 5-8, Table 5-1 presents a summary of its design characteristics as given by the manufacturer.

TABLE 5-1

Design characteristic	State	Rating
Speed, rpm...............................	Normal	0–16
	High-speed operation	53
	Maximum	1,800
Torque, lb-ft..............................	Holding (continuous)	6
	Running (intermittent)	8
Cooling-water flow, gpm...................	Normal	0.15
	Minimum	0.109
Cooling-water inlet temperature, °F..........	Normal	120
	Maximum	130
Winding temperature, °C...................	Normal	150
	Maximum (intermittent)	250
Pressure, psi..............................	....	2,500

Linear Reluctance Motor. The problem of converting rotary motion to linear motion inside a pressure shell is an extremely difficult one because of the environmental conditions. An unusual electric motor has been developed which creates linear motion directly without the need of going through rotating motion first.[2,3,8] Linear motors have been used for some time for other applications such as catapult drives[4] and X-ray tables. They are very simply adapted to pressurized reactor work. To obtain a crude feeling for the operation of the linear motor consider first the standard reluctance motor just described. If this cylindrical motor were figuratively to be sliced open at one axial place, flattened out, and then rolled up again at right angles to the previous cylinder, a structure similar to the cross section of Fig. 5-9 would be obtained. Here the field coils are nothing but circular doughnuts around a long tube. The armature consists of a series of ringlike poles on a long bar. The winding slots are cut into a thick magnetic cylinder, and the inner walls of this cylinder are backed up by the windings to take the pressure from the inside of the motor. To complete the magnetic path and also to assist in restraining internal pressures, a magnetic sleeve is placed outside the field coil struc- ture. The windings may be connected either in two phase or three phase, as shown in Fig. 5-9, and the operation and drive systems are identical

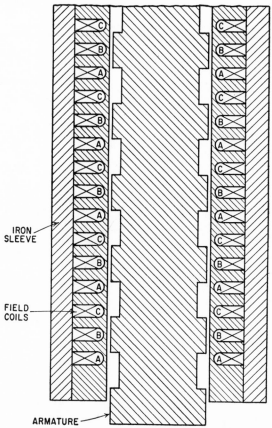

FIG. 5-9. Linear reluctance motor configuration.

with those of the rotating synchronous reluctance motor. A complete linear motor drive system for a pressurized reactor is indicated in Fig. 5-20. This motor has the additional advantage that very simple gravity scramming is provided by merely removing the current from the motor windings. The feeding system for the linear motor used as a regulator rod is indicated in Fig. 5-10.

Hydraulic Motor. In some control-rod drive systems it is more desir- able to use pipes instead of wires, particularly if a pressure shell has to be

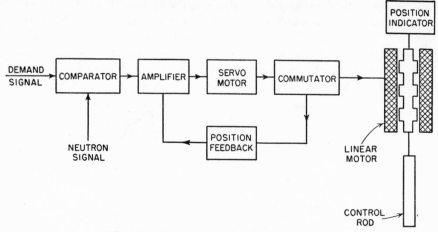

FIG. 5-10. Control system for linear motor drive.

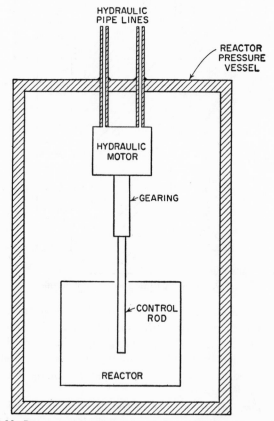

FIG. 5-11. Pressurized system using internal hydraulic motor rod drive.

penetrated many times. Hydraulic and pneumatic drive systems are available which are complete analogues to electrical driving systems. In the higher horsepower ratings some advantage in size may be obtained by using hydraulic actuators. Whether one uses electrical, pneumatic, or hydraulic systems will depend upon the load, the accessibility of the

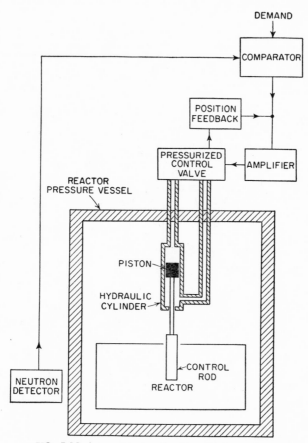

FIG. 5-12. Internal hydraulic piston driving system.

components, the speed of scramming required, and to some extent the past experience of the designer.

Figure 5-11 shows one arrangement for using a hydraulic motor completely inside a pressure shell. An arrangement of this sort is particularly advantageous if the hydraulic fluid can be the same fluid as the coolant or moderator so that any leakage from the hydraulic motor does not contaminate the system. The hydraulic motor may be of any conventional type such as a vane or reaction type motor.

Hydraulic Cylinder and Piston. The hydraulic analogy to the linear motor is the hydraulic cylinder-and-piston arrangement indicated in Fig. 5-12. Here the mechanism is shown as being installed completely inside the reactor pressure vessel. This type of arrangement may also be used with the piston mounted externally on the top of the pressure shell similar to a thimble. Again it is desirable to use the same fluid in the hydraulic cylinder as already exists inside the pressure vessel. In Fig. 5-12 a complete automatic regulating type of control system is

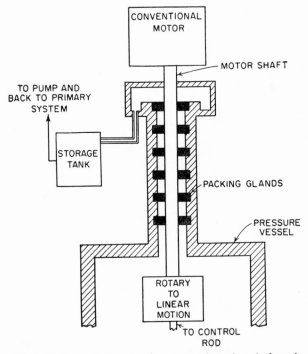

FIG. 5-13. Transmission of rotary motion through a shaft seal.

shown, although the pressurized control valve can obviously be operated manually.

Transmission of Motion through Seals. It may be undesirable for some mechanisms to use other than standard components, and for this case the problems of using conventional type motors transmitting power through seals into the pressure vessel should be explored. Seals for the transmission of rotating and linear motion are available in industry,[5,6] but the requirements of seals for a pressurized reactor system are much more stringent than are usually found in conventional plants. Most high-pressure seals permit a small amount of leakage from the inside to the outside of the pressure vessel. In the case of a reactor system, if any leakage is permitted, radioactive coolant may escape and soon make the premises uninhabitable. Consequently, the specifications for a high-pressure seal could conceivably be as severe as "should not leak one drop in a month."

Figure 5-13 indicates one of the forms that a rotating shaft seal might take. A conventional motor is used to drive a shaft into the pressure vessel. Leakage along the shaft is blocked by a series of packing glands. The packing glands serve also to reduce the pressure from the inside to the outside in gradual steps until ultimately the last gland is at atmospheric pressure. Some leakage will still result through these glands, and tap-offs are provided at various points between glands so that this leakage may be bled off into a storage tank. Figure 5-13 indicates the final tap-off at atmospheric pressure. From the storage tank another line and pump are provided to reinsert any coolant leakage back into the primary system. Similar seals for direct transmission of linear motion are also available.

5-4. Scramming Mechanisms. Thus far some of the types of mechanisms that can be used to provide the normal slow drives for control rods have been indicated. As previously mentioned, most of these drives will have some form of scramming mechanism built in, either directly at the rod or indirectly in the control-drive feed. There are two distinct types of scramming systems that must be considered, and which of these is used depends upon whether the rod is inserted into the reactor vertically or horizontally. When the rod is inserted vertically, gravity is almost always used to assist in the scramming process. When the rod is inserted horizontally, some form of power drive is involved.

Direct Magnet Release. The simplest form of scram employing gravity only is where the rod is connected directly to a mechanism by means of an electromagnet. Breaking the current through the magnet causes the rod to release by gravity. Figure 5-5 shows such a system for the pressurized type drive, and simpler systems can be devised for nonpressurized reactors.

Latch Relays. The disadvantage of the direct-magnet release lies in the fact that some designs require a large amount of magnet current which is difficult to supply and also difficult to break quickly because of the L/R time constant. A small magnet may be used to release a mechanical latch and accomplish the same effect, usually with more speed and with large decreases in driving power. One such scheme is indicated in Fig. 5-14a. Here a large arm is held against a detent in the control-rod shaft by means of the force created in a small solenoid coil. When the current is disconnected from this coil, a spring forces the large arm outward. Gravity again produces the actual scram.

It will be shown later that gravity scrams are sometimes inadequate, and consequently scramming with initial forces larger than gravity may be desirable.   One such aided acceleration gravity scram is indicated in Fig. 5-14b, in which a scram-aiding spring is inserted in order to propel the control rod into the reactor at a fast initial acceleration.   After the spring has become fully extended, the scram continues by gravity.   The

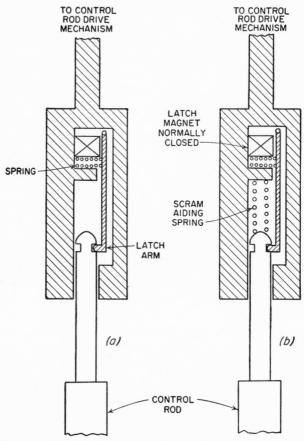

FIG. 5-14. Control-rod latching system. (a) Gravity drop. (b) With scram-aiding spring.

same effect can be obtained in other types of mechanisms by using pneumatic or hydraulic pressures in place of the spring.

Powered Scram Drives.   In horizontal rod systems or in vertical systems where there are large friction forces, power-driven scrams may be used.   This is an extremely fertile field for mechanism designers, and literally hundreds of devices have been suggested.   Figure 5-15 indicates elementary block diagrams of two simple systems.   In Fig. 5-15a advantage is taken of the fact that the reluctance motor type of motor drive described in Sec. 5-3 is a synchronous device and consequently will operate effectively at any line frequency supplied to it.   Under normal conditions the supply frequency might be a few cycles per second.   However, for scramming purposes, proper switching may be arranged so that for inward motion only the 60-cycle line will be connected to the reluctance motor.   In this way the control-drive mechanism will operate at highly accelerated rates.

Figure 5-15b indicates a system using two motors.   One motor is the normal driving motor connected to some form of mechanical speed

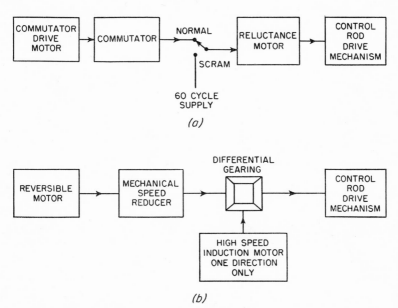

FIG. 5-15. Powered scram drives.   (a) Two-frequency reluctance motor operation.   (b) Two-motor system.

reducer driving differential gearing.   Feeding the differential gearing also is a high-speed induction motor which is capable of rotating in one direction only.   Again proper switching throws one motor or the other onto the line.

5-5. Energy Storage Devices.   All reactor control systems must provide for some form of energy storage in order to move the rods to their shutdown position in the reactor in the event of power failure.   The simplest and most direct energy storage means is gravity, when the mechanism design permits its use.   For reactors having vertical control rods, gravity dropping of the rods in the event of power failure is very practical.   For reactors with horizontal rods, gravity may also be used,

but the system is more complicated.   Any type of energy storage may be
used, and either potential or kinetic energy can be employed.

The type of storage used when gravity storage is not directly applicable
is usually hydraulic or electrical, and each specific system suggested has
a direct analogy in the other medium.   For electrical systems, storage
batteries used with d-c motors and appropriate switching provide a good
combination.   The hydraulic analogy to this system is the gravity
accumulator supplying hydraulic fluid to a hydraulic motor through

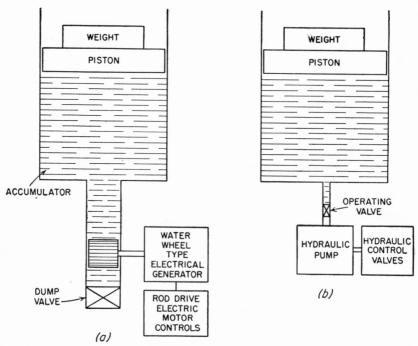

FIG. 5-16. Hydraulic tank energy storage systems.   (a) Electrical output.   (b) Hydraulic
output.

appropriate valving.   Hydraulic tanks or accumulators are used in some
present-day reactors and may be connected to supply either electrical or
hydraulic power.   Figure 5-16 indicates schematically the two types of
analogous designs.   In this figure a weighted piston is used to supply
hydraulic fluid at the proper pressure to the generator or pump.   These
elements then can ultimately drive control-rod motors.   Another form
of accumulator is the spring-loaded accumulator in which the weight is
replaced by a spring or series of springs.   The outputs are essentially the
same.

Figure 5-17 shows another way in which energy may be stored in
springs.   In this figure the rod is connected through a clutch or differen-

tial arrangement to either of two drives. One of these drives is the normal motor driving system, and the other is the scramming drive, which is powered by a previously wound spring motor. The spring drive may be connected automatically to the rod in the event of power failure. This system is most suitable for use with small light rods.

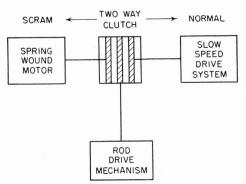

FIG. 5.17. Spring-wound-motor energy-storage system.

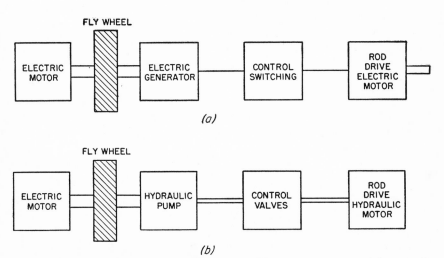

FIG. 5-18. Flywheel inertia storage systems. (a) Electrical output. (b) Hydraulic output.

The above schemes are potential energy schemes. The Brookhaven reactor employs the inertia of a flywheel in a kinetic energy system. Figure 5-18 indicates two flywheel inertia schemes. Figure 5-18a is an electrical system in which an electric motor is used to bring a flywheel up to speed. On the same shaft is an electric generator which is normally used to supply the power for a rod drive motor or scramming system.

If the charging motor power fails, the inertia of the flywheel will keep the generator operating for several minutes after the power failure.

Figure 5-18b shows the hydraulic analogy of the same system. Both of these inertia systems are such that there is a finite time after power failure in which reactor shutdown may be accomplished. For example, either the rods are inserted within 5 min after power failure or the flywheel system will coast to a complete stop. The accumulator schemes have a similar restriction if automatic operating valves actuated by power failure are used. But if manual valving is employed, the gravity storage is available at any time.

Energy storage may be provided from one source to supply several rods, or each rod may have its own storage system. The gravity or spring-loaded accumulator is more easily adapted for ganged storage, whereas the flywheel system can be placed very simply on each rod drive. Ganged storage is somewhat less desirable than individual storage in that a failure in the system could affect not one rod but all of them. For a given amount of energy storage, it can usually be shown that the flywheel system occupies less space and has less weight than the accumulator. The gravity system may be somewhat more reliable basically in that the flywheel must operate continuously and ultimately may have bearing trouble. The flywheel drive also will take more power from the supply lines, but this is generally of small consequence. In any event, the choice of one energy storage form over another will depend upon space and weight requirements and upon whether ganged or individual energy supply is desired.

The above considerations are essentially for horizontal rod drives. For a vertical rod drive system, simple or accelerated gravity drop upon power failure is preferred.

5-6. Buffers. The use of aided power drives or accelerated gravity scramming drives means that control rods are inserted into a reactor with considerable force. After the rod has reached the end of its useful travel, it must be stopped gently, as expediently as possible, so that neither the reactor nor its structure will be damaged. Springs and dashpot arrangements and conventional automobile-type shock absorbers have been used for this purpose. Figure 5-19 indicates an elementary form of spring and dashpot arrangement. The principal concern in the use of these devices is that they be mounted on such a place that bowing or bending of the drive shaft mechanism is minimized.

5-7. Rod Position Indication. In most reactors it is desirable to know where each rod is at all times in order to anticipate the state of criticality of the reactor or to determine some corollary parameter such as the amount of depletion or the amount of poisoning. Position indication is no problem at all for nonpressurized systems in that conventional a-c synchros or a-c and d-c potentiometers may be used. Proper gearing or multiple units can provide any reasonable degree of accuracy of position indication.

For pressurized systems this problem may become formidable. The accurate transmission of position through a pressure shell wall is usually accomplished by magnetic devices involving rather large air gaps. These devices take the form of canned synchro generators or canned differential

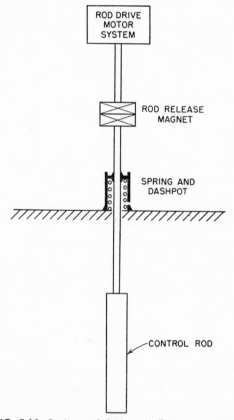

FIG. 5-19. Spring and dashpot buffer arrangement.

transformers, or they may even be built in as an integral part of the drive motor. Figure 5-8 indicates a drive motor having the rotor of a position indicator built in as an integral part of the drive motor shaft. A multipole pickup coil is used with this motor on the outside of the structure. Figure 5-20 indicates a differential transformer type of direct linear motion position indicator used with a linear motor. Here a change in inductance caused by the position of a magnetic slug is a direct measure of the position of the control rod. In many cases the indication through the pressure shell is so weak that some form of servo follow-up amplification system may be needed to bring the position information into a usable form.

5-8. Horsepower Requirements.† Until now sketches of types of mechanisms have been presented without regard to their size or rating. It is of interest to examine power requirements at this point. For normal shim-rod operation, where the motions involved are very slow, it is obvious that advantage can be taken of large gearing stepdowns and the

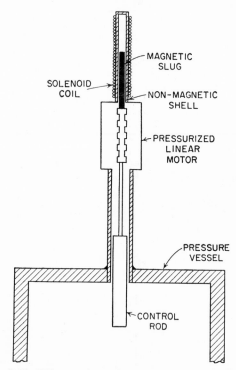

FIG. 5-20. Differential transformer type position indicator.

actual driving motor rating can easily be in the fractional horsepower class. Scramming power requirements depend upon the type of scram used, and for many gravity or aided gravity scrams very little power is needed. For horizontal systems or other powered scram drives, motor ratings of a few horsepower may be required.

The power required by a regulating rod operating in an automatic control loop is an interesting variable depending upon the desired system transient response. To examine this situation in a little more detail,

† The analysis used in this section follows that of J. M. Harrer, Argonne National Laboratories, and was originally presented in *Nucleonics*, vol. 6, no. 3, p. 58, 1950.

let us assume that we have an automatic control system of any of the types indicated in Chap. 4 and that the reactor has no negative temperature coefficient. The curve of Fig. 5-21a indicates the shape of the transient response we would expect from our control system, with P being the peak power excursion reached by the transient for an input reactivity step.

The control system removes the power transient by moving a rod in such a manner as to return the net reactivity to zero. As it would be impossible to move the rod in a stepwise motion, it is more reasonable to assume that the reactivity change created by the rod would be of the shape indicated in Fig. 5-21b. If reactivity and rod position are linearly

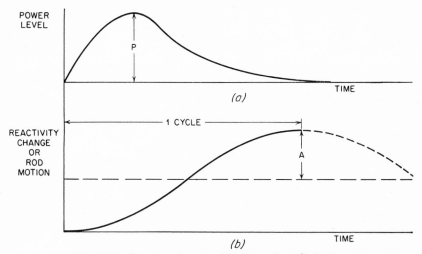

FIG. 5-21. Control-rod motion during transient elimination.

related, the rod would start to move slowly, gather speed, and then slow down as the desired end point was approached. For simplicity let us assume that this required motion is sinusoidal about the halfway point and that the sine wave has a peak half amplitude of A. The time taken by the transient to die out effectively may be considered one cycle of the rod motion sine waves.[7] This method of analysis is not strictly correct. The method used in Chap. 4 of defining a natural frequency f_n for a given control loop is a better one. However, in practice the frequency of a sine wave derived in this manner and f_n are of the same order of magnitude and either will do for rough horsepower calculations.

Now assume that the driving motor horsepower requirements must be such that this sinusoidal motion of a given frequency f and a given amplitude A can be followed by the regulator rod. If

$$\omega = 2\pi f \tag{5-1}$$

rod displacement

$$s = A \sin \omega t \qquad (5\text{-}2)$$

rod velocity

$$v = A\omega \cos t \qquad (5\text{-}3)$$

and rod acceleration

$$a = -A\omega^2 \sin \omega t \qquad (5\text{-}4)$$

For sinusoidal motion, horsepower

$$\text{hp} = Fv \qquad (5\text{-}5)$$

where the force on the rod $F = ma$, and if the rod mass $= m$, in poundals, then

$$\text{hp} = \frac{mA^2\omega^3 \sin \omega t \cos \omega t}{550} \qquad (5\text{-}6)$$

when the appropriate constants are in feet and seconds. Then as $\sin \omega t \cos \omega t = \frac{1}{2} \sin 2\omega t$, the peak horsepower required from the driving system to contain the transient is

$$\text{Peak hp} = \frac{mA^2\omega^3}{1{,}100} \qquad (5\text{-}7)$$

To obtain an idea of the magnitude of the parameters involved, let us try a numerical example. Assume the transient of Fig. 4-32, and arbitrarily state that a complete sine wave cycle would take 0.15 sec or $f = 6.67$ cycles/sec. Let us further assume that to correct for a $0.003\delta k$ step we might have to move a 200-lb control rod 2 ft.

Then the maximum horsepower would be

$$\text{Peak hp} = \frac{200 \times 8\pi^3 \times (6.67)^3}{32 \times 1{,}100} \qquad (5\text{-}8)$$
$$= 418 \text{ hp}$$

which is a staggering amount for most servo motors. Apparently either the constants of our example are impractical or we are asking for too much by way of transient response. It can be seen from Eq. (5-7) that the horsepower requirements depend most strongly on ω and A. If, in our example, ω were decreased by a factor of 10 and A by a factor of 2, the peak horsepower requirement would come down to approximately 0.1 hp, a far more manageable number. It will be recalled from Sec. 4-12 that the slowest possible control system should be chosen for safety reasons. Apparently the slowest possible system should also be chosen in order to obtain a drive of practical physical size.

The above argument has been presented on the basis of the reactor having no temperature coefficient. It will be recalled that the effect of the temperature coefficient was principally upon the front end of the transient, and the time for the disturbance to be returned to zero depended upon the external control system. Therefore, by virtue of the way in which the above horsepower requirements were obtained, the negative temperature coefficient of the reactor does not affect the answer.

REFERENCES

1. Esselman, W. H., and W. H. Hamilton: Position Control in Sealed Systems, "Proceedings of the 1953 Conference on Nuclear Engineering," University of California Press, Berkeley, Calif., 1953.
2. Shaw, V. G., G. M. Anderson, R. G. Durnal, and F. J. Walcott: A Canned Linear Reluctance Motor, *WAPD-T*-5, Westinghouse Atomic Power Division, Pittsburgh, Pa.
3. Robinson, R. C., and W. E. McCown: Direct Linear Motion in Sealed Systems, *WAPD-T*-39, Westinghouse Atomic Power Division, Pittsburgh, Pa.
4. Jones, M. F.: Launching Aircraft Electrically, *Aviation*, vol. 45, pp. 62–65, October, 1946.
5. Catalogue, Autoclave Engineers, Erie, Pa.
6. Catalogue, American Instrument Company, Silver Springs, Md.
7. Harrer, J. M.: Controlling a Power-producing Nuclear Reactor, *Nucleonics*, vol. 6, no. 3, p. 58, 1950.
8. Anderson, G. M.: Analysis of the Linear Reluctance Motor, *WAPD-T*-6, Westinghouse Atomic Power Division, Pittsburgh, Pa.
9. Harrer, J. M.: Control Rod Mechanisms, *Nucleonics*, vol. 13, no. 6, p. 48, June, 1955.

CHAPTER 6

NUCLEAR POWER PLANT CONTROL

Until now we have been discussing reactors from which no power is being taken. The reactors of Chap. 4 might be test reactors whereby the neutrons from the reactor are being used for experimental purposes or to create radioisotopes. Throughout the discussion on reactor control it has been presumed that although the reactor is giving off heat, no use is being made of this heat. This situation corresponds in our d-c generator analogy to having a generator operating at no load. We expect, of course, that if we load a d-c generator, we shall change its internal characteristics. Consequently, it is natural to expect that as we load up a reactor and attempt to obtain power from it, we shall also affect its internal characteristics. In this chapter we shall examine the operation and control of power reactors from which useful heat power is being extracted.

6-1. Introduction. We might now look broadly at the mechanism of the reaction of a load upon a reactor. For the sake of illustration an elementary block diagram of a possible nuclear power plant is shown in Fig. 6-1. Here the reactor is considered merely as a source of heat energy. This heat is extracted by passing a coolant through the reactor. The heat energy is then transferred via a heat exchanger to a turbine system, and the output shaft of the turbine can be made to drive many types of working apparatus. The primary coolant considerations are basic to this discussion, and this coolant may be gas, water, or a liquid metal.

Two external paths exist for affecting the reactor. One is a local path through its own control-rod system, and we have examined in Chap. 4 the principles of automatic control by means of control rods. The other path is the direct connection to the plant via the coolant system. Any variation in the coolant system parameters such as temperature, pressure, or flow will affect the reactivity of the reactor. Variations in the coolant parameters do not directly influence reactivity unless the coolant is also the moderator. It is the effect upon the moderator and fuel that usually causes a reactivity change, and any external influence that changes moderator characteristics can be expected to change reactivity.

The largest plant effect is usually one caused by a change in temperature. We have already seen that the temperature coefficient is an important safety and control element. The temperature of the moderator and the fuel can be affected by the internal heat of the reactor, by external variations in the load, or by a combination of these two effects.

Another effect may be the pressure of the primary system. In power plants where the coolant or moderator is either a gas or water, the primary circulating system is usually pressurized to increase the plant efficiency. The reactivity of a reactor can be a distinct function of primary system pressure, and consequently, external changes in the pressurizing system, as a function of the plant load or the pressurizer controls, can affect reactivity.

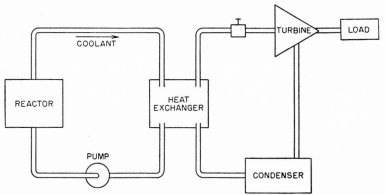

FIG. 6-1. Elementary block diagram of nuclear power plant showing essential elements.

In order to isolate these two variables we may define two coefficients. These are the temperature coefficient as the $|\partial\delta k/\partial T|_{\text{const } p}$ and the pressure coefficient as the $|\partial\delta k/\partial p|_{\text{const } T}$.

6-2. Description of Basic Elements of a Nuclear Power Plant. In order to get a better feel for the large number of items that may affect these two coefficients, we might look at a more complex block diagram than the elementary one given in Fig. 6-1. Figure 6-2 is a block diagram of a nuclear power plant indicating some of the more important auxiliary systems that may be present. In an actual power plant hundreds of auxiliary systems may be used, and each of these can conceivably affect reactor operation. We shall now briefly describe some of the more important systems of the plant.

Nuclear Instrumentation System. The nuclear instrumentation system is the multiplicity of apparatus that is used to monitor nuclear radiations over the complete range of reactor operation. It consists usually of several radiation-detection instruments and associated electronic circuitry to indicate the reactor power level and the reactor period at any instant.

This system can affect the reactor principally by giving erroneous readings. A false value of n from the nuclear instrumentation creates a wrong power demand error signal and thus causes control-rod motion. The nuclear detectors are usually calibrated against thermal detectors, and the calibration circuits are a permanent part of the system.

Temperature and Flow System. At power operating levels the power output and all the characteristics of the plant are determined by temperature and flow measurements. Measurements of these variables are complicated by the presence of radioactive coolant with no leakage whatever of the coolant usually being permitted. Because this system fur-

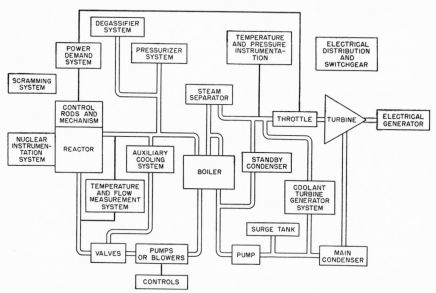

FIG. 6-2. Block diagram of a nuclear power plant indicating some of the important auxiliary systems.

nishes the basic indication of reactor power output, it will obviously be involved in the response of the secondary system output.

Reactor Shutoff and Scramming System. One control requirement peculiar to the nuclear power plant is the instrumentation setup for alarm, cutback, and scramming circuits. Alarm circuits are common in the power industry, but the peculiar notion of "scram" is one limited to the reactor field. In certain types of reactors the safety requirements are such that it is necessary to employ these types of scramming devices. However, from a practical point of view it is obvious that the plant must be kept in an operable state as continuously as possible. The plant must not be shut off every time some minor control in a secondary loop malfunctions. The control designer's problem is to limit to an absolute minimum the number of controls which can cause a scram.   For most accidents and component failures it is usually possible to cut back the reactor power level at a slower rate than scram rate or merely to ring an alarm and have an operator manually make the necessary adjustment or shutdown.

Pump or Blower Controls.   The power output of the reactor depends directly upon the rate of coolant flow.   Consequently, this flow is also involved in reactions upon the reactor.   The coolant flow may be fixed, continuously variable, or stepped in accordance with a demanded schedule.   As the power input to a pump varies with the cube of its output, it can be seen that to operate the plant at low power outputs without cutting back coolant flow usually results in a loss of efficiency.   Pumping power can become greater than 5 percent of the plant power output if precautions to change the flow are not taken.   The pump controls therefore may become quite complex in that multiple units may be switched on and off the line and variable flow schedules can be used in addition.

Pressurizer System.   If the primary loop requires a pressurizer, an interesting problem in reactor dynamics can occur.   The pressurizer in its elementary form might be a tank partially filled with coolant which, in turn, is usually covered by a blanket of gas under a specific pressure. This tank is connected to a high point in the primary coolant system via a pipe.   It can be seen that the coolant in the tank and in the pipe can represent an inertia.   The gas pressure above the coolant in the pressurizer acts as a spring.   Consequently, if insufficient damping exists in the connecting pipe, the system conditions are proper for a pressure oscillation to occur between the pressurizer and the primary loop.   This pressure oscillation obviously creates a reactivity oscillation in the reactor through the pressure coefficient.   If this problem is not considered carefully, the time delays may be such that the initial pressure oscillation can be reinforced by the reactor power oscillation.   The pressurizer system then becomes an auxiliary requiring most careful design attention in that it can violently affect the basic performance of the reactor.

Secondary System.   The secondary system of the nuclear power plant resembles a conventional steam plant.   All the necessary auxiliaries that are used in modern steam practice will be used for the nuclear power plant.   The control problem for the nuclear plant becomes very similar to the control problem of the steam plant.   A great deal must be known about the characteristics of the output load, however, before the reactions back upon the reactor can be explored.   In the case of an aircraft power plant this information might be specified in terms of aircraft speed as a function of turbine output.   For a shipboard plant the information might be supplied in the form of propeller revolutions per minute versus turbine output.

6-3. Steady-state Programming.   The pattern that the temperatures, pressures, and flows throughout the plant assume as a function of power output is called the program.   Figure 6-3 indicates again a basic plant,

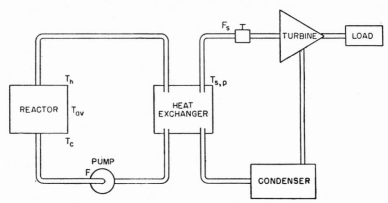

FIG. 6-3. Elementary block diagram of nuclear power plant indicating the symbols used for temperature, pressure, and flow.

and the symbols that will be used are

T_c = inlet coolant temperature to the reactor
T_h = outlet coolant temperature from the reactor
T_{av} = average coolant temperature = $(T_c + T_h)/2$
F = primary coolant flow
F_s = steam flow
p = absolute steam pressure
T_s = steam temperature

A distinct relationship exists between the temperatures and the pressures of the primary and secondary sides of the plant.   The difference between the average temperature of the primary coolant in the boiler and the steam temperature is directly proportional to the power being transferred from the primary coolant to the steam side.

$$P = K(T_{av} - T_s) \qquad (6\text{-}1)$$

where P is the total power and K is a proportionality factor which depends on the heat-transfer characteristics of the boiler.   The value of K varies slightly with coolant flow rate, thermal power, and boiler level but may be assumed constant for a first approximation.   The values of T_{av} and T_s at full power can be determined from saturation data from steam tables when the steam pressure for 100 percent power is specified.   As zero output power is approached, the difference between T_{av} and T_s converges to zero and the value at which the temperatures converge may be arbitrarily located on a temperature scale, assuming the presence of a control system to enforce the selection. The point to be made is that once the constants of the primary side of the plant are known, the secondary constants are automatically specified and vice versa. For example, Eq. (6-1) states that if one desires a plant in which the average temperature of the primary coolant is constant with power level, then the temperature program of the steam is automatically specified as dropping off as the power increases. Conversely, if one desires a given program of steam temperature as a function of power level, the average temperature program of the primary coolant is immutably fixed as long as we assume a constant K.

Constant-T_{av} Program.[1] One type of desirable program for a nuclear power plant is the program whereby the average temperature of the primary coolant is constant regardless of the power output. This type of program is shown in Fig. 6-4 for constant primary coolant flow. For reactors having a negative temperature coefficient this is the natural program of the reactor and the one that requires the least amount of external control.

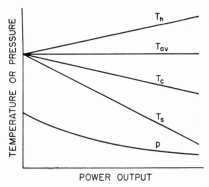

FIG. 6-4. Variations in temperatures and pressures as a function of power output for constant-average-temperature program with fixed coolant flow.

Let us examine the simple plant shown in Fig. 6-3, making the following assumptions. The steady-state program desired is the one of Fig. 6-4 with constant-coolant flow. The reactor has a negative temperature coefficient, and the plant is operating so that a steady output is being supplied to the load. Now suppose that more output is required by the load. This greater loading causes more heat to be extracted from the heat exchanger, and for a short period of time, the heat capacity of the heat exchanger and coolant can usually supply the additional load. However, this extra energy extracted from the system requires that the temperature of the coolant into the reactor must drop. If the reactor has a negative temperature coefficient, the dropping of the inlet temperature causes a drop in the average temperature, and consequently the reactor will possess more reactivity. If the reactor was initially in a critical state, it now temporarily becomes supercritical. The output temperature of the coolant rises, and more energy is then available from the reactor. Finally, in the steady state the reactor returns to its critical condition with the average coolant temperature the same as it was initially. It will be noted that without any control mechanism whatever, the reactor system has stabilized itself about a given average temperature and automatically supplies a reasonable demand placed upon it. In other words, if the plant programming calls for the T_{av} to be constant, no control-rod

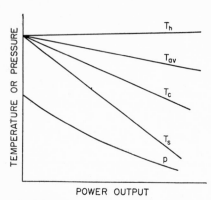

FIG. 6-5. Variations in temperatures and pressures as a function of power output for constant-outlet-temperature program.

motions or no external control means are necessary to handle changes in power demand.

Let us now assume that for some reason other than the reactor control system, it is desirable to establish a different pattern of coolant temperatures. A reasonable pattern might be that shown in Fig. 6-5. This figure shows a simple system which might be called for by some structural condition desiring to keep the outlet coolant temperature fixed at a given maximum level. Figure 6-6 shows a block diagram of a control system indicating how this condition might be achieved. Let us assume the same conditions in that our reactor possesses a negative temperature coefficient and is operating critical at a given output level. Again, as more load is required, the inlet temperature to the reactor would drop. More reactivity would be inserted into the reactor because of the negative

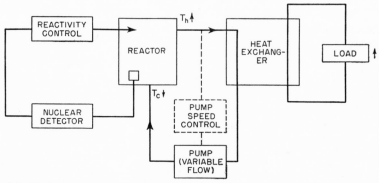

FIG. 6-6. Block diagram of control system for obtaining constant-outlet-temperature program.

temperature coefficient. The outlet coolant temperature would tend to rise, but now we must insert a control on the outlet temperature that measures the temperature and then varies the coolant pump speed in such a manner as to hold this outlet temperature constant.

In this way it is very feasible to hold the steady-state outlet temperature constant as a function of load as indicated in Fig. 6-5. However, it will be noted that the average coolant temperature must drop with load, meaning that the reactor, because of its negative temperature coefficient, would now attempt to operate in a supercritical condition. Consequently, another control loop, usually the automatic external control-rod loop such as described in Chap. 4, must be added to the system to extract the reactivity inserted by the change in average coolant temperature. It can be seen then that any program other than the constant-average-temperature program will usually require an external reactivity control to be used when the steady-state level changes.

The advantages of the constant-average-temperature program are important. If the effects of aging and poisoning could be ignored, no external reactor control would be necessary during normal operation. The reactor would simply follow throttle changes in a stable manner by means of the negative temperature coefficient. Another significant advantage of the constant-T_{av} program concerns the pressurizer. If T_{av} is constant, the volume of coolant in the primary loop is essentially constant and the required size for the pressurizer is at a minimum.

However, there are also some disadvantages to this program. The principal one is the large change in steam pressure over the power range, as seen in Fig. 6-4. A wide pressure range means larger and heavier steam piping, automatic throttling devices, special turbines, and boiler-feed pump problems. Furthermore, since the effects of aging and poisoning cannot be ignored, there always must be a feedback control loop to hold T_{av} constant even in a simple plant. This control loop, however, can be very slow and might be manual.

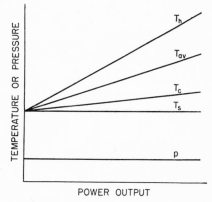

FIG. 6-7. Variations in temperatures and pressures as a function of power output for constant-pressure program with fixed coolant flow.

Constant-pressure Program. Another extreme in plant programming is to hold the steam pressure constant as a function of power level and permit the primary system temperatures to rise. This is the program of Fig. 6-7. The constant-T_{av} program is the one preferred by the reactor. The constant-pressure program is the one preferred by the secondary steam system. The advantages and disadvantages of the two systems are reversed. That is, the constant-pressure program permits optimum design of the steam plant in that it eliminates unconventional problems in automatic throttling devices, special turbines, and boiler-feedwater pumps. On the other hand, there is a large reactivity change required because of the T_{av} change, and in some cases serious primary coolant pressurizer problems can arise because of the large pressurizer volume needed.

Another disadvantage is that in going from one steady-state power level to another, the plant must fight the tendency of the negative temperature coefficient to hold T_{av} constant. Also a much larger amount of

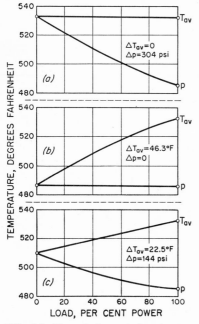

FIG. 6-8. Numerical example of constant-T_{av} program, constant-p program, and compromise program for hypothetical plant operating around 500°F.

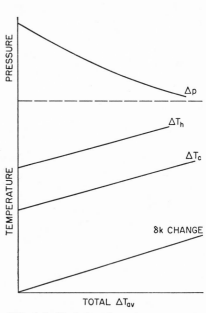

FIG. 6-9. Variations in system parameters as a function of change in T_{av}.

control-rod motion would usually be needed in a constant-pressure plant. This control-rod motion again might be made very slow.

Compromise Programs. We find ourselves, then, in a position where there are two logical extremes to the programming, and on the surface these two programs are incompatible. One program is favored by the primary loop; the other by the secondary loop. In most practical plants a compromise appears inevitable. There are two obvious methods of making this compromise. The first of these is to set up a steady-state program which is part way between these two extremes. That is, a program might be chosen in which a moderate variation in T_{av} and steam pressure would both be taken and no attempt made to hold either constant. This sort of approach is shown in Fig. 6-8, using typical numbers around 500°F for a hypothetical plant. Figure 6-8a indicates the constant-average-temperature program, Fig. 6-8b a constant-steam-pressure program, and Fig. 6-8c an attempted compromise. The practical numbers obtained indicate that a design can be made which, although it is not optimum, could be satisfactory to advocates of both primary and secondary loop optimization. A variation on these schemes is, of course, possible by varying boiler level and consequently K. This system is not considered in this discussion.

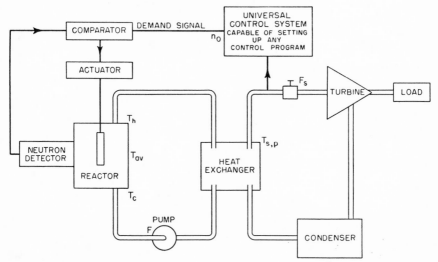

FIG. 6-10. Block diagram of plant and universal control system capable of setting up any type of control program.

The method that is used at a given power level and at a given flow is to plot a series of curves of the various parameters involved against a trial ΔT_{av}. A curve of this sort is shown in Fig. 6-9, and at any ΔT_{av} the designer of the plant may barter δk changes against temperature and pressure variations.

Time Constant Compromise.[2] The second type of compromise that might be made is on a time-constant basis. As yet we have said nothing about the transient-response consequences of steady-state programs, and this will be discussed in some detail later. From an elementary point of view, however, we can quickly see that the proper speed of response to transient changes can ease programming compromises.

Let us assume that we have an elementary plant and control system, such as is given in Fig. 6-10, which is capable of setting up and demanding any conceivable useful type of control program. To tie back to our previous case, let us assume that this system has been set up to demand the constant-steam-pressure program of Fig. 6-7. We now make the assumption that the demand signal n_0 out of our universal control device into the comparator is velocity limited. That is, let us assume by way of illustration that irrespective of any instantaneous demand changes in F_s, p, T_s, T_c, T_h, or T_{av}, the n_0 power demand signal cannot change from, say, 3 to 100 percent full power in less than 1 min.

Now let us follow through some of the typical demands that might be made on this system. Suppose we are operating at a low power level and the throttle is opened slowly. Opening the throttle slowly in times of minutes causes the demand signal n_0 to rise slowly and the nuclear loop to reposition the control rods so as ultimately to match the constant-pressure reference demand. Suppose now that the throttle is opened suddenly, say instantaneously. No new signal comes into the comparator instantaneously from the demand loop because of the velocity limit we have imposed on n_0. However, this quick transient-throttle change is reflected through the boiler into the primary loop as a change in average temperature of the coolant in the reactor, and the negative temperature coefficient of the reactor supplies a change in reactivity to match the load on a transient basis. In other words, for transient throttle operation the plant behaves as though it were operating without controls, stabilized only by the negative temperature coefficient, and for transients of short duration it behaves completely as though it were operating as a constant-average-temperature system. Ultimately a demand signal appears into the comparator and the entire system slowly changes over to a constant-pressure program.

The system responds to a change in reactivity in the reactor in a similar manner. If this reactivity change is a slow one, such as caused by aging and poisoning, the n loop signal, which is likely to be also velocity limited by virtue of the fact that the control rods are not permitted to change reactivity very fast, will handle this change slowly and safely. If a fast change in reactivity occurs, the negative temperature coefficient again takes over and the system behaves as though no external controls were present.

Apparently, then, a plant possessing a negative temperature coefficient behaves as a constant-average-temperature system for transient operation provided the control system which ultimately sets steady-state conditions is slow. Effectively, then, one can have the advantages of both constant-average-temperature and constant-steam-pressure systems with proper design.

Flow Considerations. As has been mentioned, the rate at which energy is carried by the primary coolant from the reactor to the boiler must be equaled by the power generated by the reactor. This is expressed by the simple relationship

$$P = F(T_h - T_c) \tag{6-2}$$

There may be reasons why T_h must never exceed a certain value. Problems of stress, corrosion, and wear may all be involved. Also, as previously mentioned, it is inefficient to operate the primary loop at low power output with the flow needed for full power output. These facts mean that some form of flow control will be used in the plant, and this control concerns the programming system.

Figure 6-11 indicates two types of programming changes, as a result of flow considerations, for a constant-average-temperature system. In Fig. 6-11a, the flow is constant from zero power to a given power level, and then the flow is increased linearly with power output to full power. In this way, T_h and T_c are held constant, but the power output continues to rise because of the flow change. Continuously variable speed control for pumps and blowers is more complicated than stepped control, and Fig. 6-11b indicates a two-speed type of control. Here again the flow is constant until a given power level is reached, and at this point the pump or blower speed is increased by a fixed amount, thus dropping the temperature difference required for a given output. Many variations and combinations of these two types of controls are, of course, possible.

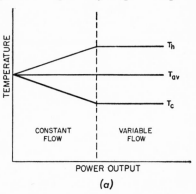

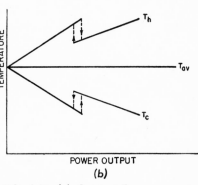

FIG. 6-11. (a) Constant-T_{av} program in which flow is variable above a given power output. (b) Constant-T_{av} program in which flow is changed stepwise at a given output level.

6-4. Elementary Thermodynamics of the Basic Loop. We have broadly examined the stability and transient response of a nuclear power plant and have come to the conclusion that the basic plant, consisting of a reactor, coolant, heat exchanger, and steam system, in itself possesses regulating ability and consequently is a basic control loop. In order to study this basic loop as a servomechanism, we must examine more carefully the elementary reactor thermodynamic structure. We shall not be able to handle anything but the simplest approximations to an actual plant, but the approach to the determination of the stability for a practical plant will be indicated. The method we shall use will be to develop the differential equations for the thermodynamics of the reactor, the transport delays in the loop, the transfer of energy in the boiler, and the use of this energy in the steam system. Once the basic form of the equations is determined, we can again change over to a transfer function approach and examine the response of an elementary nuclear power plant as a basic control loop. Figure 6-12 indicates the loop and the symbols we shall be examining.

In order to simplify the situation we shall immediately make the assumption that the coolant and the moderator of our reactor are one

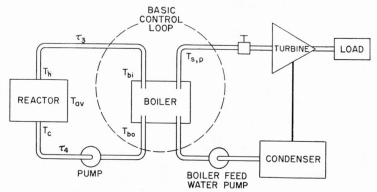

FIG. 6-12. Elementary power plant as a basic control loop.

and the same. In this way we shall eliminate double heat transfer mathematics. Many practical plants may be constructed using this system with either gas or water as the moderator. For our thermodynamics considerations we shall use both words interchangeably. It is also implied throughout this discussion that unless otherwise specified, the reactor has a negative temperature coefficient.

In the core of a reactor the fission of uranium 235 nuclei liberates energy. In addition, energy is liberated by the decay of fission products. This total energy manifests itself in a rise in the temperature of the fuel. If no energy is withdrawn from the fuel, the temperature will continue to rise indefinitely as long as fission continues. In power reactors a temperature difference between the fuel and the surrounding coolant causes heat to flow from the fuel to the coolant.

Reactor Thermal System. Figure 6-13 shows a typical section of a simplified reactor core configuration. The fuel may be a mixture of uranium and other metals in an alloy, or there may be cladding involved. We make the simplifying assumption, however, that an over-all fuel element possesses constant density and constant specific heat. In Fig.

6-13, if we consider an element of the core having a unit height and unit depth, the one-dimensional heat flow from a fuel element to the coolant can be obtained from basic thermodynamic considerations. That is, the heat generated in a given region plus the heat entering the region from the outside equals the heat expended in raising the temperature of the medium plus the heat escaping through the boundaries, where all these effects are per unit time. For our situation

$$(Q_f + Q_d)t_f + 0 = d_f c_f t_f \frac{\partial T_f}{\partial t} + 2K(T_f - T_{mod}) \qquad (6\text{-}3)$$

where Q_f = reactor specific power, defined as heat generated per unit volume per second in the fuel by fission fragments

Q_d = heat generated per unit volume by all other processes such as β and γ decay radiation

t_f = fuel thickness as indicated in Fig. 6-13

d_f = fuel density

c_f = fuel specific heat

t = time

T_f = fuel temperature

T_{mod} = coolant-moderator temperature

K = coefficient of heat transfer between fuel element and coolant (this coefficient changes as a function of coolant flow, but as we are considering only fixed flow rates in this section, K will be considered constant)

FIG. 6-13. Cross section of a simplified reactor core configuration.

Again, to simplify, we shall ignore Q_d, as it is usually less than 10 percent of Q_f and can easily be handled when more refined calculations are needed. We can now call the over-all reactor specific power Q. The partial derivative in Eq. (6-3) indicates that T_f is a function of position in the reactor core as well as of time. An average value may be determined for T_f by integration over the space coordinates of the reactor core. The corresponding integration of T_{mod} would yield the term we have been calling T_{av}. Let us mentally perform these integrations so that we may consider an entire reactor rather than just an element. Equation (6-3) would then become

$$\bar{T}_f + \tau_1 \frac{d\bar{T}_f}{dt} = T_{av} + \tau_1 \frac{Q}{d_f c_f} \tag{6-4}$$

where the time constant τ_1 is defined as $d_f c_f t_f / 2K$.

We have now replaced the partial derivative by the ordinary derivative, as $\bar{T}_f$ is a function of time only. Actually this process is crude, as the spatial variations and local effects in a reactor are going to be smeared when we consider that we shall ultimately feed back into our reactor a reactivity depending on T_{av}.

We can now set up the heat-transfer balance in a similar manner for the heat flowing out of the fuel and being carried away by the coolant. Again, we shall assume an integrated situation. This heat is the last term of Eq. (6-3), and it is carried off into the flow of coolant as

$$2K(\bar{T}_f - T_{av}) = d_{mod}c_{mod}t_{mod} \frac{dT_{av}}{dt} + \frac{d_{mod}c_{mod}t_{mod}}{\tau_0}(T_h - T_c) \tag{6-5}$$

where d_{mod} = density of the moderator coolant

$\quad c_{mod}$ = specific heat of the moderator coolant

$\quad t_{mod}$ = thickness of moderator-coolant passage as indicated in Fig. 6-13

$\quad \tau_0$ = time for a unit volume of coolant to pass through the reactor core

One of the temperatures involved may be eliminated if we return to the previous symmetrical definition of

$$T_{av} = \frac{T_h + T_c}{2} \tag{6-6}$$

Introducing this factor, we can transform Eq. (6-5) into the form of Eq. (6-4) giving

$$T_{av}\left(1 + \frac{2\tau_2}{\tau_0}\right) + \tau_2 \frac{dT_{av}}{dt} = \bar{T}_f + 2\frac{\tau_2}{\tau_0}T_c \tag{6-7}$$

where the time constant $\tau_2 = d_{mod}c_{mod}t_{mod}/2K$.

Transport Delays. With Eqs. (6-4) and (6-7) we have now related the reactor heat output to T_c, T_h, and T_{av}. We now must transport this heat to the boiler via a pipe, as indicated in Fig. 6-12. We shall assume that all our heat transfer occurs at a point in the reactor and ignore the time delays in transporting the average heat from one position in the reactor to another.

We can now examine the temperatures involved in the transportation of the heat from the reactor to the boiler. The temperatures can be given as

$$T_{bi}(t) = T_h(t - \tau_3) \tag{6-8}$$

or the inlet coolant temperature to the boiler T_{bi} is of the same form as the reactor outlet temperature, only it attains a given value after a fixed transport delay τ_3. We are assuming no heat loss in the pipe transportation system. This situation is a good approximation if our connecting pipe is well insulated thermally.

Pure transport delays may be difficult to handle analytically or by analogue methods, and for some purposes it may be desirable to approximate the time delay by a differential equation form. We shall use both forms later depending on the problem. To develop the approximate equations we may rearrange terms and expand in a Taylor series

$$T_h(t) = T_{bi}(t + \tau_3) \tag{6-9}$$

$$= T_{bi}(t) + \tau_3 \frac{dT_{bi}(t)}{dt} + \frac{\tau_3{}^2}{2!} \frac{d^2 T_{bi}(t)}{dt} + \cdots \tag{6-10}$$

For slow changes in temperature we can ignore all terms beyond the second. Consequently, we may use the following first-order differential equation to indicate the time delay between reactor outlet and boiler inlet temperatures.

$$T_{bi} + \tau_3 \frac{dT_{bi}}{dt} = T_h = 2T_{av} - T_c \tag{6-11}$$

In a similar manner we might describe the transport delay from the boiler back to the inlet of the reactor either by

$$T_c(t) = T_{bo}(t - \tau_4) \tag{6-12}$$

or by
$$T_c + \tau_4 \frac{dT_c}{dt} = T_{bo} \tag{6-13}$$

where T_{bo} is the outlet temperature of the boiler and τ_4 the transport delay between the boiler outlet and the reactor inlet.

We shall define boiler average temperature similarly to the way in which we defined reactor average temperature so that

$$\bar{T}_b = \frac{T_{bo} + T_{bi}}{2} \tag{6-14}$$

Therefore our approximate form for the reactor inlet temperature as a function of boiler temperatures becomes

$$T_c + \tau_4 \frac{dT_c}{dt} = 2\bar{T}_b - T_{bi} \tag{6-15}$$

Boiler Equations. We can now use the same type of logic and approximations in order to write the heat balance equations for the boiler.

First, on the primary coolant side of the boiler we have

$$R_c(T_{bi} - T_{bo}) = K_b A_b(\bar{T}_b - T_s) \tag{6-16}$$

or
$$2R_c(T_{bi} - \bar{T}_b) = K_b A_b(\bar{T}_b - T_s) \tag{6-17}$$

where R_c = mass rate of coolant flow

K_b = effective boiler heat-transfer coefficient

A_b = effective area of the boiler tubes

On the steam side of the boiler we may express the fact that the rate of heat storage in the boiler metal, steam, and water is equal to the difference between the rate at which heat is transferred across the boiler tubes and the rate at which it is delivered to the turbine.   Or

$$(M_m c_m + M_s c_s) \frac{dT_s}{dt} = K_b A_b(\bar{T}_b - T_s) - K_a A p \tag{6-18}$$

where M_m = mass of boiler tube metal

M_s = mass of steam and water in boiler

c_m = specific heat of boiler tube metal

c_s = average specific heat of steam and water in boiler

K_a = a throttle constant

A = relative throttle opening (full open corresponds to $A = 1$)

p = steam pressure = $p(T_s)$, a function of steam temperature

Several simplifying assumptions are again made in obtaining Eqs. (6-17) and (6-18).   First, the heat transfer between the primary coolant side and the steam side of the boiler is represented by means of a single area and a single heat-transfer coefficient.   Second, the thermal capacity of the boiler metal is lumped with that of the steam and water.   Actually there is a time delay associated with a transfer of heat between metal and steam.   Neglecting this time delay will change the shape of the initial transient of output power encountered with thermal changes, but this approximation has little or no effect on the basic kinetics of the over-all loop.   The power output has been taken to be proportional only to the flow of steam through the throttle, assuming that the enthalpy of the saturated steam is constant.   The flow of steam is then taken as the product of throttle opening and steam pressure, using a suitable proportionality constant.   The further assumption has been made that the time spent by the coolant in passing through the boiler is negligible in comparison with the time spent in the pipes and that the heat exchange in the boiler is integrated and treated as though it occurred at one point.   These assumptions limit the accuracy of the descriptive equations.   However, the errors involved in these assumptions are usually less than the amount of uncertainty in the engineering values of the coefficients used.

6-5. Transfer Function Representation of Basic Plant Components. Having the basic plant performance in mind, we can now proceed to develop the form of the transfer functions for each of the components in the basic loop. We may first start with the reactor. It will be recalled from Sec. 4-3 that the elementary reactor with a negative temperature coefficient could be treated as a simple parallel system containing a reactor transfer function and a temperature coefficient feedback path. The feedback path was fed a variation in neutron power, and from its output came a reactivity change caused by a change in average coolant temperature.

In the case of a reactor connected to a power plant, the situation becomes more complex. Figure 6-14 indicates that in addition to the simple T_{av} feedback loop, there exists another loop containing both T_c

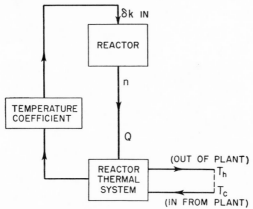

FIG. 6-14. Temperature coefficient feedback loop.

and T_h. The situation is even more complicated because of the fact that T_c and T_{av} are not independent.

Reactor-thermal-system Transfer Function. We can now develop a more sophisticated, but still approximate, transfer function for the reactor thermal system. The equations of heat flow from the reactor to the coolant were developed in Sec. 6-4 and are repeated below

$$\bar{T}_f + \tau_1 \frac{d\bar{T}_f}{dt} = T_{av} + \tau_1 \frac{Q}{d_f c_f} \qquad (6\text{-}19)$$

$$T_{av}\left(1 + \frac{2\tau_2}{\tau_0}\right) + \tau_2 \frac{dT_{av}}{dt} = \bar{T}_f + 2\frac{\tau_2}{\tau_0} T_c \qquad (6\text{-}20)$$

$$\frac{T_h + T_c}{2} = T_{av} \qquad (6\text{-}21)$$

We may eliminate the average fuel temperature $\bar{T}_f$ from these equations, change to Laplace-transform notation, and derive the following relationship between inlet and outlet temperature:

$$T_h(s) = \frac{\left\{ \frac{\tau_1 \tau_0}{2} s^2 + \left[\frac{\tau_0}{2}\left(\frac{\tau_1}{\tau_2}+1\right) - \tau_1 \right] s - 1 \right\} T_c(s) + \gamma Q(s)}{\frac{\tau_1 \tau_0}{2} s^2 + \left[\frac{\tau_0}{2}\left(\frac{\tau_1}{\tau_2}+1\right) + \tau_1 \right] s + 1} \qquad (6\text{-}22)$$

where

$$\gamma = \frac{t_f \tau_0}{t_{mod} d_{mod} c_{mod}} \qquad (6\text{-}23)$$

Factoring

$$\frac{\tau_1 \tau_0}{2} s^2 + \left[\frac{\tau_0}{2}\left(\frac{\tau_1}{\tau_2}+1\right) - \tau_1 \right] s - 1 = \left(1 - \frac{s}{\alpha_c}\right)\left(1 + \frac{s}{\alpha_{c'}}\right) \qquad (6\text{-}24)$$

and

$$\frac{\tau_1 \tau_0}{2} s^2 + \left[\frac{\tau_0}{2}\left(\frac{\tau_1}{\tau_2}+1\right) + \tau_1 \right] s + 1 = \left(1 + \frac{s}{\alpha_h}\right)\left(1 + \frac{s}{\alpha_{h'}}\right) \qquad (6\text{-}25)$$

we arrive at the form of the transfer function equation

$$T_h(s) = \frac{1}{[1 + (s/\alpha_h)][1 + (s/\alpha_{h'})]}\left[\left(1 - \frac{s}{\alpha_c}\right)\left(1 + \frac{s}{\alpha_{c'}}\right)T_c(s) + \gamma Q(s) \right] \qquad (6\text{-}26)$$

The block diagram representation of this transfer equation is shown in Fig. 6-15. Here the over-all reactor thermal transfer function artificially

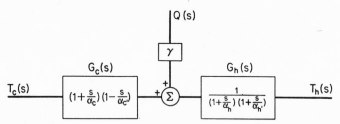

FIG. 6-15. Block diagram servo representation of a simple reactor thermal system.

appears to be in two parts, an inlet part and an outlet part, with the reactor heat feeding in between them. The generation of T_{av} is, of course, a separate external problem and its transfer function will later be obtained by combining $T_c(s)$ and $T_h(s)$.

The method for refining the over-all thermal transfer function of a reactor is now also apparent. Let us assume that a reactor is divided into a discrete number of series parts or sections, each section being farther along in the coolant flow path. Now a transfer equation of identical form to Eq. (6-26) can be derived for each individual section of the reactor. The assumption is again made that the average heat transfer from fuel to coolant occurs at a point in each individual section. The heat is then transported from section to section, and the final outlet temperature is a summation from the heats of all the individual sections.

Figure 6-16 indicates a block diagram of a two-section reactor. Here $Q_1\gamma_1 = Q_2\gamma_2$, and $G_{12}(s)$ represents the transport delay between the first section and the second. As many sections as desired may be added, depending upon the degree of refinement needed in the design of a control system for a particular plant. The tediousness of the calculations rapidly exceeds the additional utility of the more accurate results when too many sections are used.

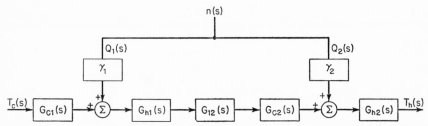

FIG. 6-16. Block diagram servo representation of a two-section reactor thermal system.

Transport Systems Transfer Functions. There are two principal delays in the primary loop of Fig. 6-12, and both of these have transfer functions of essentially the same form. First, it is necessary to transfer the heat from the reactor to the boiler, and second, after the heat exchange process has occurred, the coolant must be transferred back from the boiler to the reactor.

The equation denoting the transport delay from reactor to boiler is Eq. (6-8)

$$T_{bi}(t) = T_h(t - \tau_3)$$

and from boiler to reactor Eq. (6-12)

$$T_c(t) = T_{bo}(t - \tau_4)$$

The transforms of these equations become

$$T_{bi}(s) = T_h(s)e^{-s\tau_3} \tag{6-27}$$
$$T_c(s) = T_{bo}(s)e^{-s\tau_4} \tag{6-28}$$

The transfer functions then become the output divided by the input or

$$\frac{T_{bi}(s)}{T_h(s)} = e^{-s\tau_3} \tag{6-29}$$

$$\frac{T_c(s)}{T_{bo}(s)} = e^{-s\tau_4} \tag{6-30}$$

This is an interesting form of transfer function in that it will be recognized that there is no attenuation involved, only phase shift. The amount of phase lag in our elementary system is directly proportional to $\tau_3 + \tau_4$. Physically we have insulated our pipes perfectly and have lost no heat in getting from the reactor outlet to the boiler inlet and from the boiler outlet to the reactor inlet. The phase lag increases linearly with the length of the pipes.

The approximate differential equations expressing the equivalent delays are Eqs. (6-11) and (6-13), and the approximate transfer functions are at once recognizable as

$$\frac{T_{bi}(s)}{T_h(s)} = \frac{1}{1 + \tau_3 s} \tag{6-31}$$

and

$$\frac{T_c(s)}{T_{bo}(s)} = \frac{1}{1 + \tau_4 s} \tag{6-32}$$

This form is the so-called resistance-capacitance time delay and has a maximum of 90° phase lag as a function of frequency rather than the unlimited phase lag of the exact delay function.

Boiler Transfer Functions. We can develop the boiler transfer function in a manner completely analogous to the way we determined the transfer functions for the reactor thermal system.

The heat-flow equations for the boiler were Eqs. (6-16), (6-18), and (6-14). They are repeated below.

$$R_c(T_{bi} - T_{bo}) = K_b A_b(\bar{T}_b - T_s) \tag{6-33}$$

$$(M_m c_m + M_s c_s)\frac{dT_s}{dt} = K_b A_b(\bar{T}_b - T_s) - K_a A p \tag{6-34}$$

$$\bar{T}_b = \frac{T_{bo} + T_{bi}}{2} \tag{6-35}$$

Steam pressure p is a function of steam temperature T_s through the saturation relationship. Eliminating T_s, we may derive the following Laplace-transform equation in which the variable $T_{bi}(s)$ and $T_{bo}(s)$ now represent small deviations from their steady-state values at the power level at which the constants listed below are evaluated:

$$\frac{T_{bo}(s)}{T_{bi}(s)} = K_B \frac{1 + \tau_{bi}s}{1 + \tau_{bo}s} \tag{6-36}$$

where

$$K_B = \frac{\left(\dfrac{2R_c}{K_b A_b} - 1\right)\left(\dfrac{K_a A B}{K_b A_b} + 1\right) + 1}{\left(\dfrac{2R_c}{K_b A_b} + 1\right)\left(\dfrac{K_a A B}{K_b A_b} + 1\right) - 1} \tag{6-37}$$

$$\tau_{bi} = \frac{M_s c_s + M_m c_m}{K_b A_b\left[1 + \dfrac{K_a A B}{K_b A_b} + \dfrac{1}{(2R_c/K_b A_b) - 1}\right]} \tag{6-38}$$

$$\tau_{bo} = \frac{M_s c_s + M_m c_m}{K_b A_b \left[1 + \dfrac{K_a AB}{K_b A_b} - \dfrac{1}{(2R_c/K_b A_b) + 1}\right]} \tag{6-39}$$

$$B = \left(\frac{dp}{dT_s}\right)_{sat} \qquad \text{at corresponding value of } T_s \tag{6-40}$$

The transfer function of the boiler is then a distinct function of the power level at which the output system operates. Equation (6-37) indicates the variation in the gain term as a function of level. The variable corresponding to power level is A, the throttle opening. It is of interest to note that when $A = 0$, the throttle closed completely, $K_B = 1$. In other words, at zero power level there is no attenuation in the boiler. For $A > 0$ some attenuation will be provided by the boiler.

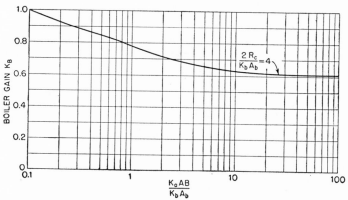

FIG. 6-17. Boiler gain as a function of throttle opening.

Figure 6-17 shows boiler attenuation as a function of $K_a AB/K_b A_b$, which is related, as indicated, to the throttle opening or load. The curve is presented for a given boiler with heat transfer characteristics such that $2R_c/K_b A_b = 4$. It can easily be seen from this illustration that the boiler does not provide much fixed attenuation even for the heaviest loads. Equation (6-37) indicates that the maximum attenuation at full load cannot be more than

$$K_{B,\max} = \frac{(2R_c/K_b A_b) - 1}{(2R_c/K_b A_b) + 1} \tag{6-41}$$

6-6. General Recapitulation of the Dynamic Performance of the Basic Plant. The general dynamic requirements of the plant are concerned with the stability of the complete system and the rate and magnitude of changes in output power expected. The requirement of stability suggests application of the familiar stability criteria of servo theory. The required speed of response depends on the particular application.

For example, at a central station power installation it may be satisfactory if power level can be changed only slowly, whereas a plant used to propel a vehicle might be required to change power rapidly.

The ability of the system to handle changes in load is affected by the bandwidth of the control system and by the thermal capacity of the primary coolant.   The coolant acts as a reservoir of energy which can absorb differences between reactor power and boiler power occasioned by relatively fast changes in output demand.   Thus reactor power may be permitted to lag behind the power delivered to the load, thereby relieving somewhat the speed of reactor control required.   However, unbalances in power result in changing coolant temperatures, and a transient is not over until the temperatures have been reset to the values specified by the steady-state program.   Hence the required speed of the control system depends on the magnitude and duration of coolant temperature excursions which can be tolerated.

The familiar frequency-response method of stability analysis is applicable for studying the natural stability of the plant and for synthesis of a control system.   The procedure is to compute the response of plant variables to sinusoidal deviations of reactor power, about an average value.   The plant variables of interest are those which are fed back through the inherent feedback paths of the plant and those which are being considered for feedback through automatic control circuits.   The analysis is usually accomplished for a fixed setting of the steam throttle, corresponding to a constant average output power.   Because of nonlinearities which inevitably arise, the frequency-response type of analysis is valid only for amplitudes of power excursions that are small compared with the average value.   The analysis may be repeated for a sequence of values of throttle setting in order to cover adequately a given power range of interest.

The source of power, the reactor, responds to changes in reactivity. The reactivity δk depends on the ratio of neutron-production rate to the rate of loss, which in turn depends on the geometry of the reactor and on variables which affect the absorption and leakage of neutrons.   These variables are effectively the temperature and pressure of the coolant, as described in Sec. 6-1, and the concentration of neutron-absorbing poisons.

Since reactivity depends on plant variables, which in turn depend on reactor power, the plant contains inherent feedback, as shown in Fig. 6-18. The dependence of reactivity on the plant variables is expressed in the form of coefficients of reactivity, assuming linearity.   The dependence of the plant variables on reactor power is determined from the frequency-response calculations.

In the following discussion we shall assume that the inherent feedback due to changes in poison concentration has a negligible effect on stability over the frequency range of interest when compared with temperature and pressure feedback.   This assumption is justified either if the changes in poison concentration are small in magnitude or if the poisoning changes occur slowly compared with the temperature and pressure changes.

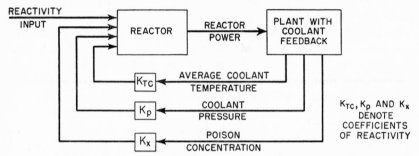

FIG. 6-18. Inherent feedback loops of a nuclear power plant.

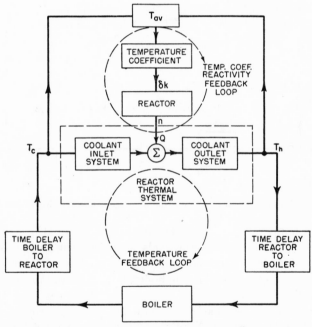

FIG. 6-19. Basic plant control loop showing temperature coefficient reactivity feedback loop and temperature feedback loop.

As we have already determined the frequency response of the reactor in Chap. 3, we must now find the response of average coolant temperature and pressure to oscillations in reactor power.   This step is accomplished by straightforward computation in an elementary plant by using the set of differential equations or transfer functions just derived in Secs. 6-4 and 6-5.

6-7. Temperature Feedback Loop Analysis. Figure 6-19 now shows a block diagram of the basic plant control loop that will be analyzed and whose component transfer functions have been developed in Sec. 6-5. Our basic control loop consists essentially of two loops: first, the temperature coefficient reactivity feedback loop involving the reactor and, second, a plant temperature feedback loop. The temperature feedback loop is the new portion of our study and is most important to stability considerations. First a quick look at this loop alone shows that it is regenerative; that is, an increase in temperature in an element of coolant at T_h is fed around through the boiler and back into the reactor as an

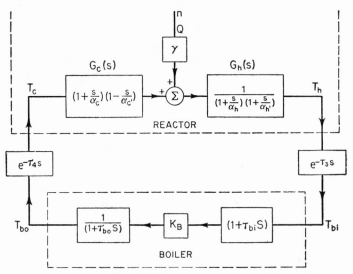

FIG. 6-20. Servo block diagram of temperature feedback loop.

increase in temperature at T_c. The only fixed attenuation in the system is at the boiler, and at low power levels, as just shown, there is only a very small amount of fixed attenuation present. The heat-transfer lags in the reactor thermal system and in the boiler, however, contain some attenuation at high frequencies.

The temperature feedback loop gain figures very prominently in all attempts to relate neutron-level changes to any temperature change in the plant. Figure 6-20 shows the temperature feedback loop with all of the transfer functions just derived. Suppose it is desired to relate the small signal sinusoidal response of the neutron level to a temperature T in the loop. Then, if the temperature feedback loop gain is denoted by $K_L G_L(s)$[3]

† An aside is necessary here concerning notation. The transfer functions that we have derived and have been using throughout this text have been in Laplace-transform

$$\frac{T(s)}{n(s)} = \frac{\text{open-loop gain from } n \text{ to } T}{1 - K_L G_L(s)} \tag{6-42}$$

The minus sign indicates that the feedback is regenerative. For example, variations in T_h as a function of variations in n become from Fig. 6-20

$$\frac{T_h(s)}{n(s)} = \frac{G_h(s)}{1 - K_L G_L(s)} \tag{6-43}$$

The term $1/[1 - K_L G_L(s)]$ appears very prominently in all stability calculations and will be used directly to determine the over-all temperature coefficient feedback. In addition, it will be needed later when controls are tied on the basic loop.

Consequently, it is now pertinent, in order to get a feeling for the properties of $1/[1 - K_L G_L(s)]$, to look at an example. Let us therefore compute $1/[1 - K_L G_L(s)]$ for a fictitious reactor plant, using simple numbers. Referring to Fig. 6-20, the following constants will be chosen for the inlet portion of the reactor thermal transfer function. Let

$$\left(1 + \frac{s}{\alpha_c}\right)\left(1 - \frac{s}{\alpha_{c'}}\right) = \left(1 + j\frac{f}{4}\right)\left(1 - j\frac{f}{3}\right) \tag{6-44}$$

where
$$\frac{\alpha_c}{2\pi} = 4 \qquad \frac{\alpha_{c'}}{2\pi} = 3$$

For the outlet portion of the reactor thermal transfer function let

$$\frac{1}{[1 + (s/\alpha_h)][1 + (s/\alpha_{h'})]} = \frac{1}{[1 + j(f/8)][1 + j(f/2)]} \tag{6-45}$$

where
$$\frac{\alpha_h}{2\pi} = 8 \qquad \frac{\alpha_{h'}}{2\pi} = 2$$

For the boiler constants we also arbitrarily choose

$$K_B \frac{1 + \tau_{bi}s}{1 + \tau_{bo}s} = 0.794 \frac{1 + j(f/0.15)}{1 + j(f/0.1)} \tag{6-46}$$

where
$$\tau_{bi} = \frac{1}{2\pi \times 0.15} \qquad \tau_{bo} = \frac{1}{2\pi \times 0.1}$$

and K_B is chosen as
$$0.794 = -2 \, db$$

---

form as functions of a complex variable s. Strictly speaking, in using these transfer functions, we are discussing transfer functions for sinusoidal signals of frequency f. We therefore should be substituting for s, $j2\pi f$ or $j\omega$. Actually, the symbol s has no meaning where we are performing nonlinear operations and is used in these following sections only to simplify notation. For all the operations involving frequency $j\omega$ is implied.

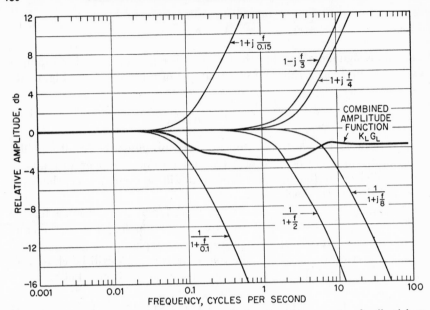

FIG. 6-21. Relative amplitude response of transfer function of temperature feedback loop $K_L G_L(s)$ showing the individual section responses.

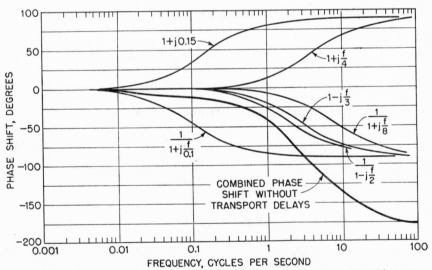

FIG. 6-22. Phase shift of transfer function of temperature feedback loop $K_L G_L(s)$ showing individual phase shifts but omitting linear phase shift of transport delay.

The coolant transport time delay constants are chosen equal to be

$$\tau_3 = 5 \text{ sec} \qquad \tau_4 = 5 \text{ sec}$$

Coolant flow is assumed to be constant at one fixed value.

Using these constants, Fig. 6-21 shows the form of the relative amplitude response of $K_L G_L(s)$. The attenuation constant K_B is not indicated in this figure, as it serves only to move the combined amplitude function down on the plot. It will be noted from this figure that as the frequency increases, the relative amplitude response does not go to zero as would be expected for most physical systems. In this case the amplitude levels off to a finite value as a function of frequency.

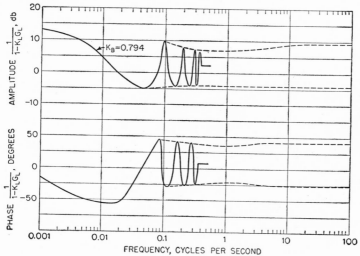

FIG. 6-23. Transfer function of $1/[1 - K_L G_L(s)]$ without mixing.

Figure 6-22 indicates the phase shift in the system without the transport delays of the pipe. It can be seen that the phase of this remainder of the system settles out at 180° phase shift at high frequencies. The transport delay phase shift that occurs is linear with frequency and will add directly onto the phase shift of Fig. 6-22.

Figure 6-23 shows a plot of the amplitude and phase of $1/[1 - K_L G_L(s)]$ for our example. The cyclic nature of the loop transfer function is due to the linear time delays causing the phase angle of $K_L G_L(s)$ to increase steadily with frequency. The peaks and valleys in the plot of the amplitude of $1/[1 - K_L G_L(s)]$ occur at frequency intervals which are roughly multiples of $1/2\tau_t$, where τ_t is the total time delay taken by the coolant in going around the primary loop. Physically speaking, the peaks and valleys occur at frequencies at which the temperature signal carried around the loop either reinforces or opposes the temperature signals introduced into the primary loop by the reactor. At high frequencies, where the phase of $K_L G_L(s)$ varies almost linearily with frequency because the linear time delay predominates, the peaks and valleys of the loop transfer function amplitude occur closer to frequency intervals of $1/2\tau_t$. The phase angle of the loop transfer function is very nearly zero at a frequency corresponding to a peak or a valley in the amplitude function. The periodicity of these plots is to be expected from any similar plant which transports heat from one heat exchange process to another by circulating a fluid heat-transfer medium.

However, the form of the transfer function of Fig. 6-23 is disturbing, as the amplitude of the periodic fluctuation does not die out as a function of frequency. This effect occurs because the amplitude of the open-loop gain $K_L G_L(s)$ settles out to a fixed value rather than diminishing to zero with frequency. In any practical physical system it can instinctively be felt that the amplitude of the open-loop gain as a function of frequency must ultimately be damped out to zero. Either our block diagram has been too simplified or we have been neglecting some aspects of the plant temperature feedback loop. One item that we have obviously left out is the mixing of the coolant as it is circulated through the loop. That is, temperatures in a given volume of coolant are not transported without being influenced by the temperatures of adjacent volume elements.

6-8. Coolant Mixing. We have been assuming that coolant temperatures flow through the system in sheetlike fashion. Actually, mixing in the circuit always takes place, particularly when there are volume changes or path-length changes in the flow path of the loop. For example, in going from the pipe into the boiler there may be many different paths that a unit volume of coolant might take. Figure 6-24 shows an illustration of what might happen at a pipe elbow. When coolant paths are of different lengths, our simple concept of transport time delay must be

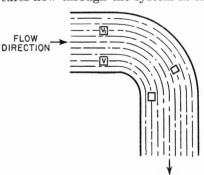

FLOW DIRECTION →

FIG. 6-24. Individual coolant volume elements at an elbow.

modified. Again, it can be felt instinctively that if a step change in temperature is inserted into a fluid flowing in a length of pipe, a clean, sharp step output in temperature will not be received at the other end of the pipe, particularly if there are different path lengths for different volume elements of coolant involved. The step input should be smeared, as some portions of the coolant at the new temperature will arrive at later times than others. Consequently, our approximate time delay formulas of Eqs. (6-13) and (6-15) might therefore really be a better representation of the two pipe delays than the pure time delay formula we have been using. Regardless of the pipe delays, however, we can certainly assume some mixing at the inlet to the reactor and the boiler and most likely also some mixing at the outlets of these components.

Mixing Transfer Functions. To develop a transfer function for these mixing effects let us consider the situation of Fig. 6-25. We shall continue to use the pure time delay representation for our pipes and assume that the mixing takes place in the inlet of the reactor or boiler. In Fig. 6-25 the large volume indicated may be the coolant in a bell or header of the reactor or boiler. We shall also assume that substantially complete mixing occurs within this volume.

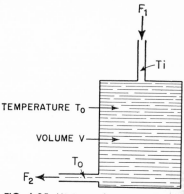

FIG. 6-25. Mixing volume representation.

Let $F_1 = F_2 = F$ = rate of flow of coolant in cubic feet per second and consider an interval of time Δt which is very small and can be made to approach zero. The input quantity of coolant then becomes $F \Delta t$.

At the end of Δt sec, the following volume and temperature conditions exist: There are $F \Delta t$ cu ft of coolant at temperature T_i; there are $V - F \Delta t$ cu ft of coolant at temperature T_0. These two volumes are mixed completely to give V cu ft of coolant at temperature $T_0 + \Delta T_0$, or

$$V(T_0 + \Delta T_0) = F \Delta t\, T_i + (V - F \Delta t)T_0 \tag{6-47}$$

or

$$\frac{\Delta T_0}{\Delta t} = \frac{F}{V} T_i - \frac{F}{V} T_0 \tag{6-48}$$

Letting ΔT_0 and Δt approach zero,

$$\frac{dT_0}{dt} + \frac{F}{V} T_0 = \frac{F}{V} T_i \tag{6-49}$$

In Laplace notation

$$s T_0(s) + \frac{F}{V} T_0(s) = \frac{F}{V} T_i(s) \tag{6-50}$$

where the initial conditions are zero, and

$$\frac{T_0(s)}{T_i(s)} = \frac{F/V}{s + (F/V)} = \frac{1}{1 + (V/F)s} \tag{6-51}$$

As V has the dimensions of cubic feet and F is in cubic feet per second,

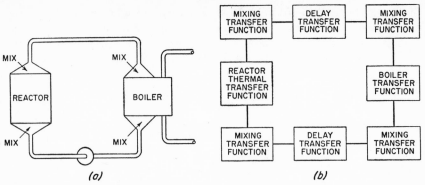

FIG. 6-26. (a) Symbolic representation of mixing in inlet and outlet of reactor and boiler. (b) Block diagram of temperature feedback loop indicating placement of mixing transfer functions.

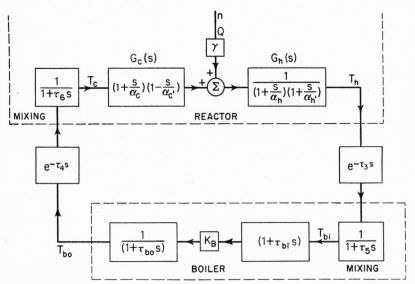

FIG. 6-27. Transfer function representation of a temperature feedback loop with two mixing terms.

V/F has the dimensions of time and consequently may be considered as a conventional time constant, or

$$\frac{T_0(s)}{T_i(s)} = \frac{1}{1 + \tau s} \tag{6-52}$$

Temperature Feedback Loop Containing Mixing. From a practical point of view we can now insert this type of mixing transfer function into the temperature feedback loop. Figure 6-26 shows one way this might be accomplished.   Of course, what we are doing is inserting some high-frequency attenuation in the open-loop gain in order to give our plant more practical characteristics.

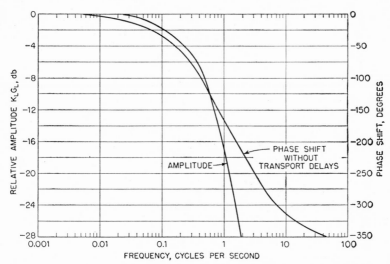

FIG. 6-28. Transfer function example of temperature feedback open-loop gain $K_L G_L(s)$ with mixing.

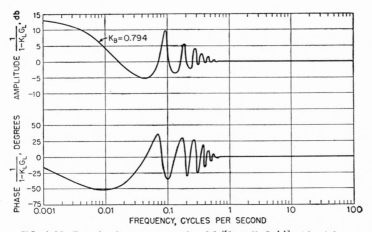

FIG. 6-29. Transfer function example of $1/[1 - K_L G_L(s)]$ with mixing.

Let us now consider the loop of Fig. 6-27, where we shall add only two mixing terms.   The two mixing time constants are τ_5 and τ_6.   In a practical plant many other mixing terms may exist and can be added to the analysis as desired.   Actually, in a real plant it is most desirable to design mixing into the reactor inlet so that any sharp transient changes in inlet temperature may be smeared promptly and not be permitted to cause rapid changes in reactivity through the temperature coefficient.

We can now return to our previous example, using the loop block diagram of Fig. 6-27, with the constants assigned from Eqs. (6-44), (6-45), and (6-46), and denote simple values to $\tau_5 = \tau_6 = (1/\pi)$ sec (break frequency 0.5 cycle/sec). We can again carry through the analysis for $1/[1 - K_L G_L(s)]$, first obtaining the amplitude and phase response of $K_L G_L(s)$ shown in Fig. 6-28. Now the open-loop gain decreases satisfactorily toward zero with frequency. Figure 6-29 shows the amplitude and phase response of $1/[1 - K_L G_L(s)]$ for our simple example, and now the periodic oscillation has been damped out to where the function is plausible.

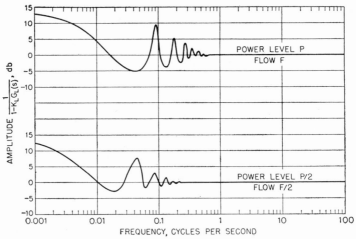

FIG. 6-30. Amplitude of $1/[1 - K_L G_L(s)]$ as the flow and power level are changed.

6-9. Flow Changes. In the previous sections we have been considering the case where the flow of coolant has been fixed at a given value and the power output of the plant has also been fixed. Let us assume that it is desired to change the power output of the plant by effectively changing the coolant flow. For illustrative purposes let us cut the flow in half, thus changing the power output by a factor of 2. If one were to examine the magnitude and phase of $1/[1 - K_L G_L(s)]$ of our simple example, it can be seen that if the frequency scale values of both the magnitude and phase were divided by 2, the resulting curves would very closely approximate the transfer functions of the new conditions.

Figure 6-30 illustrates the change in amplitude of this function for a given power and a given flow as against one-half of that power and one-half of the initial flow. It can be seen that the curves are similar, as it is apparent that all of the linear time delays in the primary coolant loop are inversely proportional to the coolant flow rate. The gain constant K_L of the loop is roughly equal to that of the boiler gain K_B, which from Fig. 6-18 does not change very much for a power output change of 2 to 1. Therefore, changing the flow through the primary loop by a limited amount changes for the most part the frequency scale only of the transfer function. The general form of $1/[1 - K_L G_L(s)]$ remains the same.

It should be emphasized again that this analysis is proper only for fixed fuel reactors. Other types of reactors, such as homogeneous reactors or boiling reactors, can be handled with the same general type of approach, but here reactivity would also be a function of flow.

6-10. Analysis for Multiple-section Reactor. Figure 6-16 indicated the form of the reactor thermal transfer function when the reactor was treated in sections. The analysis we have been carrying through up to the present has been for a simple one-section reactor. Before we proceed with the study of the reactivity feedback loop, it is of interest to point out the method of analysis that would be used for a more complicated reactor system. In order to get a more accurate representation of the reactor thermal system, the reactor is split up into sections. Figure 6-31 shows a block diagram of a temperature feedback loop in which the reactor is broken up into four series sections. The other elements in the loop are the same as indicated in Fig. 6-27. The neutron flux from the reactor may be assumed to produce equal heat in each of the four sections of the reactor, that is, $Q_1 = Q_2 = Q_3 = Q_4$. Or if it is desired to taper the heat input into the reactor representation in an effort to take care of unsymmetrical flux distribution, these quantities may have different values.

We can now use the principle of linear superposition in the following manner. Let us assume that Q_1 is finite and Q_2, Q_3, and $Q_4 = 0$. The open-loop transfer function between $n(s)$ and any temperature in the loop $T(s)$ is simply the product of all the transfer functions between $n(s)$ and $T(s)$ in the direction of signal flow. As indicated previously, the feedback loop transfer function $K_L G_L(s)$ is the product of all the series transfer functions in the primary coolant loop. Then

$$\left| \frac{T(s)}{n(s)} \right|_{Q_2, Q_3, Q_4=0} = \frac{[T(s)/n(s)]_{\text{open loop, } Q_2, Q_3, Q_4=0}}{1 - K_L G_L(s)} \tag{6-53}$$

Similarly if Q_2 is finite and Q_1, Q_3, $Q_4 = 0$,

$$\left| \frac{T(s)}{n(s)} \right|_{Q_1, Q_3, Q_4=0} = \frac{[T(s)/n(s)]_{\text{open loop, } Q_1, Q_3, Q_4=0}}{1 - K_L G_L(s)} \tag{6-54}$$

Corresponding expressions are obtained for finite Q_3 and Q_4. Therefore, assuming we are dealing with linear transfer functions, we may apply the

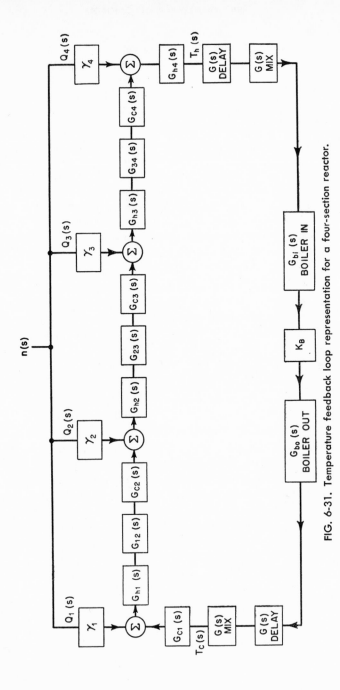

FIG. 6-31. Temperature feedback loop representation for a four-section reactor.

theory of superposition and find that

$$
\begin{aligned}
\frac{T(s)}{n(s)} &= \left|\frac{T(s)}{n(s)}\right|_{Q_2,Q_3,Q_4=0} + \left|\frac{T(s)}{n(s)}\right|_{Q_1,Q_3,Q_4=0} + \left|\frac{T(s)}{n(s)}\right|_{Q_1,Q_2,Q_4=0} \\
&+ \left|\frac{T(s)}{n(s)}\right|_{Q_1,Q_2,Q_3=0} = \frac{1}{1 - K_L G_L(s)} \left[\frac{T(s)}{n(s)}\right]_{\text{open loop, } Q_2,Q_3,Q_4=0} \\
&+ \frac{T(s)}{n(s)}_{\text{open loop, } Q_1,Q_3,Q_4=0} + \frac{T(s)}{n(s)}_{\text{open loop, } Q_1,Q_2,Q_4=0} + \frac{T(s)}{n(s)}_{\text{open loop, } Q_1,Q_2,Q_3=0} \Bigg]
\end{aligned}
$$

(6-55)

It is evident that an analysis of this sort can become quite tedious in order to obtain great accuracy. It is apparent also that if this type of analysis is carried into too many sections, distributed reactor representation should be developed. Some methods for obtaining a distributed reactor representation have been worked out in the classified literature but are beyond the scope of this book.

6-11. Application and Limitations of Temperature Feedback Loop Transfer Functions. As the relationship of all the temperatures in the temperature feedback loop to the neutron-level variations can now be derived, we can return our attention to the remainder of the basic control loop (see Fig. 6-19). This is the portion of the loop whereby the average temperature via the negative temperature coefficient changes the reactivity of the reactor. In order to obtain reactivity we note that

$$\delta k = (TC)(T_{\text{av}} - T_0) \tag{6-56}$$

where (TC) is the temperature coefficient of reactivity $|\delta k/T_{\text{av}}|_p$ and T_0 is a reference temperature.

It is apparent that we must derive an expression for $T_{\text{av}}(s)/n(s)$, where s again is to represent $j\omega$ and the entire operation is for small signal variations about given values of T_{av} and n.

Using the simple example of the block diagram of Fig. 6-27

$$\frac{T_h(s)}{n(s)} = \frac{G_h(s)}{1 - K_L G_L(s)} \tag{6-57}$$

and
$$\frac{T_c(s)}{n(s)} = \frac{T_h(s) K_L G_L(s)}{G_c(s)} \tag{6-58}$$

and
$$2T_{\text{av}}(s) = T_h(s) + T_c(s) \tag{6-59}$$

Therefore
$$2\frac{T_{\text{av}}(s)}{n(s)} = \frac{G_h(s)}{1 - K_L G_L(s)} + \frac{G_h(s)}{1 - K_L G_L(s)} \frac{K_L G_L(s)}{G_c(s)} \tag{6-60}$$

or
$$\frac{T_{\text{av}}(s)}{n(s)} = \frac{G_h(s)}{2[1 - K_L G_L(s)]} \left[1 + \frac{K_L G_L(s)}{G_c(s)}\right] \tag{6-61}$$

$$= \frac{1}{2} \frac{T_h(s)}{n(s)} \left[1 + \frac{K_L G_L(s)}{G_c(s)}\right] \tag{6-62}$$

T_{av} may be developed in a similar manner for more complex divided reactor thermal systems by the superposition technique developed in Sec. 6-10.

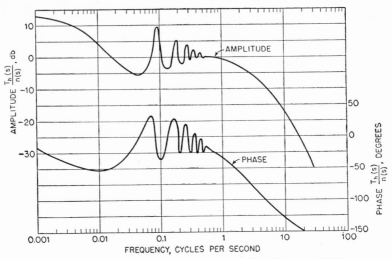

FIG. 6-32. Transfer function example $T_h(s)/n(s)$, $K_B = 0.794$.

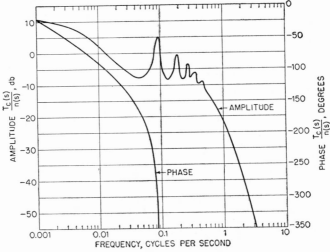

FIG. 6-33. Transfer function example $T_c(s)/n(s)$, $K_B = 0.794$.

We can now continue our numerical example for the simple loop of Fig. 6-27, using the curves of Figs. 6-28 and 6-29 for $K_L G_L(s)$ and $1/[1 - K_L G_L(s)]$. First $T_h(s)/n(s)$ is developed, using Eq. (6-57), by multiplying $1/[1 - K_L G_L(s)]$ by $G_h(s)$. This transfer function is shown in Fig. 6-32. The amplitude response is seen to fall off as a function of frequency in the same manner as $G_h(s)$. The function $T_c(s)/n(s)$ can then be obtained from Eq. (6-58) and is shown in Fig. 6-33. Here the amplitude response as a function of frequency falls off much more rapidly at high frequency because of the additional boiler and mixing high-frequency dropoffs. In other words, as the coolant progresses through the loop, high-frequency variations in coolant temperature become more and more attenuated. Consequently, the high-frequency response of $T_{av}(s)/n(s)$, shown in Fig. 6-34, closely resembles the response of $T_h(s)/n(s)$ at high frequency.

We might now examine the over-all situation, again restating the purposes and assumptions we have made in dealing with the temperature

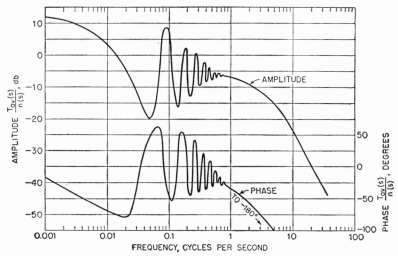

FIG. 6-34. Transfer function example $T_{av}(s)/n(s)$, $K_B = 0.794$.

feedback loop, before we proceed with the temperature coefficient analysis. The major characteristic of the nuclear power plant which has caused the oscillations to appear in both the magnitude and phase plots of the system transfer functions is the fact that the *primary coolant circulates in a closed loop*. The closed loop provides a means of reinforcement or opposition of the temperature input signals appearing in the reactor by the temperature signals carried back to the reactor by means of the primary coolant. The time delays, which are inherent in the transportation of heat from one point to another by the primary coolant, ensure that the phase angle between the input temperature signals and the feedback signals increases steadily with frequency, thus producing a series of maxima and minima in the system transfer function plots.

In a more complicated reactor analysis the reactor power is fed into the primary coolant at multiple points. The temperature signal at one point in the reactor is carried on to another point by the primary coolant. There the signal may again reinforce or oppose the temperature signal of the initial point, depending upon the phase shift acquired in passing from one point to another. The linear time delays in the primary coolant loop may cause the above-mentioned reinforcement and opposition action to occur repeatedly at regular intervals of frequency with respect to each section input of the multiple reactor.

With proper interpretation the transfer functions just derived in Figs. 6-32, 6-33, and 6-34 can provide valuable insight into the behavior of the nuclear power plant. In the first place, they may be helpful in obtaining a "feel" for the transient response of the nuclear power plant to external system disturbances without any control system. Second, Nyquist plots of this data provide a measure of the degree to which the bare reactor is stabilized by the negative temperature coefficient of reactivity. Third, the transfer functions provide basic data upon which to design a satisfactory control scheme. Finally, they may help to point out adjustments and modifications which may improve the dynamic performance of a contemplated power plant. In order to interpret these transfer functions correctly, constant reference must be made to the physical system and to the conditions and assumptions upon which these transfer functions are based.

Primarily, it must be remembered that the transfer functions or plots of frequency which have been presented in this analysis have been based on a simple example. Two basic conditions were involved: First, the throttle opening was kept constant, and second, the primary coolant flow rate was constant. The results obtained are confined solely to relating the response of the plant to reactivity or reactor power disturbances. The response to changes in throttle setting or coolant flow rate have not been specifically considered here.

These additional responses may be developed in a similar manner to those just presented. It must be emphasized again that the frequency response characteristics have been calculated for very small sinusoidal variations in the power plant variables about a specified steady-state condition for the entire plant. Predictions of the transient behavior of the plant based on the frequency response characteristics must therefore generally be confined to small transients about the steady-state conditions specified.

6-12. Temperature Coefficient Reactivity Feedback Loop. In most present-day reactors the temperature coefficient of reactivity at constant pressure is negative and the net effect is to make the reactor self-regulating. This negative temperature coefficient is, in servo terminology, degenerative and has a stabilizing influence on an unstable physical system. The actual form of the negative feedback is not derivable from the kinetic equations of a bare reactor *but depends solely on the characteristics of the physical plant associated with the reactor.* That is, an increase in reactor power results in a more rapid absorption of heat by the heat transfer medium or coolant. This increased rate of energy transfer eventually results in a higher average temperature of the coolant moderator and effects a change in reactivity. It is apparent that the form of feedback effect depends upon the characteristics of the associated plant and load rather than on the nuclear characteristics of the reactor.

This negative feedback, which is an inherent characteristic of the plant, is a control system which is already built into the plant and which cannot be removed or disconnected for either good or bad. It has one

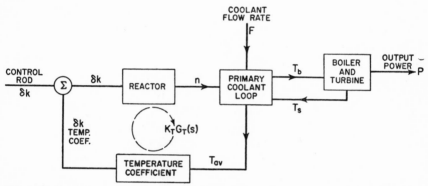

FIG. 6-35. Block diagram of nuclear power plant indicating plant temperature coefficient feedback loop.

advantage over an external control system in that it is ever reliable and never out of order. Any external control system that is desired must be designed to operate in parallel with the inherent control action in such a fashion that the over-all performance is satisfactory. Consequently, before designing an external reactor control system, one must first examine the relative stability of the reactor plant system before any controls are added.

We are now in a position to make such an analysis. A new block diagram of the plant showing how the negative temperature coefficient ties back around the reactor through the plant is given in Fig. 6-35. From this figure we see that in order to determine the stability of the complete reactor plant system about a given nuclear power level n_0 with constant coolant flow rate, throttle opening, and control-rod positions, we must examine the temperature coefficient reactivity feedback loop transfer function

$$K_T G_T(s) = (TC) \frac{n(s)}{\delta k(s)} \frac{T_{av}(s)}{n(s)} \qquad (6\text{-}63)$$

where $n(s)/\delta k(s)$ is the bare reactor transfer function as has been developed in Sec. 3-4. The poisoning feedback combination could also be added if desired. It will be recalled from Sec. 3-4 that the reactor itself is a nonlinear element, its gain being proportional to neutron-power level. For sinusoidal signals of small amplitude at a given average power level n_0, the bare reactor was represented by the transfer function of Eq. (3-41)

$$\frac{n(s)}{\delta k(s)} = \frac{n_0}{l^*} \frac{1}{s\left[1 + \sum_{i=1}^{6} \frac{\beta_i}{l^*(s + \lambda_i)}\right]} \tag{6-64}$$

Plots of the magnitude and phase of the bare reactor transfer function were presented as Figs. 3-15 and 3-16. The open-loop transfer function of Eq. (6-63) is thus the product of the temperature coefficient (TC), the transfer function for $T_{av}(s)/n(s)$, and the bare reactor transfer function.

As we have already developed $T_{av}(s)/n(s)$ in graphical form for our elementary numerical example, we may continue the example again by using the curves of Figs. 3-15 and 3-16, $l^* = 10^{-4}$ sec for the bare reactor transfer function and thus compute $K_T G_T(s)$ for the example. Figures 6-36 and 6-37 indicate the magnitude and phase of $K_T G_T(s)/(TC)$ thus obtained. From these curves it is easily seen that the system of our example possesses great stability. Negative temperature coefficients for practical reactors might range between zero and $10^{-3}\delta k/{}^\circ F$. The amplitude curve of Fig. 6-36 is at $+15$ db when the phase shift reaches -180° at 11 cycles/sec. If the temperature coefficient of the reactor under consideration were $10^{-3}\delta k/{}^\circ F$, then 60 db must be subtracted from the curve of Fig. 6-36 in order to obtain the total gain of the over-all temperature coefficient feedback loop. Then, at -180° the gain would be -45 db, a tremendous margin of stability. If the temperature coefficient were smaller, this margin would be still larger and the stability of the plant would be even greater.

The equation for the reactor feedback loop gain, Eq. (6-63), can be rewritten as

$$K_T G_T(s) = (TC) \frac{n(s)}{\delta k(s)} \frac{G_h}{1 - K_L G_L(s)} \left[1 + \frac{K_L G_L(s)}{G_c}\right] \tag{6-65}$$

Our analysis has been at a constant power level whereby $K_B = 0.8$ and is at a constant flow. Let us examine now what happens if these parameters are changed. Assume that the power level is reduced. The reactor gain $n(s)/\delta k(s)$ is nonlinear, as its gain is directly proportional to n_0, the power level at which the reactor is operating. In other words, if the power level is dropped, the gain portion of the transfer function depending upon the reactor will be reduced in a linear manner. The gain of $K_L G_L(s)$

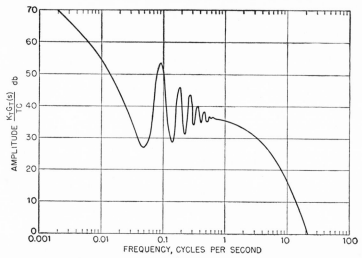

FIG. 6-36. Open-loop amplitude response of transfer function of temperature coefficient reactivity feedback loop $K_T G_T(s)/(TC)$.

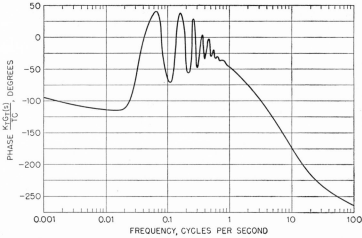

FIG. 6-37. Open-loop phase shift of transfer function of temperature coefficient reactivity feedback loop $K_T G_T(s)/(TC)$.

is also affected by power level in that it depends mostly upon boiler attenuation K_B. K_B varies inversely with power level in accordance with Eq. (6-37), so that as the power level is dropped, the gain of $K_L G_L(s)$ goes up from this cause. This effect is very noticeable because the primary coolant loop provides a regenerative feedback path as previously described. The term $1/[1 - K_L G_L(s)]$ is very dependent upon K_B. For example, from Fig. 6-17, the boiler attenuation is about 20 percent at

$K_a AB/K_b A_b = 0.5$.   That is, the boiler gain is 0.8 at zero frequency at this power level.   Therefore the value of $1/[1 - K_L G_L(s)] = 5$ at zero frequency.   At $K_a AB/K_b A_b = 0.03$ the boiler attenuation is only 2 per-cent and $1/[1 - K_L G_L(s)] = 50$.   In other words, a portion of the over-all loop transfer function gain is reduced with power level whereas another portion is increased.   Whether a net positive or negative gain change results depends upon the individual system constants.

The above reasoning was based upon constant coolant flow.   If the coolant flow is changed at the same time that the power level is changed, there are two more effects which can result.   The gain constant γ, which relates the primary coolant temperature to reactor power, is inversely proportional to coolant flow, for it will be recalled that γ was defined in Eq. (6-23) as $\gamma = t_f \tau_0 / t_{mod} d_{mod} c_{mod}$.   As τ_0 is the time for a unit volume of coolant to pass through the reactor core, it is evident that τ_0 increases directly as the flow rate is decreased.   Consequently, the loop gain becomes larger inversely with flow. K_B also changes slightly with flow, but this is usually a secondary effect.

Therefore, in examining the stability of a given reactor plant system it may be more appropriate to conduct the analysis at the lowest usable power level rather than at full power output if the flow is reduced at low power level.   If the system can then be shown to be stable at its minimum usable output, it usually can be assumed, for simple systems, that this is a worse case and the system is stable a priori at full output.   For com-plex systems in which intricate flow patterns are called for in the pro-gramming, it is necessary to examine how the heat-transfer coefficients change as a function of flow before this assumption can be taken for granted.

6-13. Transient Analysis.   The procedure for analyzing the stability of a reactor plant system without controls has just been indicated.   We would also, of course, like to examine analytically the transient response of this system.   The stability of a simple plant has been shown to be very high for reasonable values of temperature coefficient.   For small temperature coefficients the absolute stability of a plant will be even higher, but now the transient response should be poorer.   What we have is a degenerative feedback system in which the magnitude of the tempera-ture coefficient controls the feedback factor.   With a very small tempera-ture coefficient the system is extremely stable as far as sustained oscilla-tion is concerned, but a transient injected into the system would create large overshoots in all the parameters.   As the temperature coefficient becomes larger, the system will still possess good stability, but now tran-sients cause only moderate overshoots.   As the temperature coefficient becomes extremely large, sustained oscillations will result, and although the transient response may be improved, it is immaterial.   An optimum temperature coefficient or range of temperature coefficients must then exist. A minimum value should be present to prevent dangerously high transients, and the maximum value must not approach the sustained oscillation conditions.

A word defining stability is in order at this point. In conventional terms, if a system is stable, no sustained oscillations can result. An oscillation can occur when the gain of the system is greater than unity at 180° phase shift. Now, in the case of a bare reactor or for a reactor with a temperature coefficient feedback loop with a zero or positive temperature coefficient, it is recognized that at zero frequency an infinite gain results. This condition is also termed unstable, even though at zero frequency only −90° of phase shift occurs. Actually the addition of only the most minute amount of negative temperature coefficient makes the loop of Eq. (6-65) stable. Its performance, with respect to transient response, would still be very poor in that large excursions, but not infinite excursions, of all parameters would occur. Such systems can be labeled as having insufficient stability. A more proper description might be merely to say that systems having large parameter excursions, because of transient disturbances, simply have poor performance. Rigorous mathematical representation of these explanations is available[6] if desired by the reader.

The transient analysis of even a simple system such as has been used in the stability analysis of this chapter presents considerable analytical difficulty. From 10 to 20 simultaneous differential equations would be involved, depending upon how closely one wished to approximate the reactor and on how many mixing terms were used. The obvious solution is to use the technique of Sec. 4-10 and set up an analogue computer or simulator to examine the transient response. The method of designing such a simulator is given in Chap. 11. Most of the components involved in the example we have used have quite simple analogues with the exception of the linear time delays. These delays must be represented quite accurately, as a wrong representation at low power level can easily throw the temperature feedback loop $K_L G_L(s)$ into continuous oscillation. Magnetic tapes, phonograph records, or elaborate electronic networks[4] may be used to approximate the linear delays.

Two types of transients are of interest. One is a transient change in throttle opening, and the other is a transient change in reactivity similar to the transient used in checking reactor response. What is necessary is to examine the response of the reactor power output, the thermal plant output, and the significant temperatures in the plant as a function of these two types of input disturbance. As the computer set up for such a program involves obtaining numerial design data for a complete specific plant system with all its auxiliary components, we shall merely outline

here the relative types of responses to be expected from a simple plant
without using an actual numerical example.

Consider the plant of Fig. 6-38, which will be of the same type that we
have been using previously, having a common coolant moderator and an
elementary temperature feedback control loop. Let us assume that this
plant is operating at a fixed power output level and that we suddenly
open up the throttle. This effectively inserts a step change in power
demand. Figure 6-39 indicates qualitatively the results of this operation.
The first effect noted is an instantaneous increase in thermal output
accompanied by a less rapid decrease in steam temperature. The power
delivered to the turbine is available very fast because of the release of
energy stored in the heat capacity of the boiler and coolant. The

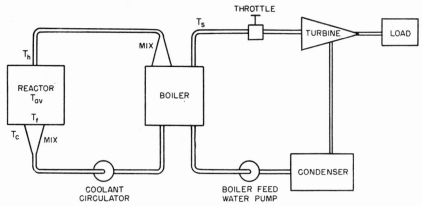

FIG. 6-38. Block diagram of elementary plant showing mixing.

decrease in steam temperature causes a decrease in primary coolant
temperature, since more heat is extracted from the coolant. The change
in temperature of primary coolant produces a significant reactivity change
at once, and the reactor power starts to rise almost immediately. The
thermal behavior of the fuel is of importance from a materials point of
view, and its general temperature pattern is similar to the pattern of the
average coolant temperature. It will be noted that after the transient
has passed, the average coolant temperature comes back to its initial
value, but now the power delivered to the turbine is the greater required
amount. A slight overshoot is seen to be present in the reactor power
output, and this overshoot serves the purpose of recharging the stored
energy in the boiler system.

For the illustration used, the plant has a moderate-sized temperature
coefficient, and the entire plant appears to be highly overdamped.
Because of this fact, it would appear possible to take a plant of this type

and increase its speed of response to a transient by means of an external control system.

The other type of disturbance we wish to examine is the disturbance caused by a change in reactivity for any reason whatever. A simple case to consider is that of a step withdrawal of a control rod. It has been shown in Sec. 3-2 that when a control rod is suddenly withdrawn, the

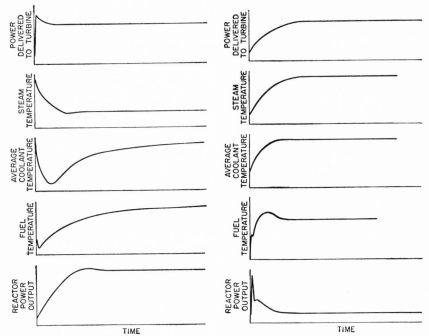

FIG. 6-39. Transient response of plant parameters to a positive step in throttle opening.

FIG. 6-40. Transient response of plant parameters to a positive step in reactivity.

reactor starts up on a positive period, the leading edge of which starts to follow the relationship

$$\frac{dn}{dt} = \frac{\delta k}{l^*} n \qquad (6\text{-}66)$$

Thus, in a very short amount of time a bare reactor would quickly reach a very high power level. However, what actually happens in the case of a reactor plant with negative temperature coefficient is that before the power level gets very high, the heat flow through the reactor fuel to the coolant raises the coolant temperature enough to stop the rapid rise. Figure 6-40 shows the effect of a step change in reactivity upon the system. The rising coolant temperature extracts reactivity and brings the reactor power level down. A small secondary peak may exist because of the emission of delayed neutrons produced at the initial high peak of power. The reactor fuel acts as a filter between the reactor power and the reactivity change. A transient heat spike can be seen in the fuel temperature, but it is completely filtered out by the time the transient arrives at reactor coolant temperature. The steam temperature and, therefore, the thermal power follow the transient much more slowly.

After the transient has passed, the reactor coolant temperature must be above its original value in order to offset the increase in reactivity caused by the rod motion. This condition causes all the temperatures of the plant to rise, and as a consequence, the thermal output power and the reactor power will rise somewhat above their original values. A completely similar, but opposite, set of curves results when negative throttle changes or negative reactivity steps are inserted.

6-14. External Reactor Control System. Having developed the temperature coefficient reactivity feedback loop, we are now in a position to

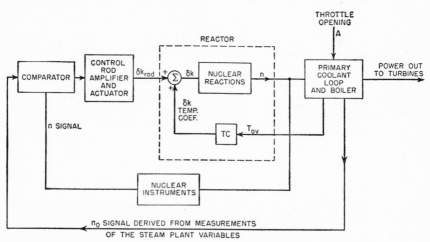

FIG. 6-41. Block diagram indicating the feedback loops which affect reactor stability.

examine a combined reactor and plant to see how the reactor responds to external controls in a manner similar to the analysis of Sec. 4-7. It will be recalled that in this previous section the temperature coefficient was handled as a simple local feedback loop around the reactor and the feedback gain was combined with the reactor gain by means of conventional servo analysis for two elements in parallel. Then when a combined reactor temperature coefficient transfer function was developed, an external control loop could be tied around the combined system. Figure 6-41 indicates how a plant can be set up to cause an external reactor control loop to control a combined reactor plant system. It is necessary, however, to determine the combined transfer function of the reactor system indicated by the dotted box of Fig. 6-41. The reactor and its feed-back loops again may be linearized for small amplitude sinusoidal varia-tions at an average power level n_0. These transfer functions are indicated in the diagram of Fig. 6-42a. The system may then be reduced to the equivalent form of Fig. 6-42b, in which the reactor and its temperature coefficient feedback system have been reduced to a single block. The function $n(s)/\delta k_{rod}(s)$ is the representation of the new combined reactor

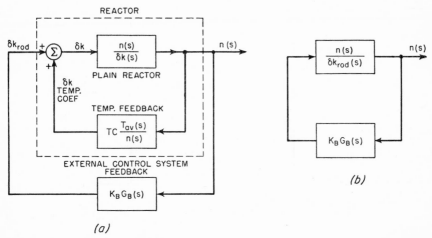

FIG. 6-42. Equivalent block diagrams of the reactor with temperature coefficient and control-rod feedback loops for small sinusoidal signals.

and temperature coefficient transfer function. $K_B G_B(s)$ again represents the external reactor control system. Then

$$\frac{n(s)}{\delta k_{rod}(s)} = \frac{n(s)/\delta k(s)}{1 + [n(s)/\delta k(s)](TC)[T_{av}(s)/n(s)]} \tag{6-67}$$

$$= \frac{1}{(TC)[T_{av}(s)/n(s)]} \frac{K_T G_T(s)}{1 + K_T G_T(s)} \tag{6-68}$$

We have then reduced the problem of reactor control in a power plant to the more simple problem of reactor control as analyzed in Secs. 4-7 and 4-8. The bare reactor had a given transfer function, and it was shown that this reactor could be controlled either with a proportional control system or with an on-off step type control system. When a simple reac-tor system containing a negative temperature coefficient, but no coolant flow, was examined, it was shown that all that was needed was to modify the reactor transfer function by combining it with a parallel reactor tem-perature coefficient feedback system. Poison feedback was handled in a similar manner. Then a new combined reactor function with all these feedbacks could be controlled by an external loop. In the case of a full plant we have now shown that the bare reactor transfer function need only be combined in parallel again with a plant temperature coefficient feedback system and an external control, either proportional or on-off type, may be analyzed in a completely analogous manner to the simpler systems previously presented.

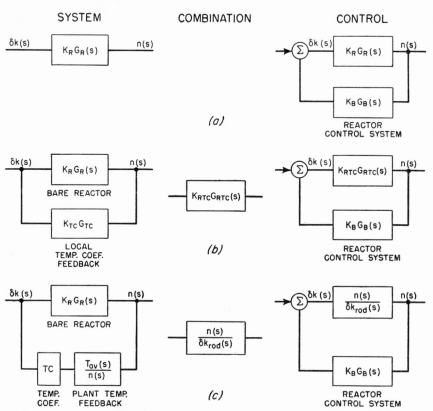

FIG. 6-43. Combinations of reactor and various feedback loop transfer functions. (a) Elementary reactor. (b) Local temperature coefficient feedback. (c) Plant temperature coefficient feedback.

Figure 6-43 indicates the sequence of combinations just described. Figure 6-43a shows a bare reactor and then an external reactor control system transfer function of any type $K_B G_B(s)$. Figure 6-43b shows the combination of this bare reactor and a local temperature coefficient effect. This is the condition of most reactors operating without external plants. Figure 6-43c shows an example of reactor control when a full plant is present. The poison feedback loop again is not shown. It can easily be seen that the analysis for any external reactor control system can always be made to have the same form by proper combination.

For illustrative purposes we can plot Eq. (6-68) for the example we have been using for a temperature coefficient of $(TC) = 10^{-3}\delta k/°F$. Figure 6-44 indicates this plot of the combined reactor and plant temperature coefficient transfer function. It is of interest to note that this transfer function is of the same general form as the combined reactor, local temperature coefficient feedback system of Figs. 4-4 and 4-6. In particular, the transfer function amplitude approaches a finite value at zero frequency. The phase shift approaches zero at zero frequency and $-90°$ at infinite frequency. Thus we see again that the example of the reactor plant negative temperature coefficient system we have been using is a most stable one, neglecting any possible long-term poison oscillations.

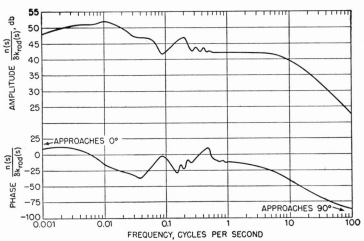

FIG. 6-44. Magnitude and phase of over-all reactor transfer function with temperature coefficient, $(TC) = 10^{-3}\delta k/°F$.

6-15. Automatic Plant Control.[5]

Reactor control by itself in a plant is of little importance. The essential problem is to obtain useful power from the plant. Reactor control then, at most, becomes a minor auxiliary loop in a power plant. Plant control must be all-prevailing and overrule local situations. We have just examined the natural stability of a plant and found that the reactor could be treated as a component in a plant system. We must now examine the basic plant when an attempt is made to superimpose an external control system upon it. Although most plants will be quite stable by themselves, it is very possible to upset this natural stability by an improperly designed external control system.

The function of an automatic plant control system is twofold. First, it must set up the ultimate steady-state temperature, pressure, and flow programs desired; second, it should improve, or at least not detract from, the transient performance of the basic plant.

To accomplish these functions requires the study of a new control loop. We have determined that the reactor plant and reactor control could be synthesized into a single loop. We now must superimpose a demand loop upon the reactor and the temperature coefficient feedback loop. Figure 6-45 shows an arrangement of a plant illustrating the position of the new demand loop.

Two different situations can arise. These will depend on whether the plant by itself has a large amount of natural stability or has poor transient performance or so-called insufficient stability. Since the type of control system required depends upon whether the plant is inherently stable or has poor performance, the two situations will be discussed separately.

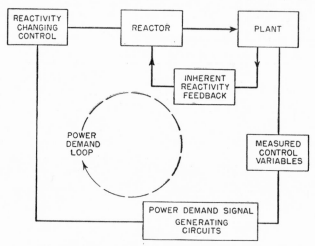

FIG. 6-45. Block diagram of power demand loop.

If an analysis shows that the plant by itself has poor performance, then complete automatic control is necessary. The automatic system must control the reactor power level according to the output demanded, in addition to maintaining the required temperatures. These requirements suggest a control system of the type shown in Fig. 6-46. Reactor power is maintained equal to a generated power demand signal by controlling the reactivity, usually by manipulation of the control rods in the reactor core. The indication of reactor power is obtained from nuclear instruments. The power demand signal is generated from measurements of plant variables and must be a measure of the load on the plant and the deviation of a variable from the value specified by the steady-state program. Usually the steam flow is a good indication of the load requirements. In fact, if the enthalpy rise through the steam generator is a constant independent of load, the power delivered is directly proportional to the steam flow. Throttle position also may be used. The particular variable used to indicate deviation from the set program might be any coolant temperature in the loop or the steam pressure. Because of the relationships that exist at steady-state conditions, only one variable is needed to control the program.

This system of control reactor power through a demand loop and a neutron-measuring reactor control loop is a necessity for a reactor containing either a positive temperature coefficient or a very small negative temperature coefficient. After a control program for such a system has been decided upon, the stability of the complete system may be studied on a frequency response basis. Again we must stipulate complete linearity. Consequently, the results are strictly valid only for small deviations. Satisfaction of familiar stability criteria and attainment of desired

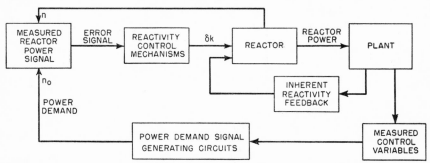

FIG. 6-46. Block diagram of control system for a plant containing inadequate natural stability.

margins of stability are readily accomplished using standard servo techniques. Whether the addition of derivative control (anticipation), integral control (reset), or other compensating networks is necessary can be determined from Nyquist and Bode diagrams in the usual manner.

If the analysis of the basic plant, such as has been carried out in the previous sections of this chapter, indicates that the plant is inherently sufficiently stable, the automatic control problem is simplified. The plant effectively controls itself supplying whatever load is imposed. Any difference between reactor power and steam load results in a rate of change of average coolant temperature. The reactivity change caused by the temperature change then alters reactor power, thus resetting the temperature and the heat balance. The speed of transient response obtained may in itself be adequate for the system application, so that in many cases automatic control of the power level for improved transient performance may not be required. The use of nuclear measurements and the generation of a neutron power demand signal become unnecessary. Thus the role of the automatic system is reduced to that of maintaining the steady-state temperature program.

The requirements for a plant that is inherently sufficiently stable suggest a control system of the type shown in Fig. 6-47.   Here the temperature or pressure error is controlled directly by insertion and withdrawal of reactivity by control-rod motion.   The inherent stability of the plant compensates for any change in reactivity by shifting the temperature level until the net reactivity is again reduced to zero.   Thus by moving the control rods a given distance, the temperatures shift to a new constant value, and direct control of the program is accomplished with no neutron information being required.   However, as in the previous example, the over-all system stability must again be studied and optimized by a frequency response method.

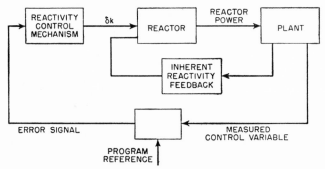

FIG. 6-47. Block diagram of control system for a plant containing adequate natural stability.

In summary, if the plant has sufficient natural stability, direct control of plant parameters may be attempted.   If the plant has poor inherent transient performance, neutron-level control should also be used.

Control Systems for Plants with Insufficient Inherent Stability.   It will be recalled that many forms of control programs may be demanded from a plant.   Obviously, each program can call for a completely different type of control, but there are recognizable patterns of control systems which can fit frequently occurring situations.   The most obvious type of control program is the constant-T_{av} program.   As has been pointed out in Sec. 6-3, this is the natural program of the reactor.   In addition, there is the constant-steam-pressure program, which is the preferred program of the secondary system.   Many in-between compromises are possible. We shall now examine a few types of control system setups for the constant-T_{av} program, the constant-steam-pressure program, and varying degrees of compromise when there is a neutron control loop involved.

Figure 6-48 indicates two types of control systems.   Figure 6-48a represents a scheme whereby the power demand signal n_0 is generated according to the equation

$$n_0 = K \left[(T_{\text{av,ref}} - T_{\text{av}}) + \frac{1}{\tau} \int (T_{\text{av,ref}} - T_{\text{av}}) \, dt \right] \qquad (6\text{-}69)$$

The n_0 signal generated in this manner is then compared with reactor power, assumed proportional to the neutron flux level, and the resultant error signal actuates the control rods. The integral of T_{av} error is necessary to provide a steady-state n_0 signal, since no T_{av} error exists in the steady state. This system, while simple, is at a disadvantage because a poor transient response results from throttle changes. As the throttle

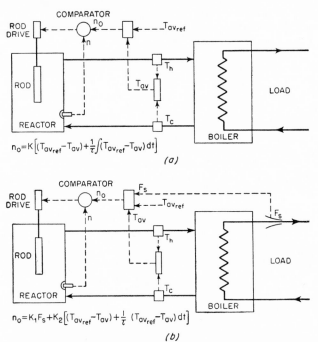

FIG. 6-48. Two types of control systems for constant-average-temperature program. (a) Indirect control. (b) Direct control.

opening is increased, steam flow increases immediately, thus withdrawing more power from the primary coolant and lowering the average coolant temperature. The reactor power is increased to supply the demand, preventing further depletion of the reservoir of energy stored in the coolant. The sooner reactor power equals the steam demand, the shorter the duration of the transient. The control system of Fig. 6-48a requires that an error in T_{av} exist for a length of time following a throttle change, in order to furnish the necessary change in demand signal n_0, since the accumulated integral of the T_{av} error is the only contributor to n_0 in the steady state. In other words, this system behaves pretty much in the same manner as would the natural plant stability by itself. The T_{av} signal ensures that the long-term depletion and poisoning changes are wiped out.

Figure 6-48b shows a control scheme that does not have the limitations just described.   In this system we again assume that the enthalpy of the steam generator is essentially constant throughout the power range. Since power at any level is then the product of steam flow and enthalpy, the thermal power being delivered is directly proportional to steam flow F_s.   The generated demand signal then becomes

$$n_0 = K_1 F_s + K_2 \left[(T_{av,ref} - T_{av}) + \frac{1}{\tau} \int (T_{av,ref} - T_{av})\, dt \right] \quad (6\text{-}70)$$

Here the demand signal is nearly directly proportional to steam flow and a change in steam demand immediately changes n_0.   The reactor power

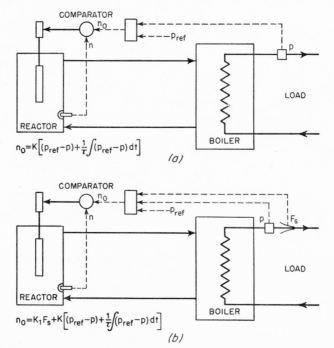

$$n_0 = K \left[(p_{ref} - p) + \frac{1}{\tau} \int (p_{ref} - p)\, dt \right]$$

(a)

$$n_0 = K_1 F_s + K \left[(p_{ref} - p) + \frac{1}{\tau} \int (p_{ref} - p)\, dt \right]$$

(b)

FIG. 6-49. Two types of control systems for constant-steam-pressure program.   (a) Indirect control.   (b) Direct control.

is adjusted much more rapidly than in the system of Fig. 6-48a, where a temperature error was required for a length of time.   The integral of T_{av} error is included to supplement the steam-flow signal in regions where the steam-flow indication may be in error.   The value of K_1 should be very close to unity; that is, $K_1 = 1$ percent reactor power demand per 1 percent steam flow. The scheme of Fig. 6-48b may be called the direct method of controlling n_0; that of Fig. 6-48a the indirect method.

Two comparable schemes can be set up for controlling a constant steam pressure program, and these are indicated in Figs. 6-49a and 6-49b. Figure 6-49a employs the pressure error to generate the power demand signal which is then compared with reactor power in a similar manner as was the T_{av} error. This system has the same inherent limitations as Fig. 6-48a in that an error is required during a transient to supply the steady-state n_0 signal. The circuit of Fig. 6-49b again controls n_0 directly, using the steam-flow measurement to represent the actual power

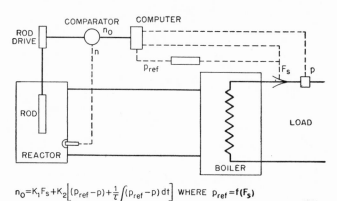

$$n_0 = K_1 F_s + K_2\left[(p_{ref}-p) + \frac{1}{\tau}\int(p_{ref}-p)\,dt\right] \quad \text{WHERE} \quad p_{ref} = f(F_s)$$

FIG. 6-50. Universal control system based on a variable pressure reference.

demand, plus a function of the pressure error to reset the power demand signal.

A system capable of handling any program ranging from constant T_{av} to constant p is indicated in Fig. 6-50. The scheme essentially is the same as that of Fig. 6-49b, except now the pressure reference is not constant but may be programmed in any predetermined manner, linear or nonlinear, by the steam flow. In other words, if a constant-T_{av} program is desired from this system, the pressure reference can be tapered to drop off in the proper manner as a function of power demand. By means of a universal control scheme of this type, any program can be set up by measuring and controlling from secondary system variables. No measurements of primary loop temperatures are thus required.

Control System for Plant Having Sufficient Inherent Stability. Once it has been determined that the natural stability of a plant by itself will be satisfactory for the intended service, the superimposed control system becomes considerably simpler. No reactor control loop as such is needed, and direct control of the parameters is possible.

The first system that comes to mind is the very elementary one of manual control.   Figure 6-51 shows two possible manual control schemes, one for holding the average temperature constant and the other for holding steam pressure constant.   The human link in the system is specified to be deliberately slow, and his action consists merely of setting a meter reading.   The plant takes care of itself through its own natural stability, and only occasional shimming by the operator is necessary.

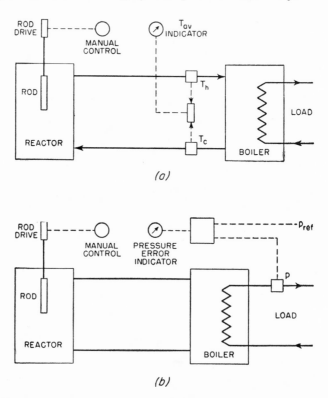

FIG. 6-51. Two manual control systems.   (a) Constant-average-temperature program. (b) Constant-steam-pressure program.

If, on the other hand, automatic control is desired, systems similar to those of Figs. 6-52 and 6-53 may be used.   Here a temperature or pressure error is made to actuate control rods directly and thus take care of removing the specified system parameter error.   Any neutron indication that is present in the system is used only for such information as giving alarms and is not tied back into the control.   Both systems of Figs. 6-52 and 6-53 are slow shimming operations and may be used either with proportional control or with on-off control.

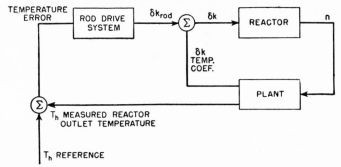

FIG. 6-52. Automatic control system for a plant with sufficient inherent natural stability using outlet temperature as the primary control variable.

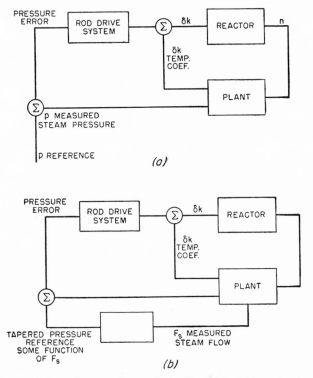

FIG. 6-53. Automatic control system for a plant with sufficient inherent natural stability. (a) Primary control variable, steam pressure. (b) Primary control variable, steam flow.

6-16. Stability Analysis for Demand Loop.   The analysis of any of the plant control systems just presented should again be in two parts, that is, a stability analysis based on frequency response and a transient analysis. As the transient analysis would in practice be accomplished by simulation technique on analogue computing machines for a very specific reactor plant, we shall confine our attention to a general approach to the stability problem.

As before, two variations of the problem exist in that there are two different types of demand loop, depending upon whether the plant by itself has adequate natural stability or not. In an actual plant design, at this point the problem becomes one of synthesizing the demand loop. The process is a tedious one of actually optimizing component constants for maximum stability and for meeting operating specifications.

Frequency Analysis for Plant with Reactor Control Loop. Let us first consider the case of a plant having inadequate natural stability where a

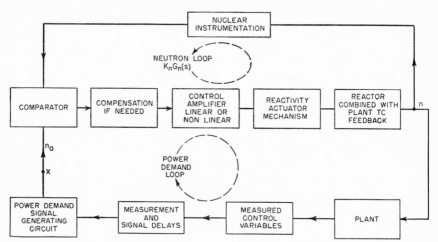

FIG. 6-54. Power demand control loop for a plant with insufficient natural stability.

reactor control loop is specified. The power demand loop for this condition is shown in general form in Fig. 6-54. The stability analysis for this loop is outlined in the following manner. Let us break the loop at some convenient place such as between the power demand signal generating circuit and the comparator at the point marked X on Fig. 6-54. We can now examine the power demand open-loop gain and phase shift by injecting a small sinusoidal variation in n_0 into the comparator and examining the output of the power demand signal generating circuit. The over-all loop gain is then examined for phase margin and gain margin, and if necessary, appropriate compensating circuits can be added to the loop. Symbolically the open-loop gain consists of two parts:

$$\text{Open-loop gain} = \frac{n(s)}{n_0(s)} \frac{n_0(s)}{n(s)} \tag{6-71}$$

where $n(s)/n_0(s)$ is crudely the reactor system portion of the over-all transfer function and $n_0(s)/n(s)$ is the plant portion of the power demand loop transfer function. The term $n(s)/n_0(s)$ consists of an external reactor control loop around the combined reactor plant temperature coefficient feedback loop transfer function $n(s)/\delta k_{rod}(s)$. If we denote this neutron loop gain by $K_n G_n(s)$, then

$$\frac{n(s)}{n_0(s)} = \frac{1}{1 + K_n G_n(s)} \tag{6-72}$$

$K_n G_n(s)$, of course, contains all of the nonlinearities previously examined in that the reactor gain is a function of level, the comparator gain an inverse function of level, and the control amplifier, if it is of the contactor type, may have its gain of the form $(V/b)A_{b/a}(|x|/b)$, where the output is a discontinuous function of its input. Nevertheless, how these nonlinearities may be handled has been pointed out in Chap. 4, and $K_n G_n(s)$ may be found in a logical manner.

The power demand signal n_0 will usually be similar in form to the following terms, as indicated in Sec. 6-14:

$$n_0 = f_1(F_s) + f_2(T) \text{ or } f_2(p) \tag{6-73}$$

That is, the power demand signal first consists of some term generally directly dependent on thermal power output or its direct relations such as steam flow or throttle opening. Second, there will be an error-reducing term which will be used to set up the plant program around some variable such as a plant temperature or steam pressure. The transfer function can be found as

$$\frac{n_0(s)}{n(s)} = \frac{f_1(s)}{n(s)} + \frac{f_2(s)}{n(s)} = g_1 \frac{F_s(s)}{n(s)} + g_2 \frac{T(s)}{n(s)} \text{ or } g_2 \frac{p(s)}{n(s)} \tag{6-74}$$

For a more specific example let us assume that the plant operating conditions call for T_h to remain constant as a function of power level. The following equation might then apply for a given control system:

$$n_0 = K_1 F_s + K_2(T_{h,ref} - T_h) \tag{6-75}$$

then
$$\frac{n_0(s)}{n(s)} = K_1 \frac{F_s(s)}{n(s)} - K_2 \frac{T_h(s)}{n(s)} \tag{6-76}$$

As all the other terms of this equation are essentially fixed by the principal components of the plant, the synthesis of the demand loop would usually consist of optimizing the constants K_1 and K_2.

Two details must be mentioned at this point. The first is that, although the procedure for obtaining $T_h(s)/n(s)$, $T_c(s)/n(s)$, and $T_{av}(s)/n(s)$ has been previously outlined, no mention has been made of $F_s(s)/n(s)$. The method used to determine $F_s(s)/n(s)$ is taken directly from the differential equation of (6-18),

$$(M_m c_m + M_s c_s) \frac{dT_s}{dt} = K_b A_b(\bar{T}_b - T_s) - K_a A p \tag{6-77}$$

and the additional relationship

$$F_s = (BK_a A)T_s \tag{6-78}$$

where the symbols are as defined in Sec. 6-4 and the constants are greatly dependent on the specific secondary plant used.

Another detail which must be included in the demand loop over-all gain is the fact that the information on plant conditions is not available instantly. For example, a thermometer of some sort would be used to

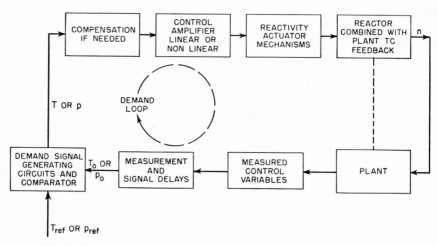

FIG. 6-55. Demand control loop for a plant with sufficient natural stability.

measure primary loop temperature. In conventional practice such a thermometer might have a time constant ranging from 0.2 to 30 sec. This time constant can have a very serious effect on the stability of the demand loop. In addition, in some types of hydraulic or pneumatic measuring devices, a transport time delay may also be involved before the temperature or pressure signal arrives at the power demand signal generating circuit. Therefore, in general, additional delays of the form $1/(1 + \tau s)$ and $e^{-\tau s}$ in combination may be expected in a practical plant demand loop.

Frequency Analysis for Plant with Sufficient Natural Stability. For this second type of control system we may examine the block diagram of Fig. 6-55. Here the separate reactor control loop is eliminated and a comparison is made directly between some demanded temperature or pressure reference (linear or nonlinear with power output) and the actual temperature or pressure existing in the plant. The demand open-loop gain now becomes

$$\text{Open-loop gain} = \frac{n(s)}{T(s)} \frac{T(s)}{n(s)} \tag{6-79}$$

or
$$\text{Open-loop gain} = \frac{n(s)}{(ps)} \frac{p(s)}{n(s)} \tag{6-80}$$

depending on whether we are using a temperature or a pressure as a reference. The term $n(s)/[T(s)$ or $p(s)]$ then becomes the combined reactor plant temperature coefficient feedback transfer function in series with the control amplification and actuation mechanism. The demand signal may take forms such as

$$T = T_{ref} - T_0 \tag{6-81}$$

where T_0 may be any function T_c, T_h, or T_{av}, or

$$p = f(F_s) + f_2(p)$$

leading to transfer functions for the plant portion of the loop of the form

$$\frac{T(s)}{n(s)} = \frac{T_c(s)}{n(s)} \text{ or } \frac{T_h(s)}{n(s)} \text{ or } \frac{T_{av}(s)}{n(s)} \tag{6-82}$$

or for the case where pressure is the reference

$$\frac{p(s)}{n(s)} = K_1 \frac{F_s(s)}{n(s)} + K_2 \frac{p(s)}{n(s)} \tag{6-83}$$

It must be pointed out again that all analyses such as have been indicated above should be examined for stability at various power levels, as most of the parameters being used are a function of level or flow or both.

Analyses conducted in the above manner will usually result in a limitation being placed on the reactor system for stability. This limitation can, in most cases, be boiled down to the simple problem of permissible rate of reactivity change. The condition that is found in a practical case is that above a given control-rod speed of motion the system is unstable. It can be shown that below this speed the system will be stable. It is important to note at this point that practical reactor operating conditions, such as transient poison burnout, also impose requirements on control-rod reactivity change rates from a reactor safety point of view. Some of these requirements may call for the control rods moving at a faster rate than a given amount. These requirements will be examined in detail in Chap. 9. Thus, offhand, the over-all problem of plant control system design for power range operation is going to depend upon finding conditions of overlap between control system stability and reactor operational limitations.

REFERENCES

1. Schultz, M. A.: *Trans. AIEE,* vol. 71, paper 53-31, 1952.
2. Schultz, M. A.: Temperature Programs and Control Systems for a Nuclear Power Plant, "Proceedings of the 1953 Conference on Nuclear Engineering," University of California Press, Berkeley, Calif., 1953.
3. Brown, G. S., and D. P. Campbell: "Principles of Servomechanisms," John Wiley & Sons, Inc., New York, 1951.
4. Single, C., and G. Stubbs: "Transport Delay Simulation Circuits," *WAPD-T-38,* Westinghouse Electric Corporation, Pittsburgh, Pa.
5. Grace, J. N.: Synthesis of Control Systems for Nuclear Power Plants, "Convention Record of the IRE 1954 National Convention," pt. 9, "Medical and Nuclear Electronics," Institute of Radio Engineers, New York, 1954.
6. Truxal, J. G: "Automatic Feedback Control System Synthesis," McGraw-Hill Book Company, Inc., New York, 1955.
7. Stubbs, G. S.: Constant Reactor Outlet Temperature Control System, *IRE Trans. on Nuclear Science,* vol. NS-1, no. 1, September, 1954.

CHAPTER 7

REACTOR CONTROL RADIATION DETECTORS

We have seen in the preceding chapter that certain types of control systems call for the use of a radiation-measuring loop. The radiation-measuring devices involved are unique and therefore will be described separately in this chapter as control components. Actually many types of radiation detectors exist, but very few are suitable for control purposes. We shall attempt to define the requirements and operational ranges for the instruments. We shall also look at the limitations of radiation-detection instruments as power indicators and control elements. Finally we shall examine the problems involved in calibration of these detectors.

7-1. Measurement Problem. In considering what to measure in a reactor in order to obtain a signal for control purposes, it is evident that one desires to obtain a measurement of reactor power output. In a complete plant operating at a high power level it seems possible that a thermal measurement of the temperature rise across the reactor times the flow of coolant might be used. This method has two disadvantages: First, the information is slow; second, over much of the reactor operating range at low power levels there is no appreciable temperature rise involved. Also, for reactors without a plant attached, this method may be unfeasible.

In searching for a suitable parameter to use for power-measuring purposes, it is evident that the total power emanating from the reactor consists of the sum of all the energies involved in the nuclear disintegrations in the reactor. As over 90 percent of the energy involved comes from the direct fission process and less than 10 percent by indirect beta and gamma radiations, it seems reasonable to use the incidental neutrons from the fission process as a measurement parameter. In addition, the beta and gamma power does not directly follow the fission power time-wise but may come from long-lived decay activities. Consequently, attempting to monitor on gamma radiation alone, for example, would lead to an erroneous answer.

The power level of a nuclear reactor is then generally assumed to be proportional to the number of neutrons in its core. Operating conditions arise where the relationship between neutrons and power is much more complex, but for most purposes the simple assumption of direct proportionality is essentially correct.

The problem exists of measuring a given fixed fraction of reactor neutrons with conventional radiation detectors and to relate the output of these detectors to reactor power. It can be assumed to start that the neutron flux distribution in a reactor is not a constant but varies with time and position in the core. In order to read power output directly, it is then necessary to measure continuously the average core flux. Two means of making an average flux measurement are at once apparent. First, a large number of detectors might be placed as uniformly as possible throughout the core and an average taken of their output readings. Second, a detector might be placed so far from the core that the core can be considered a point source of neutrons and local neutron density variations in the core will be insignificant. Both methods require compromises to be at all applicable, with the second approach being the one most generally used.

7-2. Ranges of Measurements. The fact that the detecting instruments are usually placed at some distance from the reactor imposes severe limitations on instrument sensitivity and range. First a nuclear reactor is really never shut off. In a conventional power plant whose normal full power output might be 1,000 kw, if the output were turned down to 1 kw, one would consider that the plant was essentially shut off and could be ignored. In the case of a nuclear plant operating at the same level, because of the unique self-multiplying characteristics of the medium at any power level 1 kw still represents a great many neutrons. If these neutrons are not monitored continuously and the possibility of creating a multiplication factor greater than unity exists, then the plant is capable of ultimately destroying itself, starting from any conceivable power level. Neutrons must then be monitored at all times and at all levels. In the case of a power reactor this requirement may call for as much as 10-decade instrumentation for complete monitoring of the entire operating range from source strength to full power output.

No one present-day instrument is capable of covering such a range. In conventional instrumentation, instruments usually can operate usefully over 3 or at most 4 decades. Consequently, to cover the wider requirements of the nuclear power plant, over-all coverage may be obtained by using multiple instrumentation with overlapping ranges, or a very sensitive instrument may be used and its position changed with respect to the reactor as a function of power level. Figure 7-1 indicates the multiple instrument overlapping-range system. Figure 7-2 illustrates the movable instrument system. The diagram of Fig. 7-2 shows an interesting servo-type instrumentation system in which the detector position is continually moved so that the detector always operates in a constant neutron flux. In this way the position of the instrument with respect to the reactor becomes a measurement of the neutron level.

The advantage of the movable instrument system is that only one type of detector is needed to cover the entire operating range. The principal disadvantage is that the neutron level as a function of distance from the

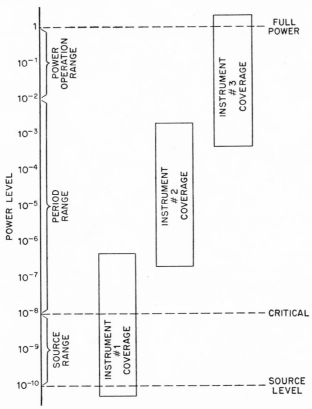

FIG. 7-1. Typical instrument-range coverage for a multiple fixed instrument system.

reactor is usually very nonlinear and may contain sharp slope changes at the boundaries of different materials. Although these effects may be calibrated out of the instrument, they are apt to change with time. Consequently, the overlapping-range type of instrumentation is the more prevalent system at present. However, moving an instrument a fixed amount to reduce its sensitivity or to protect it from high neutron or gamma radiation levels is done quite frequently.

Figure 7-1 also indicates the conventionally used terms to denote the operating ranges of the reactor. Three ranges are usually considered, although separate instruments may not necessarily be used to cover each range as such.   These ranges are the source, or startup, range, the period range, and the power operation range.

The source range is the range of neutron level between the points where the reactor is shut down as completely as possible and where the reactor is critical.   At the complete shutdown level the detector sees only its fraction of those neutrons emanating from the source as multiplied by the subcritical multiplication factor of the reactor.   The point at which a reactor goes critical depends upon how fast reactivity is removed from the reactor.   This level is usually between 20 and 1,000 times the source

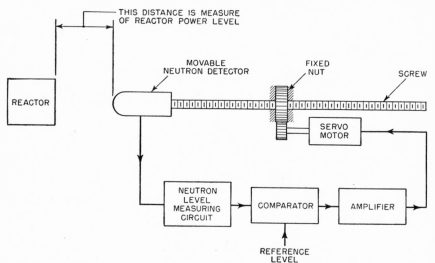

FIG. 7-2. Block diagram of movable instrument system in which the detector is automatically positioned to sit in a constant neutron flux.

level.   Once criticality is reached, the reactor is brought up to a level where thermal power can be measured.   This rise is usually restricted to a given rate or period.   This interval in level is called the period range. The period used for specific reactors depends upon their operational requirements and may vary from 3 sec to a few minutes.   In this range circuits providing both level and period information are usually connected to the detector.

The power operation range is where the reactor is producing an amount of power close to its rating.   This range usually extends downward no more than 2 decades from full power rating.

7-3. Description of Instruments.   The many types of instruments that might be considered for reactor control can be divided into two types, classified by the operation of the external circuit to which they are connected.   These are pulse-counting types of circuits and current-integrating types. Some of the detectors may be operated with either type circuit. Many specific types of neutron-detecting instruments are available. Those used principally with power reactors are BF_3 counters, boron-lined counters, fission counters, ionization chambers, compensated ionization chambers, neutron thermopiles, and scintillation counters. The requirements for a reactor control instrument include high neutron sensitivity, gamma radiation insensitivity, operation at high temperatures, wide plateaus, and construction to be such that neutron-induced radioactivity in the detector is held to a minimum. A brief description of each of the types of instruments mentioned follows.

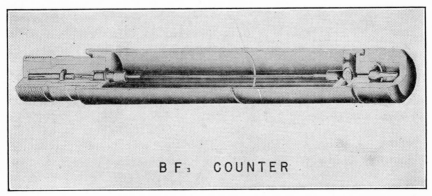

FIG. 7-3. BF_3 proportional counter. (*Courtesy of Westinghouse Electric Corporation.*)

BF_3 *Proportional Counter.* The most sensitive types of pulse-counting instruments used are usually the BF_3 counter or the boron-lined counter. The BF_3 proportional counter, in common with most other neutron detectors, relies on the detection of ionized particles which are produced by a neutron-induced reaction. In the case of the BF_3 counter this reaction is

$$B^{10}(n,\alpha)Li^7$$

Briefly, the counter consists of a metal cylinder with a small-diameter collecting electrode suspended coaxially within the cylinder. The cylinder is filled with BF_3 gas, which in turn is ionized by the boron alpha particle emitted in the reaction. The electrons formed in the primary ionizing events are accelerated toward the collecting electrode by the electric field in the counter tube. In so doing, the electrons acquire sufficient energy to ionize other molecules. The sum total of these electrons collected at the center electrode causes a voltage pulse to appear across a load resistor. The rate at which these pulses appear is a linear function of the neutron flux level in which the counter is located. The theory of proportional counters (BF_3 and others) is extensively treated elsewhere.[1-4]

A picture of a conventional BF_3 proportional counter is given in Fig. 7-3. Several other configurations are presented in the literature.[1] The instrument has a plateau in counting rate as a function of applied voltage, and the plateau of a typical detector is presented in Fig. 7-4. These instruments are usually connected to an electronic circuit which selects pulses above a given size to be counted. In this way spurious pulses and noise may be partially eliminated. The performance of a detector and circuit connected in this manner is determined by a so-called integral bias curve. Such a curve is presented in Fig. 7-5 for a typical BF_3 counter. Sensitivity of tubes of the type of Fig. 7-3 ranges from 0.1 to 2 counts per unit of neutron flux.

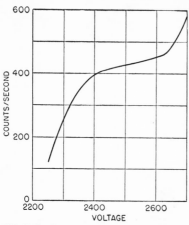

FIG. 7-4. Counting rate versus voltage for a typical BF_3 counter.

Boron-lined Counter.[1] The boron-lined counter usually consists of cylindrical electrodes coated with boron, which are enclosed in an inert

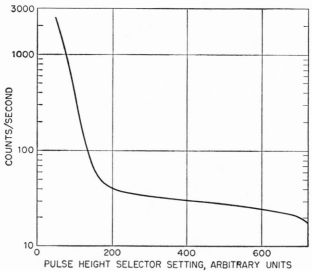

FIG. 7-5. Integral bias curve for typical BF_3 counter showing counting rate as a function of pulse height selector setting.

gas atmosphere. Its external appearance and performance are similar to the BF_3 counter. Its advantages over the BF_3 counter are that it does not contain a fine wire electrode and that it usually operates at a somewhat lower voltage between electrodes. Its principal disadvantage is that for equal volumes it is usually less sensitive than the BF_3 counter and has a shorter voltage plateau. This shorter plateau usually means that the tube will perform more poorly in the presence of large gamma fields.

Fission Counter. The fission counter detects neutrons by utilizing the highly ionized fission fragments that result when a neutron causes a nucleus to undergo fission. In general, the instrument consists of an

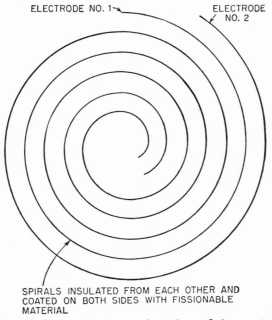

ELECTRODE NO. 1

ELECTRODE NO. 2

SPIRALS INSULATED FROM EACH OTHER AND COATED ON BOTH SIDES WITH FISSIONABLE MATERIAL

FIG. 7-6. Cross-sectional view of spiral type fission counter.

ionization chamber type detector which contains fissionable material in the form of a thin foil or coating on the counter electrodes. By a proper choice of this coating material and by the use of neutron shields placed around the outside of the counter it is possible to design a tube that is sensitive to neutrons of a particular energy range. At present it is the measurement of thermal energy range neutrons that is of importance in most reactor control problems.

Two types of fission counters are available, a spiral type[1] and a cylindrical type.[5] Figure 7-6 indicates a drawing cross section of the spiral type of fission counter. Two separate foils, usually coated with uranium, are wound concentrically and electrically insulated from each other with a very small spacing of about 0.02 in. The spirals are mounted into a container and after suitable outgassing, the container and contents are filled to a high pressure with inert gas. The over-all size of the counter may be from $\frac{1}{2}$ to 2 in. in diameter. The spiral type of counter is used in an effort to pack as much fissionable material as possible into a given small space. Although the pulses coming from a fission counter are usually quite large without the use of any gas multiplication, the sensitivity of the tube is generally lower than that of the BF_3 counter. The

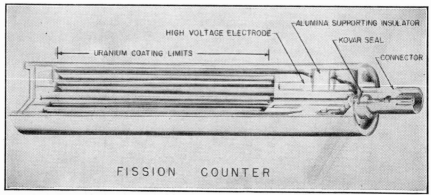

FIG. 7-7. Cylindrical fission counter. (Courtesy of Westinghouse Electric Corporation.)

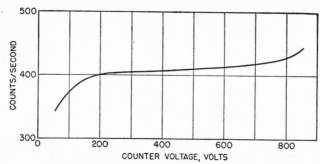

FIG. 7-8. Counting rate versus voltage for a typical cylindrical fission counter.

sensitivity of the tube depends upon how many atoms capable of undergoing fission are present in the tube volume and upon the cross section of the material for the process involved.

Figure 7-7 indicates the cylindrical type of tube. This tube does not have as close spacing of its elements as the spiral type and consequently is quite rugged. Its size ranges from 2 to 4 in. in diameter, and it may be as long as 18 in. It obtains its sensitivity by using large cylinders. Figure 7-8 indicates the plateau in counting rate as a function of counter voltage for a fixed pulse height setting. It can be seen that this type of tube operates at a much lower voltage than does the BF_3 counter. Figure 7-9 shows an integral bias curve for a fission counter which uses a uranium 235 coating. As this material gives off a spontaneous alpha particle of fixed energy, the tube circuit must be biased to select pulses above a given amount to eliminate counting these alpha particles. A ratio range 10:1 to 100:1 in neutron to alpha-particle output is usually set up by the pulse height selector circuit.

Ionization Chamber. In the period range and power range, neutron-sensitive ionization chambers are normally used for neutron flux measurements in reactors. These are the instruments which are usually connected to the automatic control system as indicators of power level. The detector consists of chambers in which large surfaces may be coated with boron 10 and the ionization from the recoil alpha particles again collected as current.[1]

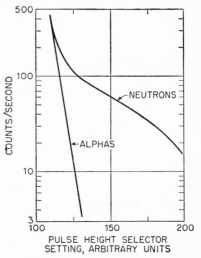

FIG. 7-9. Integral bias curve for uranium 235 coated cylindrical fission counter, showing counting rate as a function of pulse height selector setting.

The range of intensity over which neutron flux may be detected is limited by the gamma-ray background in which the chamber must operate. The ratio of neutron flux to gamma flux at the normal operating position of an ionization chamber in a reactor core or shield structure is usually such that the signal caused by the neutron flux is about 1,000 times that caused by the gamma rays. Therefore, when the reactor is in the power range, gamma-ray background is no problem. However, the gamma-ray intensity does not vary directly with reactor power as does the neutron intensity. Thus, a lower limit is set for neutron detection at the level where the ionization caused by neutrons equals that caused by gamma rays.

Ionization chambers at present are of the parallel-plate type or cylindrical type. That is, the internal electrodes may consist of a series of parallel disks or concentric cylinders or cups coated with boron. The literature[6,26,27] contains in detail the proper design procedures to obtain maximum sensitivity from an instrument. The tubes usually may be treated as constant-current sources having characteristics as shown in Fig. 4-16.

Compensated Ionization Chamber. The neutron-detection ranges of an ionization chamber can be increased by gamma-ray compensation, that is, by balancing out the component of the signal caused by the gamma rays. This balancing is accomplished by effectively using two similar chambers, one of which is sensitive to the neutron and gamma rays as indicated above and the other sensitive to gamma rays only. These chambers are connected electrically so that their output subtracts. Convenient designs consist of concentric cylinders or cup-shaped electrodes connected as shown in Fig. 7-10.[7]

Since the gamma flux in and around a reactor varies widely from point to point, the ionization produced in two equal volumes by the gamma rays

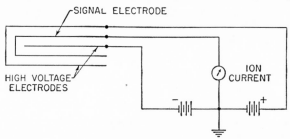

FIG. 7-10. Circuit arrangement for compensated ionization chamber operation.

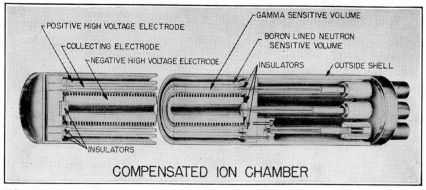

FIG. 7-11. Electrically compensated ionization chamber. (*Courtesy of Westinghouse Electric Corporation.*)

is seldom the same. For this reason it is necessary, after the chamber is installed, to adjust the compensation so that the currents caused by the gamma rays from the two volumes are equal. This adjustment may be accomplished by mechanically changing one volume or by electrically changing the effective volume. The electrical compensation is caused by having one electrode consisting of a number of teeth or sections.[8] The effective chamber saturation volume is changed by voltage in that the saturation can be made to extend into the serrated structure by increasing the voltage. In this manner compensation is set up electrically without the use of moving parts in the tube. Figure 7-11 shows a photograph of such a compensated ionization chamber.

Neutron Thermopiles. The instruments just mentioned are the ones principally used in reactor control. However, many other devices have found considerable use. One of these detectors is the neutron thermopile.[9,10,27] This instrument consists of several thermocouple junctions connected in series, alternate junctions of which are coated with boron. The instrument is a small one and in the past has taken two forms, one a cylinder roughly the size of a fountain pen, the other a disk about the size of a half dollar. These instruments are rugged and reliable and do not require the high-voltage insulation of the previous instruments. One disadvantage of the instrument is that its design usually must make a compromise between sensitivity and response time. And as the sensitivity of the instrument is quite small because the volume of boron present is small, most of the instruments attempt to favor increased sensitivity. Consequently, time constants in the order of one to several seconds result and the instruments have not been used in the past for direct reactor control. Another disadvantage of these instruments is that they operate in quite high neutron fluxes and ultimately suffer from boron depletion.

Scintillation Counter. Although the scintillation counter has received wide publicity as a prospecting instrument and laboratory tool, it has not as yet seen much service as a reactor control device. The principal reason is that most scintillation crystals or liquids which are sensitive to neutrons are also very sensitive to gamma rays. Also, the multiplier portion of the detector is very susceptible to heat in that the noise level of the tube increases greatly with temperature. As the vicinity of most power reactors is thermally warm, the scintillation counter is at a disadvantage for power reactor usage. However, scintillation counters are used as gamma detectors in low-power reactor safety setups. Several excellent descriptions of scintillation counters are found in the literature.[11–14]

7-4. Effect of Gamma Radiation on Instrument Responses.† A problem always encountered in determining the usefulness of a neutron-detecting instrument in a reactor system is the ability of the instrument to operate under gamma irradiation. The existence of large gamma intensities around a power reactor must be taken for granted, and provisions made to live with them. The gamma radiation might originate in the decay of fission products or from reactor materials which capture the incident neutrons. The instruments are most likely to be affected by capture gammas in the shield or the instrument itself. For most purposes the gamma equilibrium radiation at any instant in the reactor operating cycle can be considered as a first approximation to fall off exponentially

† Sections 7-4 to 7-7 were originally presented by J. C. Connor and the author in Reactor Power Calibration, *Nucleonics*, vol. 12, no. 2, February, 1954.

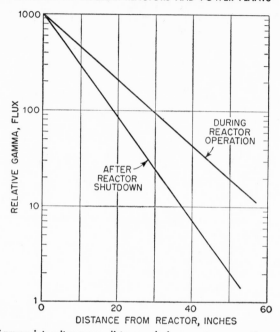

FIG. 7-12. Gamma intensity versus distance, during reactor operation and shutdown.

with distance from the reactor.

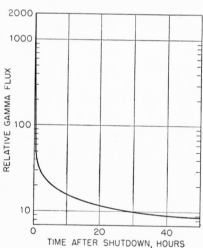

FIG. 7-13. Gamma intensity versus time after reactor shutdown at a fixed point in a reactor shield.

Gamma-level problems then are substantially reduced as the instrument is placed farther away from the reactor. Figure 7-12 shows a typical gamma flux falloff with distance for a water-iron shielding mixture under two operating conditions.

Figure 7-13 shows how the gamma radiation at any given point in a shield might drop off as a function of time after shutdown of a reactor. Here the initial sharp dropoff is a function of the shutoff of the fission-product gamma radiation. The slow tail of the curve depends upon the half lives of the materials at the particular point under consideration. The curve shown is for a structural material containing iron and manganese.

Gamma radiation affects the response of the neutron-detecting instruments or their circuits directly in an adverse manner. The effect of gamma radiation is different on each of the instruments described in Sec. 7-3. A brief discussion follows on how BF_3 proportional counters, fission counters, and ionization chambers are disturbed.

Present-day BF_3 proportional counters suffer direct characteristic changes from high gamma irradiations. Figure 7-14 indicates a typical integral bias curve for a BF_3 counter and amplifier operating with and without a superimposed gamma field. With no gamma radiation present

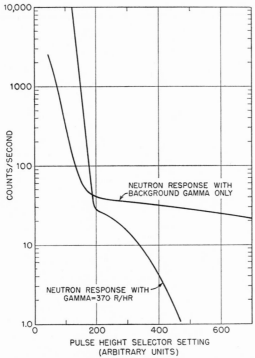

FIG. 7-14. Integral bias curve for BF_3 counter with and without gamma radiation background.

other than the normal laboratory background, a conventional plateau type curve is obtained, giving counting rate as a function of pulse height discriminator settings. As the gamma background is increased, the tail of the curve at high discriminator settings begins to fall off and ultimately reaches a point where no usable plateau range exists. This point may occur between 50- and 1,000-r/hr gamma background, depending upon the design of the counter. No permanent damage appears to occur to the instrument at these gamma levels. However, it is known that at 10^5 r/hr some form of semipermanent damage does occur. After even short exposures to these very high levels the counters do not operate properly, and several weeks may be required for the instrument to return to its original operating characteristics. BF$_3$ counters are ordinarily not used at such high gamma levels, but the damage may occur even if the counter is disconnected and sitting in this ambient. The mechanism of this instrument damage is not fully understood but is related to decomposition of the BF$_3$ gas and the amount of gas amplification which is obtained in the tube.

Fission counters have been irradiated in gamma fluxes approximating 5 × 10⁵ r/hr. No permanent damage occurs under these irradiations. However, the electronic circuits which connect to the fission counter suffer a form of partial blocking because of the immense gamma pulse pile-up. In order to minimize the blocking effect it is usually necessary to use extremely short time constants in the electronic circuits. These differentiating networks are generally placed as close to the detecting instruments as possible.

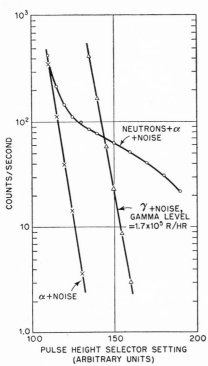

FIG. 7-15. Integral bias curve for fission counter operating under gamma radiation background.

Figure 7-15 indicates the performance of a typical fission counter under high gamma radiation conditions. From the curve it can be seen that operation at higher pulse height discriminator settings reduces the gamma contribution to the counting rate much more rapidly than the contribution of the neutrons. Any reduction in neutron sensitivity caused by operating at higher pulse height settings must be charged directly to the gamma background radiation.

Ionization chambers, as described in Sec. 7-3, collect all ion pairs created within them. A current proportional to neutron flux is usually obtained by a secondary process such as the ionization from the alpha particle emitted by the reaction of a thermal neutron with boron 10. This secondary process must compete directly with the ionization caused by the gamma flux inside the volume of the chamber. An ionization chamber may be designed which will have a 3- to 4-decade neutron range in the presence of a gamma field of 200 r/hr. To extend this range farther it is necessary to compensate the instrument against the gamma radiation. This compensation is usually accomplished by providing two operating chamber volumes—one volume which is sensitive to neutrons plus gamma rays and the other sensitive to gamma rays alone. A subtraction process then enables the instrument neutron range to be extended for roughly $2\frac{1}{2}$ more decades. A typical response of an ionization chamber operating on a reactor shutdown problem is shown in Fig. 7-16, and it will be noted that the amount of compensation shifts as a function

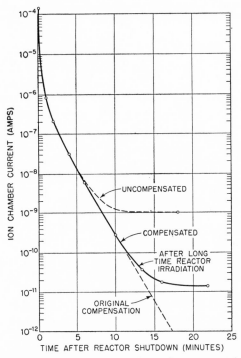

FIG. 7-16. Ionization chamber current versus time after reactor shutdown for various degrees of compensation.

of time. This shift is usually caused by changes in the gamma gradient adjacent to the instrument as the reactor builds up the longer half-life emitters to a fixed activity.

7-5. Effects of Reactor Operation and Rod Shadowing on Neutron Measurements. Having once established the calibration and placement of the nuclear detector, it is necessary to see how this calibration changes with time and operating conditions. For proper calibration of a thermal-neutron detector, the thermal-neutron flux at the detector location must be a function of power only. As far as the response of a particular instrument is concerned, the reactor may be regarded as a neutron source surrounded by an attenuating medium. Consider for a moment that the reactor is a point source at a fixed position emitting a constant number of neutrons each second.   The neutron attenuation between the source and a particular point in the shielding structure depends upon distance, the scattering and absorption cross sections of the shielding materials, and the physical arrangement of the shielding structure.   Since a reactor is far from a monoenergetic neutron source, it is clear that even if the rate of emission of neutrons remains constant, changes in their energy distribution will result in flux variations at the detector, because the neutron cross sections of the shielding material are a function of energy.

In addition to energy variation problems, a reactor ordinarily cannot be considered as a point source of neutrons unless the distribution of neutrons as a function of their position in the core remains constant for all operating conditions.   As has been mentioned, a power-producing reactor must contain enough excess fissionable material to maintain criticality as fuel depletion occurs.   Fuel depletion reduces reactivity, and if the reactor has control rods of any type, the depletion may be compensated for by rod motion.   A rod movement can cause a change in the neutron flux distribution within the core.   It may be necessary or desirable to move control rods for any one or a combination of the following reasons:

1. To calibrate control-rod effectiveness or reactivity
2. To compensate for fission-product poisoning
3. To compensate for fuel depletion
4. To compensate for reactor temperature changes
5. To change the flux distribution within the core in such a manner that fuel depletion occurs uniformly or in a prescribed manner
6. To change the power level

The relative effect of these rod movements on neutron instrument calibration depends principally upon the design of the reactor in question. Figures 7-17a and 7-17b are two views of a thermal reactor containing four absorber type control rods which can move parallel to the Z axis. Loss of reactivity for reasons such as fuel depletion or fission-product poisoning must be compensated for by withdrawing these control rods. The curves to the right of Fig. 7-17a show what might happen to the neutron flux distribution along the Z axis in the core if all four control rods are moved uniformly from position A to position B.   It is apparent that the reading of a neutron detector located beneath the reactor decreases, since the peak in the flux distribution shifts up and away from the instrument.   The reading of a detector located on the X axis would increase, since the flux peak moves toward the axis of the instrument.

The curves plotted to the right of Fig. 7-17b show what might happen to the neutron flux distribution along the Y axis for a nonuniform rod withdrawal.   Curve C shows the symmetrical flux distribution present if all rods are at a uniform height. Curve D shows that the peak in the flux distribution shifts toward a detector located on the Y axis if reactivity changes are compensated by withdrawing rods 1 and 2 while rods 3 and 4 remain at the same height. Other rod withdrawal programs might be hypothesized, but it is clear that no detector location or rod program exists for a reactor of the design shown which is not subject to some neutron-detector sensitivity shift because of changes in flux distribution.

Instrument calibration changes caused by rod motion are called rod shadow effects. Planning an experiment to determine the magnitude of a particular effect may be complicated by the simultaneous presence

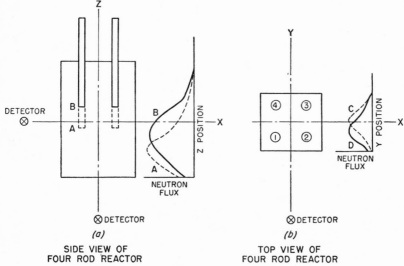

FIG. 7-17. Reactor flux distributions as a function of control-rod positions.

of many other variables. Some idea of the order of magnitude of the calibration changes because of rod movements alone may be obtained from the following example. Suppose we have a reactor, as shown in Fig. 7-18, containing four control rods equally spaced radially from the center of the core. If the reactor contains a separate neutron source, a particular instrument may have a given source-level counting rate with the reactor subcritical and all control rods inserted. Figure 7-18 is a plot of the counting rate data that might be obtained by withdrawing and reinserting one rod at a time as a function of angular position of the rod measured with respect to a line between the detector and the center of the core. Note that the maximum effect occurs for those rods closest to the detector. The dashed curve through the four rod position points indicates the counting rates which might be obtained if the reactor had more than four control rods.

Rod shadow effects of this nature are greater the closer the instrument is to the core. At points in the shield far from the reactor, the neutron flux is more closely proportional to the total number of neutrons in the core. Unfortunately, choice of distance between core and instrument is usually dictated by instrument sensitivity. The highest power level detectors, however, may be placed farthest away from the core, thus minimizing rod shadow effects for power operation.

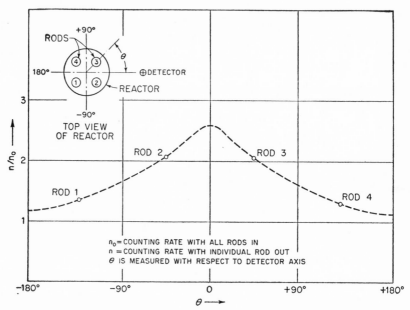

FIG. 7-18. Magnitude of instrument reading change as control rods are pulled one at a time.

7-6. Temperature Effects on Neutron-measuring Instruments.

Most pile operating conditions, in addition to causing control-rod movement, create more complex disturbances on the neutron-detector calibrations. For example, consider the case of a change in reactor temperature. The neutron flux at a detector location in the shielding structure depends to a large extent on the thermalizing of fast neutrons from the reactor in the immediate vicinity of the detector. If the temperature of a reactor changes sufficiently to cause the density of the moderator to decrease, it is apparent that the number of fast neutrons reaching the detector will increase. Changes in the energy distribution of neutrons in the reactor may accompany temperature variations. The leakage flux of fast neutrons and hence the neutron-detector calibrations depend upon the magnitude of these effects.

In addition, temperature may affect the instrument reading directly, even assuming a constant flux. Figure 7-19 shows the operation of a commercial BF$_3$ counter at various temperatures. It can be seen that unless great care is taken in the instrument design and usage, counting rate is tremendously dependent on temperature.

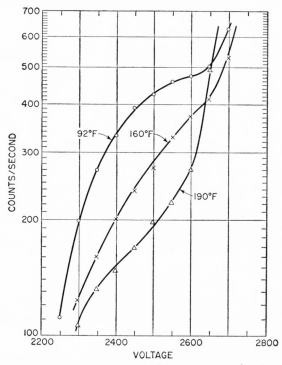

FIG. 7-19. Characteristic curves of commercial BF$_3$ counter as a function of temperature.

7-7. Instrument Calibration and Intercalibration. Despite the many difficulties pointed out above with neutron-radiation detectors, they are still most useful, particularly once they have been directly calibrated in terms of power level. Three basic types of power calibration are usually available. These are foil measurements at low power levels, a direct energy calibration generally made at low power levels, and a conventional calorimetric calibration usually made at high levels. With multiple-instrument arrangements such as are indicated in Fig. 7-1, intercalibration between any of these methods and the neutron detectors can be accomplished.

Low-level Calibrations. Before bringing a newly designed reactor safely to its rated power, it is desirable to check such items as the adequacy of the biological shield, control effectiveness, and criticality configurations.

Experiments of this type are most easily conducted at low power when radiation levels around the core are low enough to permit physical access to all parts of the plant.   Data obtained at low levels can then be extrapolated to higher power operations.   Thus instrument readings and calibrations at low power are important to assure that such reactor design items as shield adequacy will be proper at higher power.

The first calibration method, experimentally troublesome but capable of yielding reasonable accuracy in a thermal reactor, is to determine the average thermal-neutron flux by irradiating foils at various locations in the core for a known length of time and measuring the induced activity.[2]   The power P developed within the core is given by the product of the number of fissions occurring per second, and Q, the energy release per fission event.

$$P = nv\Sigma_f Q \qquad (7\text{-}1)$$

where n is the total number of neutrons in the core, v is their velocity in centimeters per second, and Σ_f is the macroscopic cross section for fission. Σ_f may be calculated for the particular reactor in question, and Q (3.2×10^{-11} watt-sec per fission) is a known constant.   Unfortunately, the usual indium-cadmium-foil counting techniques determine only that portion of the neutron flux below an energy of 0.6 electron volt.   It is possible, however, to measure average thermal flux to within 10 percent by this method.   A large number of measurements are required to determine average core flux if the core structure is at all complicated.   Access to the core for removal and insertion of foils must also be possible.

A second method of low-level calibration which does not require a highly accessible core is to bring the reactor to exact criticality, insert a neutron source of known strength, and plot the resultant rise in counting rate of the neutron instruments as a function of time.   By solving the pile kinetic equations subject to the proper boundary conditions, it can be shown that the rate of change of neutrons with time after an initial transient, and consequently the rate of power increase, is linear and proportional to the source strength.   The following type of derivation may be used.   We may start with the familiar kinetic equations

$$\frac{dn}{dt} = \frac{\delta k - \beta}{l^*}\, n + \sum_{i=1}^{6} \lambda_i C_i + S \qquad (7\text{-}2)$$

$$\frac{dC_i}{dt} = \frac{\beta_i}{l^*}\, n - \lambda_i C_i \qquad (7\text{-}3)$$

where the symbols have their usual meanings and S is the neutron source strength.

These equations are to be solved subject to the following conditions. The source S is to be inserted into a critical reactor ($\delta k = 0$) at time zero. The boundary conditions are that when $t = 0$, $n = n_0$, $C_i = C_{i0}$, $dn/dt = S$, $dC_i/dt = 0$. The terms n_0 and C_{i0} are the values of the neutron density and delayed-emitter concentration present prior to the insertion of the source and are constants.

We can first try a simplified solution using lumped delayed emitters, having a single decay constant $\lambda \approx 0.1$ sec^{-1}. For this situation we find that

$$n = n_0 + \frac{\beta S/l^*}{[\lambda + (\beta/l^*)]^2} e^{-[\lambda+(\beta/l^*)]t} + \frac{\lambda St}{\lambda + (\beta/l^*)} \qquad (7\text{-}4)$$

when $t \gg 10$ sec. In this type of solution for large values of t and any reasonable value of l^*, the negative exponent of the transient term in the solution becomes quite large, and after an initial waiting time, dn/dt approaches the value

$$\frac{dn}{dt} = \frac{\lambda}{\lambda + (\beta/l^*)} S \qquad (7\text{-}5)$$

In other words, after an initial transient, the reactor neutron level rises linearly with time.

If the kinetic equations are solved using all six delayed-emitter groups, the expression for n would contain six transient terms, each of which decays after several half lives to a negligible value. Then, after a given time determined by the half life of the longest-lived delayed emitter, dn/dt is given by

$$\left(1 + \frac{\beta_1}{l^*\lambda_1} + \frac{\beta_2}{l^*\lambda_2} + \cdots + \frac{\beta_6}{l^*\lambda_6}\right)\frac{dn}{dt} = S \qquad (7\text{-}6)$$

or
$$K\frac{dn}{dt} = S \qquad (7\text{-}7)$$

For a graphite-moderated reactor of $l^* = 10^{-3}$ sec, $K \approx 100$, and for this type of reactor

$$\frac{dn}{dt} \approx \frac{S}{100} = 10^{-2}S \qquad (7\text{-}8)$$

The expression for dn/dt may be integrated, giving

$$n = n_0 + 10^{-2}St \qquad (7\text{-}9)$$

where n_0 is the neutron density at a time $t = 0$ chosen after the initial transient is past and the reactor is rising linearly with time. For our example, if D is the time required for the counting rate of a neutron-measuring instrument to double

$$n_0 = 10^{-2}SD \qquad (7\text{-}10)$$

To maintain a consistent set of units, n must be the total number of thermal neutrons in the core if S is the total source strength in the core expressed in neutrons per second.

We must now relate power output to neutron level by means of Eq. (7-1), $P = nv\Sigma_f Q$. In order to put the equation for P in a more useful form, it is necessary to develop an equivalent expression for $v\Sigma_f$.

The mean lifetime l^* of a thermal neutron in a given core may be defined as

$$l^* = \frac{\Omega}{v} \tag{7-11}$$

where Ω is the mean free path and v is the velocity of a thermal neutron in the core.   The probability that a neutron will be absorbed is simply the ratio of absorption to production.   If Σ_a is the macroscopic cross section for absorption in nonfissionable material or the probability of such absorption, then

$$\Omega(\Sigma_a + \Sigma_f) = \frac{\text{absorption}}{\text{production}} \tag{7-12}$$

If ϵ is the number of neutrons produced per fission,

$$\Omega(\Sigma_a + \Sigma_f) = \frac{nv(\Sigma_a + \Sigma_f)}{\epsilon n v \Sigma_f} \tag{7-13}$$

Solving for $v\Sigma_f$,

$$v\Sigma_f = \frac{v}{\epsilon\Omega} \quad \text{or} \quad v\Sigma_f = \frac{1}{\epsilon l^*} \tag{7-14}$$

The equation for power level now becomes

$$P = \frac{nQ}{\epsilon l^*} \tag{7-15}$$

We can continue our example for the case of the graphite-moderated reactor and find that

$$P = \frac{n_0 Q}{\epsilon l^*} = \frac{10^{-2}SDQ}{\epsilon l^*} \tag{7-16}$$

The accuracy of power calibration measurements made in this manner depends upon the validity of the assumptions made in the derivation, the power level at which the measurements are made, and the strength and calibration accuracy of the neutron source.

High-level Calibration.   The difficulties experienced in obtaining a power calibration at low levels largely disappear at high powers where the reactor is developing sufficient heat to allow calorimetric measurements to be made.   The procedure is first to obtain intercomparison data between whatever overlapping low- and high-level neutron instrumentation is present at some convenient set of power points. The high-power instruments can be calibrated at a given reactor power output by measuring coolant flow and temperature rise across the core, power being proportional to the product of these two variables. Having obtained a calibration of the high-level instruments, the low-level detectors may be intercalibrated. The accuracy of power calibrations made in this manner may be as good as that of the temperature- and flow-measuring instruments.

It is of interest to examine how the thermal calibration standard itself may vary as a function of time and operation and to see also the variations

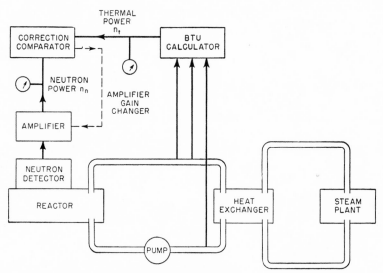

FIG. 7-20. Block diagram of automatic calibration system for nuclear instrumentation.

that might occur in the process of intercalibration. Let us assume that we have a nuclear power plant containing a neutron-measuring system which is used to read the power output of the reactor. It is desired to set up some form of continuous power-level calibration. Figure 7-20 indicates a block diagram of a nuclear power plant which attempts to provide such a calibration. Thermal power in the reactor loop is obtained directly by means of a so-called Btu calculator. This calculator computes the product of the coolant flow and the temperature difference across the reactor. Neutron power is measured by a neutron detector. The signal is amplified and then compared with the output signal from the Btu calculator in a correction comparator. The output of this comparator then adjusts the gain of the amplifier in such a manner that the neutron power reads the same as the calculated thermal power.

Let us examine now what the Btu calculator actually reads. It certainly reads all of the thermal input to the coolant loop. This includes pump power, incidental beta-gamma power from the reactor, and fission power from the reactor. The neutron detector reads essentially fission power as modified by all of the local operating conditions previously mentioned. Let us assume that the amplifier gain changing mechanism sets the neutron power measurement to be equal to the calculated over-all thermal power measurement at full power output of the plant. In some plants under these conditions, pump heat input might be estimated at 10 percent of the calculated thermal output, and beta-gamma power might be 6 percent of the total output. The neutron instruments would then be automatically set up to read high by a factor of 16 percent compared with fission power.

Let us now suppose that a power demand change is made on the system calling for 10 percent power output instead of 100 percent. Immediately after this change is met by the plant, the beta-gamma power given off by the reactor has not changed appreciably from its high power level and might now represent a full 60 percent of the actual thermal power output. The pumping losses at low power outputs can probably be considered negligible if the coolant flow is reduced in the power-changing operation. The neutron instruments will now be reading fission power of 4 percent full power plus a 16 percent correction factor and would indicate that the power output is 4.5 percent instead of 10 percent. Ultimately the Btu calculator time constants, which should be quite long in order not to disturb the control system, will catch up with this situation and all meters will read 10 percent. This correction might conceivably take as long as $\frac{1}{2}$ hr. Of course, at this new level of operation the beta-gamma power would eventually decay out and ultimately become 6 percent of the new power output level, and further continuous corrections would have to be applied to the neutron-measuring instruments.

7-8. Instrument Circuits. The amplification, counting, and integrating circuits which follow the detecting elements just described are a complex subject, and considerable literature is available on their design and usage.[16,17] These circuits fall into two categories: pulse counting and current integrating types. The essential thing, from a control point of view, is that the output of these circuits is always a d-c signal which is in some manner proportional to a neutron signal into the detector.

The circuits which are peculiar to reactor control are the period circuits which give outputs proportional to rate of change of neutron level. Period outputs are obtained by first starting with a signal proportional to level. The logarithm of this signal is then obtained in a logarithmic amplifier, and finally the derivative of the logarithmic signal is taken to provide an inverse period signal. The heart of this operation is the logarithmic amplifier which also is used to compress the wide range required. Considerable work has been accomplished in the field of logarithmic amplifiers.[18,19,23,24,28]

The principal design problem is the one of obtaining utmost reliability in the circuits. Multiple circuit configurations are generally used,[20] and efforts are made to use as few vacuum tubes as possible.

REFERENCES

1. Rossi, B., and H. H. Staub: "Ionization Chambers and Counters," McGraw-Hill Book Company, Inc., New York, 1949.
2. Curran, S. C., and J. D. Craggs: "Counting Tubes: Theory and Application," Butterworth & Co. (Publishers) Ltd., London, 1949.
3. Korff, S. A.: "Electron and Nuclear Counters: Theory and Use," D. Van Nostrand Company, Inc., New York, 1946.
4. Wilkinson, D. H.: "Ionization Chambers and Counters," Cambridge University Press, New York, 1950.
5. Baer, W., and R. T. Bayard: A High Sensitivity Fission Counter, *Rev. Sci. Instr.*, vol. 24, no. 2, pp. 138–140, February, 1953.
6. Goodman, C. (ed.): "The Science and Engineering of Nuclear Power," vol. 1, Addison-Wesley Publishing Company, Cambridge, Mass., 1946.
7. Murray, R. L.: "Introduction to Nuclear Engineering," Prentice-Hall, Inc., New York, 1954.
8. McCreary, H. S., Jr., and R. T. Bayard: A Neutron-sensitive Ionization Chamber with Electrically Adjusted Gamma Compensation, *Rev. Sci. Instr.*, vol. 25, no. 2, pp. 161–164, February, 1954.
9. Barbaras, G., et al.: The Design and Construction of Boron Coated Thermopiles for Use in Neutron Fields, *AECD*-2485, 1949.
10. Barbaras, G., et al.: The Design and Construction of Boron Coated Thermopiles for Use in Neutron Fields, *AECD*-2975, 1950.
11. Marshal, F., J. W. Coltman, and A. I. Bennett: Photomultiplier Radiation Detector, *Rev. Sci. Instr.*, vol. 19, pp. 744-770, November, 1948.
12. Gilette, R. H.: Calcium and Cadmium Tungstate as Scintillation Counter Crystals for Gamma-ray Detection, *Rev. Sci. Instr.*, vol. 21, pp. 294–301, April, 1950
13. Morton, G. A.: Photomultipliers for Scintillation Counting, *RCA Rev.* vol.. 10, no. 4, p. 526, 1949.
14. Hofstadter, R., et al.: Detection of Slow Neutrons, *Phys. Rev.*, vol. 82, p. 749, June 1, 1951.
15. Schultz, M. A., and J. C. Connor: Reactor Power Calibration, *Nucleonics*, vol. 12 no. 2, February, 1954.
16. Elmore, W. C., and M. Sands: "Electronics: Experimental Techniques," McGraw-Hill Book Company, Inc., New York, 1949.
17. Lapp, R. E., and H. L. Andrews: "Nuclear Radiation Physics," Prentice-Hall, Inc., New York, 1954.
18. Meagher, R. E., and E. P. Bently: Vacuum Tube Circuit to Measure the Logarithm of a Direct Current, *Rev. Sci. Instr.*, vol. 10, p. 336, 1939.
19. Wade, E. J.: Instruments Used with Experimental Reactors, "Convention Record of the IRE 1954 National Convention," pt. 9, "Medical and Nuclear Electronics," Institute of Radio Engineers, New York.

20. Stephenson, R.: "Introduction to Nuclear Engineering," McGraw-Hill Book Company, Inc., New York, 1954.
21. Dunlap, G. W.: Detection and Measurement of Nuclear Radiation, *Elec. Eng.,* August, 1948.
22. Cochran, D., and C. A. Hansen, Jr.: Instrumentation for a Nuclear Reactor, *Nucleonics,* August, 1949.
23. Connor, J. C., R. G. Durnal, and V. G. Shaw: Photomultiplier Log Level-Period Meter for Reactor Control, *Nucleonics,* vol. 11, no. 11, November, 1953.
24. James, W. G.: Logarithms in Instrumentation, *ORNL* 413, Oak Ridge National Laboratories, Oak Ridge, Tenn.
25. Cooke-Yarborough, E. H., and E. W. Pulsford: An Accurate Logarithmic Counting Rate Meter Covering a Wide Range, *Proc. Inst. Elec. Engrs. (London),* vol. 98, pt. 2, p. 191, 1951.
26. Jaques, T. A. J., H. A. Ballinger, and F. Wade: Neutron Detectors for Reactor Instrumentation, *Proc. Inst. Elec. Engrs. (London),* vol. 100, pt. 1, p. 110, 1953.
27. Carmichael, H.: Design of the Chalk River Ion Chambers, *Natl. Research Council Can. Rept.* 276.
28. Jordan, W. H., H. B. Frey, and G. Kelley: An Instrument for Measuring the Logarithms of Neutron Level and the Period of a Pile, *Oak Ridge Natl. Lab. Rept.* 110, November, 1948.

CHAPTER 8

OPERATIONAL CONTROL PROBLEMS: STARTUP

In considering the startup of a nuclear reactor the primary fact exists that operation is required over many decades. As we have shown, the range from zero to full power is a range covering nuclear fissions resulting in a few neutrons per second to many billion neutrons per second. Unless adequate control is maintained, particularly in the startup range, an accident is most likely to occur. The primary reason that startup range is the most dangerous one is because here the measuring instruments are poorest. This is not because the instruments are poor in a physical sense, but at low neutron levels the statistics of the instrument circuits usually demand instruments having slow responses. In the event that the neutron level in a reactor starts to rise rapidly in the startup range, the information may not be received by a control or an observer until it is too late to do anything about it.

The basic startup problem is first getting the initial neutron level up high enough that the detecting instruments can measure their fraction of the neutrons with good statistics. Many factors enter into setting this initial startup level, and these will be examined in this chapter.

We are not concerned here with the startup of a nuclear power plant, but rather with starting a reactor by itself. A power-plant startup is a complete series of details depending upon the design of the plant and generally can be considered as a form of preheating the plant. For example, the temperatures of large metallic masses such as are involved in shielding structures, pressure vessels, or boilers cannot be changed too rapidly for fear that dangerous stress forces might develop. Consequently, before a reactor is brought up to power, the plant is usually made ready for it by proper preheating and pressurizing where necessary.

There are essentially two types of reactor startups that will be described: first, the initial cold startup of the reactor and, second, subsequent hot startups in a ready plant. We shall first discuss sources of neutrons that set instrument levels, and then we shall examine these types of startups. A large portion of the chapter will be spent on the so-called startup accident. Finally we shall outline some of the systems under which a reactor may be brought to power level.

8-1. Neutron Sources. As the power level of a reactor must be under observation at all times, there must be available neutrons at all times for the instruments to measure. Actually cosmic rays or spontaneous fission will create a few neutrons in a reactor, but their number is usually too few to be satisfactorily detected. Consequently, a physical source of neutrons is deliberately inserted into a reactor, and it is the multiplication of the neutrons from this source which is usually observed by the startup range-detecting instruments. In a practical operating reactor there are usually two other types of created sources of neutrons. These are, first, photoneutrons created by gamma radiation and, second, the delayed neutrons emanating from fission-product decays. We shall examine these three sources in order.

Radioactive Sources. There are several nuclear reactions whereby a free neutron is given off when a given substance is bombarded by another particle. (α,n) reactions are very prominent, and the $Be(\alpha,n)C$ reaction is the one generally used. The alpha particle can be obtained from the natural radioactive decay of Ra or Po. The most common type of neutron source is the Po^{210}-Be source. This source is used in preference to the Ra-Be source in large sizes because it is relatively inexpensive.

The number of neutrons emanating from a Po^{210}-Be source depends upon the number of curies of activity in the initial Po and upon the efficiency of converting the alpha particles into neutrons. Geometric considerations are most important. In a typical source the efficiency might be such that one curie of Po-Be can be made to give off in the neighborhood of 2×10^6 neutrons per second.

Actually it is not this source strength which is important, nor even the neutron flux created by these emanations, but rather the number of counts per second or current produced in a neutron-detecting instrument in a given fixed position with respect to the reactor. The detecting instrument is usually calibrated in terms of neutron flux, and as has been shown in Chap. 7, fairly elaborate means must be used for calibration. It is quite obvious, however, that the larger the source rating in curies, the more counts per second will be indicated by the detecting instruments. The only limit to the size of a radioactive source is the practical one of how large a source can be safely handled in the fabricating and installation technique of placing the source into the reactor. On occasion a small factor may be gained by splitting the source into a number of discrete pieces, each piece being more easily handled than the over-all source itself. Physically the source can be made quite small. Commercial sources of neutron radiation are available as small capsules roughly ¼ in. in diameter by a few inches long, or they are also available in thin sandwich type plates.

Because of the fact that Po^{210} is radioactive with a half life of only 138 days, the neutron emission from the Po-Be source drops off rapidly with time. It is actually necessary to consider reactor assembly time and rated operational life in the design of the low-level instrumentation because of this source strength dropoff. Figure 8-1 indicates the relative source strength of a Po^{210}-Be source as a function of time. If the source must be installed in an early stage of the reactor construction, far more sensitive instruments may have to be used. For example, if the time from the initial insertion of the source to the end of the life of the

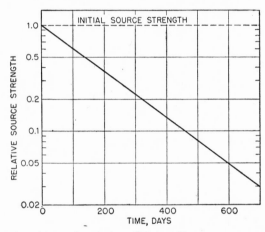

FIG. 8-1. Radioactive decay of polonium 210–beryllium source as a function of time.

reactor is 2 years, then the source will have fallen off by a factor of approximately 30. Obtaining an instrument sensitivity increase of a factor of 30 may well be an impossible task. Consequently, it is of interest to examine induced source levels in a reactor that has operated for some time.

Photoneutron Sources.[2,4,5] After a reactor has been run at power level, it is desirable that some form of induced radioactivity be built up to take the place of the decaying fixed radioactive source. As will be recalled from Chap. 7, an inevitable large gamma flux exists around power reactors. Use may be made of this gamma radiation in an effort to create new neutrons by a (γ,n) reaction. In order to produce a neutron by this method the gamma energy must be at least equal to the binding energy of the neutron to the nucleus in question. This energy is about 8 Mev for most nuclei except for some of the light ones. Deuterium and beryllium have threshold energies of 2.21 and 1.62 Mev respectively, and for this reason they are feasible for use in induced neutron sources.

The type of neutrons emitted from these reactions is usually monoenergetic and does not have the fission neutron energy spectrum.

The process involved in this artificial source is that following a shutdown of the reactor after any appreciable power operation a large gamma flux exists in and around the core. Now if the reactor contains either beryllium or water in its structure in any form, new neutrons will appear in this structure. Heavy water exists in normal water in a concentration

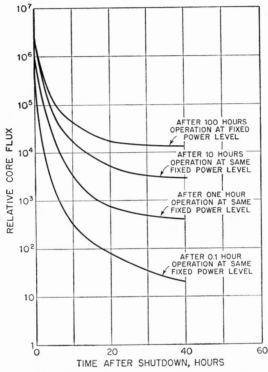

FIG. 8-2. Relative core flux after shutdown caused by photoneutron production in D_2 for various power-level operation times.

by weight of 0.016 percent. In a water-moderated plant, many thousands of pounds of water would be available and consequently a great many deuterium nuclei would be available for the (γ,n) reaction. The cross section for the (γ,n) reaction with deuterium is sufficiently high that a large photoneutron source exists for a considerable time after shutdown. It will be recalled from Fig. 7-12 that the gamma radiation drops off rapidly after shutdown. It is consequently to be expected that the photoneutrons would also drop off. Figure 8-2 indicates the relative behavior of the photoneutrons as a function of time after the reactor has been shut down. This series of curves shows that the number of photoneutrons depends upon the past history of operation of the reactor; and the longer the reactor has been operated at power levels prior to shutdown, the higher will be the photoneutron flux level.

At present beryllium and water have existed in most of the reactors designed, and consequently it has not been necessary deliberately to design materials into a reactor for specifically increasing the number of neutrons at shutdown. The curves of Fig. 8-2 also indicate that whenever possible after a reactor has been shut down, it should be started up immediately. Obviously after a sufficiently long time has elapsed, the photoneutron source will completely die out.

It should be noted in passing that gamma radiation existing in the shield or external structure of a reactor container is not useful from the standpoint of photoneutron production. Only neutrons that can be multiplied by the reactor fuel assist the instrument-level measurements.

Fission-product Delayed Neutrons. After any reactor operation, delayed neutrons are emitted from the fission products. These delayed neutrons are given off at various times, but after a sufficient time interval the number of neutrons present in the core from fission products has been shown to decay on a fixed 80-sec period. After a power level operation, then, in going to a shutdown condition the initial reduction in power level is a function of how much negative reactivity is injected into the reactor in a given amount of time. After a few minutes, however, the 80-sec period decay predominates. Figure 8-3 indicates the relative amount of fission-product delayed neutrons decaying on this 80-sec period, and for most reactors at the end of 20 min there is no substantial measurable contribution from the fission-product delayed neutrons. Another bench mark may then be set for desirable reactor operation. That is, in the event a reactor must be turned off from its power-level operation, all efforts should be made to start it up again in less than 20 min in order to use the fission-product delayed-neutron source.

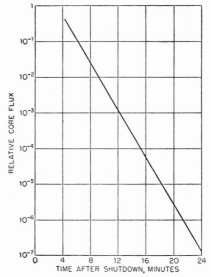

FIG. 8-3. Relative core flux after shutdown caused by fission-product delayed emission.

8-2. Initial Reactor Startup. After a reactor has been assembled, the dramatic moment finally comes when it is necessary to start it up.

Many questions are in the minds of the designers.   The first question is: Will the reactor go critical at the point that the calculations have indicated?   The reactor at this stage is presumably cold and at room temperature.   Any plant that might be used with the reactor is not in operation.   The instruments are set at their most sensitive positions and probably would be connected to scalers rather than counting-rate meters in that higher sensitivities are more easily obtained.   The use of the scalers means that the operation will take a fairly long time.   Low counting rates will initially be used, and large time constants will be necessary to obtain proper readings.

Bringing the reactor to initial criticality can be done in a number of ways depending upon its design.[1]   Some reactors, such as the water boiler, add liquid uranium fuel mixture to a container until a sufficient amount is present that the reactor becomes critical.   Other reactors such as the NRX reactor add moderator in the form of heavy water to such a level that the system becomes critical.   Still other heterogeneous reactors have fixed fuel and moderator and remove control rods so that the multiplication is increased to where the reactor system becomes critical. In any case, the effect is always the same.   A multiplication factor is brought from some fractional value to unity.   As the initial operation is apt to be a very slow and careful one, the performance of the reactor is such that it appears to be operating on the subcritical multiplication formula.   That is, the instruments will be reading a signal proportional to $1/(1 - k)$, or the counting rate from an instrument channel will be

$$\text{c.r.} = A \, \frac{1}{1 - k} \tag{8-1}$$

where c.r. is the counting rate and A an instrument constant.   As k approaches unity very slowly, the counting rate approaches infinity. It is customary to plot $1/\text{c.r.}$ as a function of the process that is changing the multiplying factor.   In this way, when $1/\text{c.r.}$ approaches zero, the reactor approaches criticality.   In a small water-boiler-type reactor the plot might be $1/\text{c.r.}$ as a function of grams of uranium added.   For the large heterogeneous reactor the abscissa of the plot might be rod travel in inches.   Figure 8-4 shows such a plot for bringing a water boiler to criticality.   As the uranium is being added, the curve constantly can be extrapolated to zero to predict where the reactor will go critical.   The shape of the curve as the reactor approaches criticality will depend on the position and type of detecting instruments.   If an instrument is located very close to the reactor, it will effectively see the source for a long period of time and the shape of the curve will be concave downward.

As will be recalled from Sec. 2-7, as criticality is approached in this manner, the reactor will take longer and longer to settle out at a fixed neutron level or counting rate. At criticality the reactor level will continue to rise indefinitely because of the additive neutrons from the source. Actually, criticality will be reached at such a high level that the source probably will be contributing only in the neighborhood of a fraction of a percent of the over-all counts read by the instruments.

If the source is removable from the reactor, then another technique can be used. The reactor is brought close to criticality by the above-described methods and then the source is quickly removed from the reactor. If the reactor were exactly at critical, the counting rate would stay

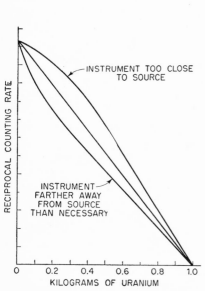

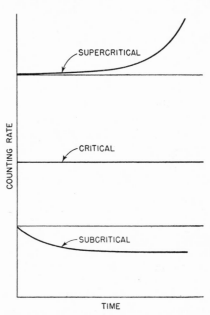

FIG. 8-4. Plot of 1/c.r. versus amount of uranium solution for a small water boiler reactor, showing the effect of instrument placement.

FIG. 8-5. Counting rate versus time after source is dropped for a reactor at or near critical.

constant. If the reactor were subcritical a slight amount, the counting rate would drop off slowly, and if the reactor were supercritical, the level would rise. Curves of the form of Fig. 8-5 might be obtained. In a supercritical case, before any rapid rises are permitted to occur, some reactivity would be removed from the reactor. Experimental reactors would usually have provisions for removing the source. Large power reactors probably would have fixed sources.

Once initial criticality has been obtained, it is desirable to examine the reactor's characteristics. Measurements would then be made of such parameters as the effectiveness of the control rods and their shutdown capabilities, relative rod effectiveness, rod calibrations, instrument rod shadowing, and other theoretical calculations.

8-3. Subsequent Reactor Startups. After the initial startup or several initial startups of the type just described, confidence is gained in the repeatability of reactor startup phenomena and the reactor can be taken gradually to higher and higher power levels. After rated power-level operation has been reached and the reactor then shut down, there are many other contributors to the reactor shutdown neutron-level instrument indications. The three source contributions will be as described in Sec. 8-1. The second major effect will be the change in subcritical multiplication caused by changes in reactivity, which in turn are caused by temperature and poisoning.

The magnitude of these effects may best be seen by a simple example. Let us assume that we have a reactor whose design is such that the normal cold shutdown multiplication factor $k = 0.9$. The subcritical multiplication factor of this shutdown reactor would then be 10. Let us now assume that the reactor has a negative temperature coefficient of $10^{-4}\delta k/°F$ and that the normal hot operating temperature of the reactor is 1000°F. Then an additional negative reactivity of 0.1 would be placed into the reactor in changing its temperature from cold to hot. The over-all hot k would now be 0.8, and the subcritical multiplication factor would be 5. In other words, if the shutdown reactor were preheated up to its normal operating temperature, the counting rates of the instruments would drop off by a factor of 2.

Similarly, as shown in Sec. 2-14, after a reactor has been operated at a high power level for a while, the so-called peak xenon effect will build up in accordance with a curve similar to that of Fig. 2-9. A peak of negative reactivity would be inserted into the core at approximately 11 hr after shutdown. The amount of negative reactivity this poisoning would insert would depend upon the reactor design, its sepecific power, the length of operation at any given power level, and the time after shutdown that the reactor is started up. It is well within conceivable probability to have the poisoning effect also change the counting rate up to another factor of 3 or 4.

After long-term operation at power level some of the fuel has been burned up. This uranium depletion also changes the subcritical multiplication factor but usually no more than a few percent.

We therefore find that the startup neutron level of a reactor depends very much upon the time after shutdown the reactor is again started up. The fixed source, photoneutron sources, delayed-neutron sources, temperature, poisoning, and depletion all may change the readings of the neutron-detecting instruments. The degree of variability may be plus or minus from the initial startup cold level and may be measured in thousands of times the initial level. This degree of variability is a severe headache to the instrumentation and control designer, and efforts to cut this range by reactor design and operational procedures are usually greatly appreciated.

Getting the Reactor Critical. A starting level having been established at a given time, and with some knowledge and confidence of the reactor and the plant, the first problem is: How fast should the reactor be brought up to critical? We shall look at this problem from the reverse point of view of seeing how fast the reactor becomes critical under given operating conditions, and we shall later examine how proper operating specifications and conditions should be laid down.

Figure 3-9 is repeated as Fig. 8-6 in order that we may describe it in terms of a startup problem. This figure shows that at infinitely slow rates of change in reactivity the reactor never becomes critical and follows a hyperbolic curve approaching criticality. At finite rates of reactivity change the reactor becomes critical at lower and lower levels as the rate is increased. At large values of subcriticality all the curves merge and the rates of change of reactivity do not matter. Figure 8-7 indicates the period that might be obtained by a given reactor as a function of the reactivity remaining in the reactor, as this

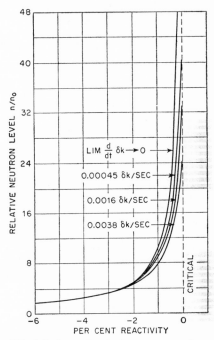

FIG. 8-6. Power level of a reactor as function of percent reactivity remaining in the reactor for given linear rates of change of reactivity.

reactivity is inserted linearly up to the critical point. Here different rates of reactivity are shown, indicating clearly the relationship of Eq. (2-11) that the period is

$$P = \frac{-\delta k}{d(\delta k)/dt} \tag{8-2}$$

That is, the period changes linearly with the reactivity as long as the reactivity is being inserted at a given linear rate. This equation holds only for large values of subcriticality, as when the reactor approaches critical at a finite rate the curves start to bend over, as is seen in Fig. 8-7.

Equation 8-2 may be combined with the subcritical multiplication factor equation giving the level

$$L = \frac{1}{-\delta k} \qquad (8\text{-}3)$$

and the relationship between period and level derived as

$$L = \frac{1}{[d(\delta k)/dt]P} \qquad (8\text{-}4)$$

In other words, any subcritical period may be obtained at any subcritical level depending upon how fast reactivity is inserted into the reactor.

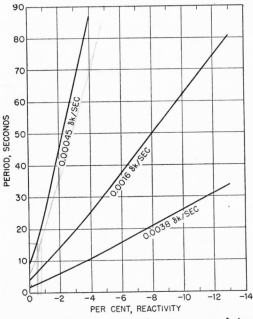

FIG. 8-7. Period versus reactivity of a reactor for given rates of change of reactivity.

Equation (8-4) obviously also does not hold when the level gets too close to critical, but for operation at 60-sec periods or longer the formula is usually quite valid. It can be seen that instrument sensitivity in counts per second can therefore be swapped off directly against time. For example, a given reactor with normal rod extraction rates might go critical in 10 to 20 min. One can gain approximately a factor of 10 in the instrument counting rate at any reasonable period by taking 2 hr to get this reactor to its critical level.

Obviously, then, the reactor can also go critical at any desired period. Figure 8-8 indicates the type of curve that can be obtained showing reactor period at criticality as a function of reactivity insertion at various rates. This curve is based on approximate calculations for a given reactor. This curve changes slightly as a function of l^*, but the general shape of the curve would be as shown in Fig. 8-8.

Rod Effectiveness. Until now we have been talking about linear rates of change of reactivity. In a practical reactor, linear rates exist only under short-term conditions. In problems involving large motions of control rods, the reactivity as a function of time is mostly nonlinear. These nonlinearities are important from three points of view: (1) that of startup, (2) that of automatic control, and (3) for scramming considerations. In this section we shall discuss only changes in rod effectiveness from the startup point of view.

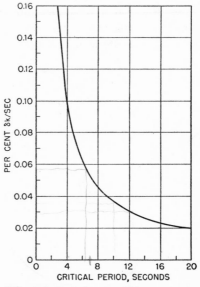

The effectiveness of a control rod depends upon its position in the core and the value of the neutron flux at that point of insertion of the rod. An approximate formula can be used that the effectiveness of a control rod varies as the square of the neutron flux in which it is placed. Thus a rod or group of rods is most effective at the center of a reactor and least effective in the outer edges or in the reflector. The control rods in a ther-

FIG. 8-8. Period on which a reactor would go through criticality by inserting reactivity at given linear rates.

mal reactor reduce the reactivity in two ways. They absorb thermal neutrons at a rate which is proportional to the thermal-neutron flux at the point in question before the insertion of the rod, and they also increase the thermal leakage from the reactor. Physically the presence of the rod decreases the number of fissions in its vicinity. Thus for a given total power output the flux must be higher in some other portion of the reactor. In a large reactor containing many rods the total effectiveness of a bank of rods is only slightly less than the sum of the individual values for each rod used alone. This is the condition whereby the rods are not too close together, since the shadowing of one rod by another will depend upon the distance between rods. For a small reactor the effectiveness of the rods is not even approximately additive, as the insertion of a single rod greatly distorts the flux distribution throughout the entire reactor.

The effectiveness of a control rod then is usually fairly small when it is completely inserted into a reactor. It becomes larger as the rod is extracted to approximately halfway out, and then near where it is completely withdrawn from the reactor its effectiveness again is quite reduced. For approximate calculations a rod worth value of the form $\int \sin^2 x \, dx$ can be used where x is the distance the rod is extracted out of the reactor. This form is illustrated in Fig. 2-10.

From a startup point of view it is the rate of reactivity change of a control rod when the reactor is close to criticality that is important. From Fig. 8-6 it has been shown that at greatly subcritical operation almost any reasonable reactivity rate produces the same results but close to criticality the level and period are sharply dependent upon reactivity

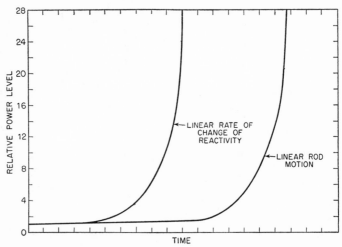

FIG. 8-9. Power level versus time for a reactor being started up on either linear rate of change of reactivity or linear rod motion.

rate. Therefore the effectiveness of the control rods must usually be considered as that value of reactivity rate which the rods possess as the reactor approaches criticality. If the rods are at their maximum effectiveness, criticality will be reached at lower levels and shorter periods.

Another effect of the rod effectiveness is to lengthen the startup time. With all of the variability in startup level that exists and additional variability in rod worths and effectiveness as a function of position and poisoning, etc., reactor startup systems usually must be designed, for safety reasons, on the basis of maximum rod effectiveness. Consequently, the rods are at a lower effectiveness most of the time. Hence, it takes longer for the reactor to attain criticality. Figure 8-9 illustrates this effect by showing a reactor startup to criticality using linear reactivity rates and then linear rod motion rates on a rod setup whereby the rods have an effectiveness of the form $\int \sin^2 x \, dx$ with the maximum effectiveness equal to the previous linear reactivity rate. The length of time to reach critical for this particular startup from -13 percent in reactivity is nearly doubled.

It should be mentioned in passing that intermittent rod motion, such as pulling a rod for a given length of time and then stopping and then pulling again, etc., is sometimes used. For analysis purposes the rates of change of reactivity and consequent levels and periods for this type of motion can be obtained to a good degree of approximation by merely taking the straight-line average of the intermittent reactivity change.

8-4. Operational Startup Requirements. The usual approach to a given power level is on a period basis; that is, the reactor will be brought

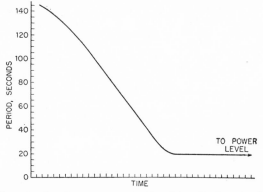

FIG. 8-10. Period versus time for a reactor starting from shutdown and going to power level.

up to its power operating point from criticality on perhaps a 30-sec period or possibly a 20-sec or shorter period. As these values of period can be reached before the reactor goes critical at given rates of reactivity withdrawal, control-rod motion may be slowed down in actual practice or stopped before criticality is reached. Figure 8-10 indicates a possible period versus time sequence in a reactor startup. From this figure, once a 20-sec period is reached, either an operator or an automatic circuit manipulates the control rods to maintain this period until the desired power level is attained. In this type of operation criticality is of no importance whatever. The reactor is brought through the critical point without the operator's knowing or caring where it is.

There are several requirements upon which the startup time or the required reactivity rates of change of a reactor control system may be based. These considerations usually are of three types: (1) operational considerations, (2) safety startup considerations, or (3) poisoning override considerations. We shall discuss these considerations in order.

Operational Considerations. If one were permitted by operational requirements to start up a reactor in a day's time, the operational and safety requirements would be unimportant and only poisoning override would have to be considered in startup problems. In discussing a power-producing nuclear plant for electrical generation or a military propulsion plant, it is quite apparent that this plant must be in a power operative condition for as large a percentage of the time as possible. Scramming such a reactor is most undesirable, and shutting the reactor down to fixed source level is equally undesirable. If the reactor plant is such that it must supply power continuously to some of its own auxiliaries, then a fixed minimum operating level exists. This level might conceivably be a few percent of the plant full-power output rating. It then would take the reactor only a minute or so to get up to a useful output level from this stand-by type of state. This step presupposes that the steam plant and auxiliaries are always ready to run. Starting from source level is rarely done for this type of plant.

On the other hand, research or experimental reactors need such operation cycles that are turned on every morning and turned off every night. Startup times should be minimized so that the day is not wasted in getting to an operational level. Other types of output programming are possible, and the operational startup requirements for each reactor must be considered on an individual basis.

In order to get a feel for the numbers involved let us again examine an elementary example. Let us assume that we have a reactor which for some reason must be brought up to power in 20 min. If one considers a 10-decade startup, roughly 2 decades will be necessary to get to critical and 8 decades will be used in bringing the reactor up to power. If the power level is attained on a 30-sec period, 9.2 min will be consumed by this operation. Therefore 10.8 min are available to bring the reactor to critical. If the startup is made from a shutdown value of reactivity of -13 percent, such as has been used in some of the previous examples, the average reactivity rate required for this startup would be $2 \times 10^{-4} \delta k \text{ sec}^{-1}$. This elementary type of reasoning may be what determines reactivity insertion rates for a reactor plant provided the safety and poisoning considerations can be met.

8-5. Safety Startup Considerations. The fundamental premise upon which safety startup considerations are based is that the speed at which reactivity may be inserted into a reactor can be that speed at which the protection system ensures a safe shutdown in the event of accident. The faster reactivity is inserted into a reactor, the shorter will be the period at a given power level and the greater the possibility that the reactor power level might overshoot any safety stops. Normally it is assumed that nothing would go wrong in starting up a reactor, but many possible accidents may be hypothesized. One of these accidents appears to be much more severe than the others. This is the so-called startup accident, and we shall examine it in detail as an extreme case.

The startup accident is that condition in which reactivity is continually inserted into a reactor at a given rate and nothing is done to stop it. In the case of a reactor being started up by withdrawing its control rods, the situation might easily be hypothesized that a relay controlling a motor driving the rods becomes stuck. The motor keeps turning, and the rods are extracted from the reactor until they are all the way out. In this way the reactor is brought from a subcritical condition through critical and through prompt critical. It is presumed that safety stops or emergency means of stopping rod motion are not available until the reactor power level reaches a given overpower amount.

The problem then becomes: How bad is this accident, and what sort of periods are involved? If the level of reactor power rises too rapidly, an overshoot of the top protection level signal may result and the reactor be damaged. The parameter that is important is the period attained by the reactor in that this is a measure of the time available to do something about the accident.

Two methods of analysis of reactor power level and period are available. The first method is to attempt to solve the reactor kinetic equations for various rates of reactivity change starting from various subcritical levels. The method of solution would be similar to that outlined in Sec. 3-3. This method is tedious and restrictive in that the entire range of probable periods and levels involved cannot be seen without many numerical calculations. Another method that might be used is to solve for the boundary cases of maximum and minimum periods that may be involved in a startup accident and to attempt to design a startup system to handle the worst case.

We shall indicate here how to develop such period bounds.† Intuitively there will be two such bounds, the first an upper bound on how short the period can get as the reactor becomes greatly supercritical and the second a lower bound at greatly subcritical conditions. The upper bound should be dependent in some way upon neutron lifetime l^*. On the other hand, for greatly subcritical conditions there must be a certain minimum period involved which will depend upon the rate of insertion of reactivity.

The upper bound will be handled in the following manner: We may start by first rewriting the familiar pile kinetic equation

---

† The development of the period upper bound follows that of H. W. Newson in the classified literature. The lower bound analysis presented was first accomplished by F. Engel, Jr.

$$\frac{dn}{dt} = \frac{\delta k - \beta}{l^*} n + \sum_{i=1}^{6} \lambda_i C_i + S \tag{8-5}$$

If we note that the last two terms on the right-hand side of the equation are always positive, then

$$\frac{dn}{dt} > \frac{\delta k - \beta}{l^*} n \tag{8-6}$$

As the period P is defined as

$$P = \frac{n}{dn/dt} \tag{8-7}$$

it follows that

$$P < \frac{l^*}{\delta k - \beta} \tag{8-8}$$

for $\delta k \geq \beta$. For $\delta k < \beta$ the inequality of Eq. (8-8) loses its significance with regard to fixing the magnitude of the period. However, this inequality establishes a real upper bound for the period when the reactor is above prompt critical.

We have then established a maximum limit on the period a reactor can possess by saying that within a given upper criticality range the period cannot be larger than a specified amount.

A lower bound to the period in the subcritical range may also be established. It can be seen from the subcritical multiplication formula $P = \dfrac{-\delta k}{d(\delta k)/dt}$ that this lower bound will depend on the rate of change of reactivity. Defining this rate of reactivity change by the symbol γ, in δk sec^{-1},

$$P = \frac{-\delta k}{\gamma} \tag{8-9}$$

as the subcritical relationship.

For reactors subcritical by a large amount it has been shown that this formula is exact, but as the reactor approaches criticality, the formula does not hold. The formula is inaccurate because it assumes that all neutrons are effectively prompt neutrons. As criticality is approached in a startup, the delayed neutrons become more and more important, in that the rates of change of level become comparable with delayed-neutron-emission times. It is felt intuitively from a control point of view that the effect of the delayed neutrons is to slow down any level changes, thus increasing the reactor period. Therefore Eq. (8-9) represents an intuitive lower bound. A rigorous analysis will now be presented which substantiates this feeling.

For simplicity, consider the pile kinetic equations for the lumped-delayed-emitter situation; that is

$$\frac{dn}{dt} = \frac{\delta k - \beta}{l^*} n + \lambda C + S \tag{8-10}$$

$$\frac{dC}{dt} = \frac{\beta}{l^*} n - \lambda C \tag{8-11}$$

For the subcritical condition the reactor must ultimately reach some equilibrium. This equilibrium may be defined as when the concentration of the delayed-neutron emitters $C(t)$ is constant. Here neutrons are lost at the same rate they are being produced.

Thus at equilibrium

$$\frac{dn}{dt} = \frac{\delta k - \beta}{l^*} n + \lambda C + S = 0 \tag{8-12}$$

and

$$\frac{dC}{dt} = \frac{\beta}{l^*} n - \lambda C = 0 \tag{8-13}$$

Substituting Eq. (8-13) into Eq. (8-12)

$$\frac{dn}{dt} = \frac{\delta k}{l^*} n - \frac{dC}{dt} + S = \frac{\delta k}{l^*} n + S = 0 \tag{8-14}$$

or

$$n = \frac{-Sl^*}{\delta k} \tag{8-15}$$

which must hold in the equilibrium state and is independent of whether we use one lumped delayed emitter or six individual ones. If we now make a small change in δk about this equilibrium state,

$$\Delta n = n - n(0) = Sl^* \left(\frac{1}{\delta k_0 + \Delta \delta k} - \frac{1}{\delta k_0} \right) \tag{8-16}$$

$$\Delta n = \frac{Sl^* \Delta \delta k}{\delta k_0 (\delta k_0 + \Delta \delta k)} \tag{8-17}$$

The time required for δk to change by an amount $\Delta \delta k$ is

$$t = \frac{\Delta \delta k}{\gamma} \tag{8-18}$$

where γ is the previously defined rate of change of reactivity. Then if we are considering a startup whereby we are inserting reactivity, the equilibrium value of the neutron flux level must be greater than the level before equilibrium is established for any subcritical δk. The greatest possible value for the time rate of change of the neutron flux level then would be

$$\frac{\Delta n}{\Delta t} = \frac{Sl^* \, \Delta \delta k}{\delta k_0 (\delta k_0 + \Delta \delta k)} \frac{\gamma}{\Delta \delta k} \qquad (8\text{-}19)$$

$$= \frac{Sl^* \gamma}{\delta k_0 (\delta k_0 + \Delta \delta k)} \qquad (8\text{-}20)$$

If one obtains the time derivative of n in the following manner

$$\frac{dn}{dt} = \lim_{t \to 0} \frac{\Delta n}{\Delta t} < \frac{Sl^* \gamma}{(\delta k)^2} \qquad (8\text{-}21)$$

the period lower bound becomes

$$P = \frac{n}{dn/dt} > - \frac{Sl^*}{\delta k} \frac{(\delta k)^2}{Sl^* \gamma} = - \frac{\delta k}{\gamma} \qquad (8\text{-}22)$$

This expression could have been obtained by a direct differentiation of Eq. (8-15), but the above process appears to have greater validity.

An upper and a lower bound for the period of a reactor involved in a startup type accident have thus been established. Figure 8-11 illustrates these bounds for several conditions. It will be noted that the upper bound depends only on l^* and the amount of reactivity present in the core at a given time. The lower bound, however, is a function of the rate of insertion of reactivity. Figure 8-11 also indicates a possible startup accident when reactivity is being inserted at the linear rate of $1.2 \times 10^{-4} \delta k$ sec^{-1} into a reactor having an l^* of 10^{-4} sec. At large subcriticalities the reactor follows the lower period bound. Above prompt critical the period closely follows the upper bound.

It will be noted, of course, that the upper bound is really in the wrong direction as far as safety design considerations are concerned. That is, it would be desirable to know that a reactor could never get on a period shorter than a given amount. However, above prompt critical, the period follows the upper bound as developed so closely that this bound may also be used as a practical value of the minimum period. Using this limit type of approach, the severity and time involved in a startup accident may be seen without the necessity of performing a complete calculation of the kinetic equations for ramp input functions.

It is to be stressed that no temperature coefficient is considered in this approach as presented. The lower bound picture would probably not be affected by temperature coefficient, but the upper bound would be drastically changed.

The period attained in the intermediate region between the bounds as developed depends upon how far subcritical the reactor is at the start and the reactivity change rate. Consequently, the period attained at any level above the startup level is a function of from how far below that level the initial reactivity insertion started.   Let us assume, for example, that we have established by the safety system a protection level above

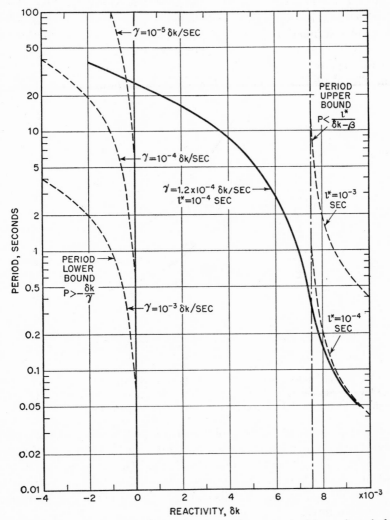

FIG. 8-11. Period as a function of reactivity indicating upper and lower bounds for a startup accident.

which a signal is given for a scram or some emergency means to reverse rod motion.   A good example might be that when the reactor power level exceeded 200 percent of full power, a signal would be provided to the scramming system to insert all the control rods as quickly as possible. The problem then exists of how much time is available from when the dangerous level is noted by an instrument and the rods actually start moving in. This available time depends upon the period that the reactor is on at this level. In turn, the period that may be attained depends upon how far below this protection level the startup accident began. Figure 8-12 indicates the period attained by a reactor at a given protection level as a function of the decades of rise in reactor power level before the protection level is reached. The curves again are for the example that the reactor was originally −13 percent subcritical. It can be seen from Fig. 8-12 that if only a few decades of power-level change are

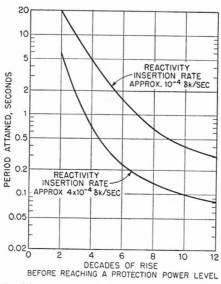

FIG. 8-12. Period attained by a reactor during a startup accident at a given fixed protection level versus the number of decades below the protection level reactivity insertion started. Startup from −13 percent in reactivity. No temperature coefficient.

involved between the startup point and the protection level, the periods attained are quite modest and a comparatively long amount of time is available to initiate some protection device. On the other hand, if an accident occurs when the reactor is started possibly 10 decades below the protection level, very fast periods can occur, particularly at high reactivity insertion rates.

Once a period has been established in this manner or from boundary conditions, then the amount of time available to do something about protection is directly established. Figure 8-13 indicates the relative power level that a reactor would attain above the protection trip level as a function of the time delay in doing something about the rising power level. In other words, while waiting for the protection signal to act following a trip signal, the delay time in the protection system is most important, as the power level could conceivably become very high during this delayed interval.   Conversely, Fig. 8-13 indicates that if a 200 percent absolute power level is needed to protect a reactor, then if a protection signal is provided at 100 percent full power, the protection system must reverse the reactivity and cause the power level to start coming down with a delay of less than 0.7 sec, provided that the reactor is on a 1-sec period.   We shall discuss these overshoots in greater detail in Chap. 10.

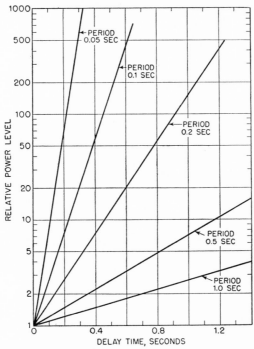

FIG. 8-13. Relative power level attained by a reactor on a given period as a function of the time delay in doing something about it.

Level Considerations with Temperature Coefficient.   The considerations until now have been based upon the reactor having no temperature coefficient.   We have seen in the case of automatic control that the addition of a temperature coefficient has a tremendous effect.   In startup control also the no-temperature-coefficient case is a very pessimistic one, and with any sized negative temperature coefficient the situation improves considerably.   It can be shown that for a given negative temperature coefficient there exists a corresponding reactivity insertion rate under which the reactor can be protected from a startup accident by virtue of the temperature coefficient alone.   Subsequently, for the same given temperature coefficient there exists a higher reactivity insertion rate during startup, whereby the reactor system can be protected either by stopping the control rods or reversing their motion during a startup accident. Obviously a still higher reactivity insertion rate can be used in starting a reactor, provided both a negative temperature coefficient and a scram are used as the ultimate protection system.

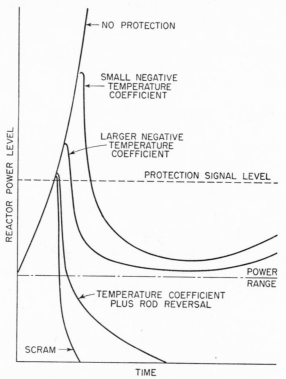

FIG. 8-14. Reactor power level as a function of time for several types of protection systems.

Let us crudely examine the process that exists during the startup accident for several types of protection systems. Figure 8-14 illustrates some of these situations. Let us assume that the reactor comes into the power range on a given period. Curves similar to those in Fig. 8-12 can be used to determine this period. With no protection system, obviously the reactor power level would continue to rise on a fast exponential until the reactor destroyed itself. If even the smallest negative temperature coefficient is available, then a form of protection exists in that ultimately the temperature of the reactor will rise to such a point that sufficient negative reactivity will be inserted into the reactor to overcome the positive reactivity put in by the startup accident.   When this occurs, the power level must reverse itself and the reactor will tend to reach an equilibrium position between the startup accident reactivity and the negative reactivity being inserted by the temperature coefficient.   Eventually, however, if rod pulling continues, the average temperature of the reactor will continue to rise to match this rod pulling and the power level will gradually follow, assuming some simple coolant flow pattern.   This second rise following the first sharp peak is usually a long time effect taking in the order of minutes, and presumably several different types of protection systems may be employed to handle this second rise.

As the temperature coefficient is increased, the peak level reached in the startup accident becomes smaller and smaller until with a very large temperature coefficient the actual useful power output of the reactor itself may be limited.   As a matter of fact, in some reactors this is the method of startup and operation.   That is, the rods are pulled all the way out deliberately and the power level rises to such a point whereby the negative reactivity set by the average temperature comes into balance with the positive reactivity set up by rod removal at some maximum power level.   However, for most reactors having large excess reactivities there are temperature limitations that make this type of operation dangerous.

If the temperature coefficient is insufficient to restrain the power level to a safe amount under any attainable period, then it is necessary to apply external means for protection.   One simple means is to stop the rods externally from moving by any convenient mechanical device.   A second scheme is to reverse the rod motion at the same speed at which the rods are being extracted.   The ultimate in protection is, of course, attained by a scram in which all available reactivity is injected into the reactor as violently as possible.   It will be noted in Fig. 8-14 that for internal protection the power level remains high at some point where a balance in reactivity can be obtained whereas for external protection schemes involving rod movement the reactor is ultimately shut down.

From these types of considerations design criteria curves against the startup accident may be derived.   Figure 8-15 indicates such curves. It is first necessary to assume that a situation exists below which the reactor is always protected or safe and above which some damage may be caused.   This situation may be defined in terms of reactor fuel temperature, moderator temperature, or power level.   These parameters, of course, are related.   For convenience, the safe condition is usually defined in terms of a power level.   To go back to our previous example, the design of a reactor may be such that below 200 percent of its rated power level the reactor is always safe.   If the power level is permitted to rise above 200 percent full power, something will occur that will damage the system.

Once such a criterion has been established, then various combinations of temperature coefficient, reactivity rates, and protection systems may be examined. The curve of Fig. 8-15 illustrates the shape of the data for a given reactor. If any negative temperature coefficient exists, there are certain rates of reactivity insertion permitted whereby the startup accident cannot cause any trouble with the temperature coefficient alone providing the protection. If there are other forms of protection in the system in combination with a negative temperature coefficient, then faster

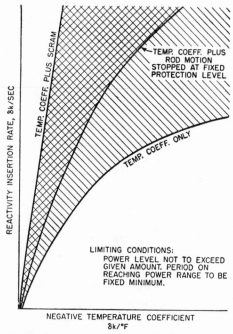

FIG. 8-15. Design criteria curves against the startup accident. Permitted rates of reactivity for various negative temperature coefficients and protection systems.

reactivity insertion rates may be used. And ultimately if a scram is used, extremely high reactivity rates may be used in startup, provided nothing can possibly happen to disable the scramming system. This last hedge usually would limit the rate of reactivity insertion in a practical design. It can be seen from Fig. 8-15 that, if possible, an attempt should be made to design the reactor and its plant so that protection depends upon its internal temperature coefficient only, in that nothing can go wrong with this mechanism.

8-6. Poison Considerations. The startup of a reactor from the point of view of operational requirements and safety has been examined, and now we might look at a special safety case called poisoning override. It is a well-known phenomenon, as explained in Sec. 2-14, that after reactor operation at power level, a given amount of so-called equilibrium xenon poisoning builds up in thermal reactors. A thermal reactor also loses reactivity for approximately 11 hr after shutdown, following which time the reactivity is then returned to its normal value in approximately 60 hr after shutdown. Figure 2-9 illustrates this peak poisoning effect. The peak poisoning after shutdown (as well as the equilibrium poisoning) depends upon the previous long-time operating flux. If we define poisoning as the ratio of the thermal neutrons absorbed by the poison to the

TABLE 8-1

Long-time operating flux	Equilibrium poison	Maximum poison after shutdown
10^{12}	0.0054	0.0055
10^{13}	0.028	0.03
10^{14}	0.045	0.20
2×10^{14}	0.046	0.38

thermal neutrons absorbed in the fissionable material, Table 8-1, showing the relative amounts of poison, can be computed from Glasstone and Edlund.[7]

Once the poisoning has reached its peak, it starts to decay back to its normal condition. During the time of this decay, reactivity is being added to the reactor in a manner similar to actually pulling control rods. The maximum slope of this reactivity insertion may occur at approximately 20 hr after a power-level shutdown. If at this time the reactor is at critical or close to critical, this can be a dangerous condition. The addition of this amount of reactivity must be compensated for by the insertion of control rods or other poisons, or else the power level will rise rapidly under conditions similar to a startup accident. In other words, the control rods must be capable of being inserted at a given minimum rate in order to counteract the poisoning effect. We have previously been discussing how fast the control rods might be extracted from a reactor, but this present consideration concerns how fast they must be inserted during startup.

A special extreme case exists, which may or may not be taken into account, depending upon the automatic control philosophy selected for power operation. The curve of Fig. 2-9 is for the case of poison build-up with the reactor at zero power. The second case is the condition whereby the reactor is turned on at the time peak xenon is reached and then immediately run at full power. Here the xenon poisoning is burned out very rapidly. Strictly speaking, this is not a startup problem and will be mentioned again under operational power problems. Once full power is reached, these fast rates of rod motion will have to be considered by any automatic or manual control system.

To determine the speed of control rods for any of these poison conditions, minimum rod effectiveness must be considered. We can conceivably get into a situation whereby it is necessary to move the rods to compensate for a given amount of reactivity per second insertion by the poison. At maximum rod effectiveness it might be very easy to overcome this poison, but at minimum rod effectiveness it might well be impossible. If the reactor structure is at all complicated, the rods can conceivably be at any position at critical. Therefore provisions must be made in the control system for maintaining at least sufficient rod effectiveness which can be inserted at a given rate to take care of this poisoning decay during startup. Scramming to override this burnout is, of course, undesirable.

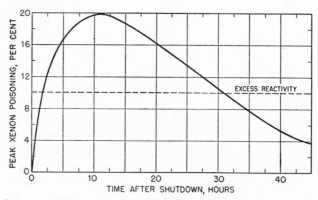

FIG. 8-16. Poisoned startup example in which the reactor is not capable of overriding peak xenon.

Although the problem of safety does not exist, if one attempts to override the initial portion of the xenon build-up curve of Fig. 2-9 between 1 and 10 hr, there may be an operational reason for inserting reactivity at a rate faster than the poisoning is inserting negative reactivity. The front edge of this curve has a slope approximately 10 times that of the rear end, and if this poison effect must be overridden, a rate 10 times faster than that previously required would have to be used.

Many reactors do not provide for complete xenon override. That is, they do not have sufficient excess reactivity to overcome the poison even when their rods are all the way out. For these reactors, in the event they are shut down after an extended operational period, a startup must be made within a given time; otherwise a waiting period is involved. Figure 8-16 indicates an example of this type of operation. Assume that a reactor has built in a maximum excess reactivity of 10 percent and the xenon poisoning is capable of building up to 20 percent after shutdown following a given power-level operation. Figure 8-16 indicates that unless this reactor is started up within 1¾ hr after shutdown, a wait will be necessary until 31 hr after shutdown before the reactor can again be brought to critical. Once any substantial power level is reached, the poison will rapidly be burned out.

As also mentioned in Sec. 2-14, the problem of xenon override is particularly severe in reactors operating on an 8- to 12-hr day and then being shut down. It is quite evident that this sort of operation requires that the reactor always start up near peak xenon poisoning.

8-7. Startup Control Systems. The specifications for control-rod speeds during startup having been examined, we can now briefly look at startup control systems. The first and most obvious control system would be a manual one. The problem is simply to increase the multiplication factor of a reactor to such a state that the reactor power level rises on a given period until a desired power output is reached. Figure 8-10 indicates a period versus time curve for such an operation. A manual control on reactor rod motion would simply be first to extract the rods at a given rate until the reactor reached the specified period, in the case of Fig. 8-10, in 20 sec, and then rod motion would be stopped or changed manually to maintain this period. The operator would watch two meters, a period meter and a power-level indicator. The reactor would be maintained at the fixed period until the specified power level was reached. Then the reactor would be returned to exact criticality, and this power level maintained.

Because of the hazards involved in manual reactor startup, some form of override or interlock protection is usually provided. The most common system is of the permissive type. In this sort of startup operation, control rods may be moved in or out provided the reactor period is not shorter than a fixed amount. Once shorter periods are achieved, the rods are automatically stopped by the interlocks or they may be moved in, either manually or automatically. Figure 8-17 illustrates a permissive type of operation about a 20-sec period. Here the reactor is started up and is gradually brought from long periods toward a 20-sec period. For periods longer than 25 sec the control rods may be moved either in or out by an operator. As the period shortens to 20 sec, interlocks prevent the rods from being withdrawn any farther and rod motion is stopped. In the event that a 15-sec period is reached, interlocks take over and cause control-rod motion inward. This form of semiautomatic control provides a simple, safe means of getting the reactor to power level.

Automatic Period Control. An automatic control loop can, of course, be used to replace the manual or permissive operation just described. Figure 8-18 shows such an automatic control system for period control.

This loop is very similar to the rod control loops of Chap. 4. The principal difference is that instead of the level demand being placed into the comparator, a period demand signal is used. For the example of Fig. 8-10, a period demand of 20 sec would be set into the comparator as a fixed voltage. The reactor, through the neutron detector and period cir-

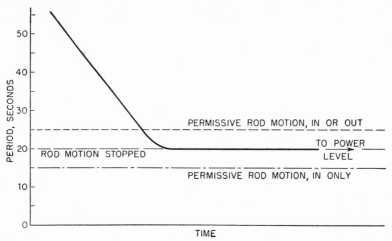

FIG. 8-17. Permissive type startup control. Period controls direction of rod motion.

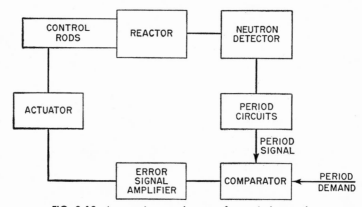

FIG. 8-18. Automatic control system for period control.

cuits, would create a matching voltage, and any error signal would be amplified to initiate control-rod motion to reduce this error signal to zero. Similar types of analysis to those presented in Chap. 4 may be used to determine the constants and compensations needed for this type of control loop. The error-signal amplifier may be of the on-off type or proportional type.

Combination Period and Level Startup Control.[3][†]   It is desirable, if the complexity of the control system permits, to provide a startup control whereby both period and level are used to control the motion of the rods. For the purpose of automatic control it is essential only that the reactor be at such a level that good period information is obtainable from the instruments.   It is unimportant whether an initial startup or startup after scram is involved.   Consider the block diagram of Fig. 8-19a.   This control loop is similar to the previously described loop of Fig. 8-18, with the exception that a level and a period detector and a level and a period demand signal have been inserted to feed information into the comparator.   Let us now follow a startup program by observing the operation of

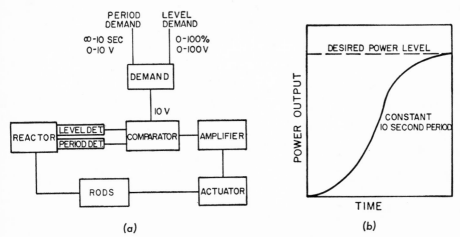

FIG. 8-19. Combination period and level control, "magic-number" system. (a) Block diagram of control system.   (b) Approach to power-level operating curve.

this loop.   If the reactor is initially at a very low level, we can assume that no significant output is available from the level detector.   We might also arbitrarily assign numbers on the basis of the voltages that one might expect in the comparator.   That is, for example, a variation of level from 0 to 100 percent full power might be interpreted in terms of 0 to 100 volts into the comparator.   A variation in period or period demand from infinity to 10 sec might correspond to a variation in voltage from 0 to 10 volts.   The level detector may be expected to give out information only during the top 2 decades of power operation.   If we now start at some arbitrary low level, for example 8 decades below full power, and we demand into the comparator a 10-volt signal corresponding, for example, to either 10 percent of full power or a 10-sec period, then the rods will be extracted from the reactor by the actuator mechanism which has been given an error signal.   This signal corresponds to the fact that

† This section was originally presented by the author in *AECD*-3163, 1950.

insufficient voltage is coming out of the period detector to match the 10-volt input to the comparator. It will be recalled from Figs. 8-9 and 8-10 that even though the rods are pulled at some maximum permitted speed, for a long time the reactor will not be able to attain a 10-sec period. Consequently, a large error signal is maintained into the amplifier and actuator mechanism, and the rods are removed from the reactor at maximum permitted speed. However, as soon as the period detector gives out a 10-volt signal, the error is reduced to zero and the rod motion is stopped or possibly reversed. This condition presupposes that the servo loop has a fast time constant compared with a 10-sec period. The period of the reactor has now leveled off at 10 sec and is maintained by the servo loop. The reactor goes through criticality on a 10-sec period and on up in power for approximately 4 more decades on this same 10-sec period with the servo system acting completely on period information alone.

As soon as the reactor approaches the power operating range, some information begins to come out of the level detector. This information, plus what is coming out of the period detector, must now match up against the 10 volts. This situation automatically calls for the output of the period detector to be reduced, and consequently, the pile must now operate on a longer period. As the level increases still farther, the servo system gets less and less information from the period channel and more and more information from the level detector. This action is as shown in Fig. 8-19b. Here the reactor comes up through the startup range and period range on a 10-sec period, and this period slowly levels off into infinity as the reactor approaches the desired power.

The system just described is a so-called magic number system wherein, by the proper choice of voltages corresponding to period and level, only one input is needed to the comparator. Other automatic systems are possible, and a very flexible one is a system whereby a discrete period and level can be demanded independently. A third system of merit is one whereby period information is the controlling factor until the power level is reached and then level information only takes over and period information drops out. The system that the designer selects is one which fits the time constants of the measuring instruments and amplifiers as well as the desired operating program. For example, if the level information is available from the instruments in a matter of milliseconds and the period information is not available in less than 10 sec, it is futile to build a fast servo system for level control and expect to be able to use period information with this system. In general, with the instruments available at present, there is a higher resistance and capacitance time constant associated with period information than with level information. If the time constants of both pieces of information are comparable, then the same speed servo system obviously may be used. If the two time constants differ widely, then modifications have to be made to the servo system to set up a different response time in the period range from that in the power range.

Another type of interesting comparator circuit for use when the time constants are not widely different is shown in Fig. 8-20. Here power and period information are received from the respective measuring circuits. The circuits give voltage outputs proportional to neutron density and reactor period. Period demand is varied by changing the amount of reference voltage used to balance the period information. Power demand

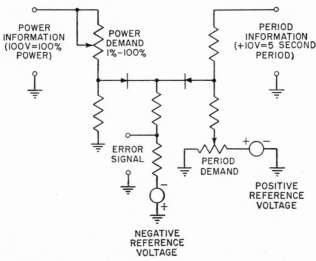

FIG. 8-20. Simplified schematic diagram of a comparator using both period and level information.

is varied by changing the gain of the information received from the power-measuring circuit. The diodes separating the demand circuits are used in such a manner that only that voltage which is most positive will assume control of the rod-actuating mechanism. The negative voltage reference shown is to set up a zero position for accompanying amplifiers. A system of this type effectively switches over automatically from period to power demand at about 90 percent of the power demand level. Yet a rein is held by the period control which prevents the reactor from ever changing its level too fast.

REFERENCES

1. Murray, R. L.: "Introduction to Nuclear Engineering," Prentice-Hall, Inc., New York, 1954.
2. Bernstein, S., et al.: Yield of Photoneutrons from U^{235} Fission Products in Heavy Water, *Phys. Rev.*, vol. 71, p. 573, 1947.

3. Schultz, M. A.: Automatic Control of Power Reactors, *AECD*-3163, 1950.
4. Bernstein, S., et al.: Yield of Photoneutrons from U^{235} Fission Products in Be, *AECD*-1833, Feb. 20, 1948.
5. Ergen, W. K.: Hard Gamma Emitters among Fission Fragments, *ANP*-59, May 3, 1951.
6. Moore, R. V.: The Control of a Thermal Neutron Reactor, *Proc. Inst. Elec. Engrs.* (*London*), vol. 100, pt. 1, p. 90, 1953.
7. Glasstone, S., and M. C. Edlund: "The Elements of Nuclear Reactor Theory," D. Van Nostrand Company, Inc., New York, 1952.

CHAPTER 9

OPERATIONAL CONTROL PROBLEMS: POWER OPERATION

In this chapter we shall consider the operation of a power reactor at its rated power level.   It will be recalled that the power range was defined as the top 2 decades of output below the full power rating of the reactor. It is the problems that occur within this range which will be discussed.

The operation of a stable reactor plant in the power range is a dull process.   Once the plant achieves this operating range, the temperature coefficient plus the control system maintains any desired power level. Occasional control-rod motions of a slow sort are required, and it is the causes of these motions plus some of the physical means for creating the reactivity changes that will occupy our attention.

9-1. Requirements for Reactivity Changes at Power Level.   There are six items that might cause a reactor system to require a change in reactivity at power level.   These items are programming, temperature changes, pressure changes, depletion, poisons, and flux distribution control.   These may appear singly or in combination and may be compensated for manually or automatically.   Each item is important, both from an operational point of view and from a design point of view, in that each individual condition sets a requirement for a maximum change rate of reactivity that must be designed into the control system.

Programming.   Problems in programming arise directly when a reactor power-level change of any sort is required.   The operational program may require any of the types of temperature and pressure variations called for in Chap. 6.   The question to be answered is: What are the limitations that should be imposed upon a reactor plant in changing from one power level to another?   In a large plant one usually looks outside the reactor for the limitations.   It has been shown that the reactor can change its level quite fast.   The boiler may have a temperature change rate limitation, or the turbine may not be able to handle power as fast as the primary system can deliver it.   In any event, it is reasonable to assume that some type of limitation will be placed on the system.

In casually considering what sort of a limitation should be imposed upon reactor power changes, we might first look at a period limitation such as we had in the startup range. For illustrative purposes let us say that the reactor plant should not be capable of having its power level changed from 1 percent of rated output to full output in a time faster than 1 min with a minimum period restriction being imposed. Figure 9-1 illustrates the ultimate condition of making this entire level change at the fastest possible period. From the figure this period can be seen to be approximately 13 sec. This type of period limitation means that in the first 13 sec the power level would increase from 1 to 2.7 percent of rated

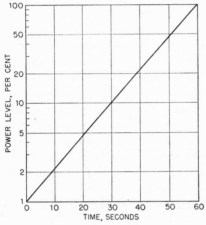

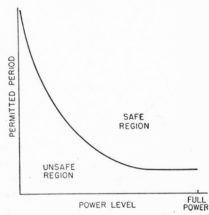

FIG. 9-1. Permitted power-level change versus time for a fixed minimum period operation.

FIG. 9-2. Permitted period as a function of power level.

power and in the next 13 sec from 2.7 to 7.4 percent, and so on. In other words, the absolute power level rises very slowly at first and then much faster on a percentage basis as the level is increased. In the last 13 sec of the operation the power level would go from 37 to 100 percent. This sort of period limitation is rather useless, then, as it appears to be in the wrong direction. It is far more desirable to slow up the rate of change of power level as full power is approached to prevent overshoot if nothing more.

The reactor is a somewhat unique device in that it effectively operates on an exponential basis rather than on a linear basis. If it turns out that the reactor is the limiting component of the system in the speed of changing power level, then a combination of linear level and period type of limitation may be usefully considered. It will be recalled from the startup accident that the danger which exists in going from one power level to another is a function of the distance between these levels. Therefore if only a comparatively small level change is called for, this change can be handled safely at a faster period than if a larger change is made.

Figure 9-2 illustrates a type of combination level-period restriction that permits a given safe period operating area for each power level. At any given operating power level, period signals longer than a prescribed amount can be tolerated. As the power level approaches full power, a minimum period situation is set up. However, if the reactor is at a low power level, only slow rates of change are safely permitted. This system has the same disadvantage as the one above of permitting an operation into full power at an ever-increasing percentage change as a function of time.

Most physical apparatus is apt to have a percentage power type of limitation. A boiler might have a limitation that it can handle power changes of, say, 1 percent of full power per second or a similar type of rating. We can see, therefore, that operational power-level changes as a

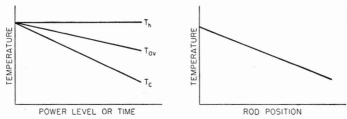

FIG. 9-3. Rod position used as a thermometer for constant-T_h, constant-coolant flow program.

function of time should not have limitations similar to startup range limitations. Instead, percentage change limitations appear more useful.

The maximum reactivity change rate required from the control rods to change level depends directly upon the type of program. For the constant-average-temperature program, with negative temperature coefficient in the reactor, the level change can be made without any rod motion at all. For other programs some maximum rate of reactivity change or rod motion will be needed.

Temperature Changes. Changes in reactor temperature can cause changes in reactivity and vice versa through the temperature coefficient effect. We can see that the control-rod position can actually be used as a thermometer for short-term variations once the temperature coefficient is established. We might use an example with the constant-T_h constant flow program such as is given in Fig. 9-3. As power-level changes are made, T_{av} is changed, thus causing a reactivity change and ultimately a shifting of control-rod position to compensate for this temperature shift. If the reactor in question has a temperature coefficient of $10^{-5}\delta k/°F$ and a control-rod worth over a small range can be considered linear and worth

$10^{-5}\delta k$ per inch of motion, then this control rod as a thermometer has the calibration of 1°F per inch of motion.

Pressure Changes. If the reactor plant system is of the pressurized type, using gas or water as a moderator, changes in pressure can also cause changes in reactivity. Reactivity pressure coefficients are usually quite small, and they may be either positive or negative.

There are many causes for a pressure change in a reactor primary system. The principal one is likely to be the pressurizer control system. Variations in the pressurizer tank level caused by the local control are reflected back into the reactor. If insufficient damping exists between the pressurizer and the reactor, it is even possible to have an oscillation set up.

In a manner similar to the temperature effect, control rods may also be used as pressure gauges for short-term operations providing the temperature is held constant. For example, if a reactor has a pressure coefficient of $10^{-6}\delta k$/psi and a control rod has a linear effectiveness of $10^{-4}\delta k$/in., then the calibration of this rod in terms of pressure is 100 psi/in.

Depletion. Depletion, sometimes called burnup, does not usually figure as a factor in day-to-day reactor operation. The amount of depletion in terms of reactivity is a major design problem concerned with refueling cycles and how much burnup of fuel is permitted. From an operational point of view the effect of depletion is noted only on a long-time basis. Therefore, rod motions caused by depletion can usually be neglected when compared with those caused by temperature and pressure changes.

Poisons. By far the largest factor in causing rod motion on a steady-state basis is the build-up of poisons. It will be recalled from Secs. 2-14 and 4-4 that these poisons originate chiefly in a thermal reactor from xenon 135 and the concentration varies both at a steady power level and after reactor shutdown. Figure 9-4 indicates how equilibrium xenon builds up during operation at a fixed power level. In this figure, after 8 to 10 hr the xenon reactivity change has reached a fixed limit, but because operation continues at a fixed power level, a small amount of depletion reactivity continues to be lost. In a practical operation one cannot isolate the depletion from the equilibrium poison build-up, and the solid line curve of Fig. 9-4 is the one usually measured experimentally.

Figure 9-5 shows again the familiar xenon build-up and decay curve after shutdown. In the curve shown here the peak xenon builds up to 20 percent in reactivity. It was mentioned under the startup accident that this peak xenon could be burned out very rapidly at full power and that this rate in some reactors constituted a maximum requirement on the rate of change of reactivity. Figure 9-5 indicates this rate of burnout for full power operation and a corresponding burnout rate for a partial power operation.   If we scale this curve, assuming a 20 percent peak xenon, we find that the burnout rate is approximately $7 \times 10^{-5} \delta k/\text{sec}$ for full-power burnout.   It will be noted that in the process of burnout

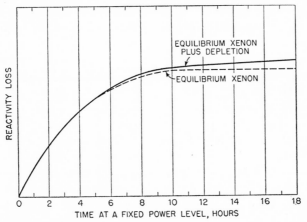

FIG. 9-4. Equilibrium xenon and depletion build-up versus time for a continued fixed power-level operation.

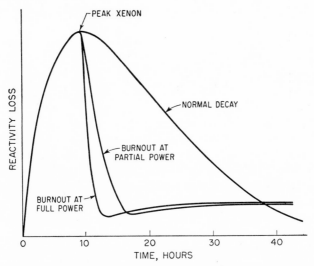

FIG. 9-5. Peak xenon build-up and burnout for different power operations.

for the illustration given, the reactivity change drops below that caused by equilibrium xenon during burnout but, after a long-term steady operation at the burnout rate, equilibrium xenon level is again achieved. The equilibrium xenon depends upon the neutron flux level as indicated in Eq. (2-26).

It can be seen from Fig. 9-5 that the xenon reactivity is constantly changing and calling for rod motion. A good example of how this level changes on a daily cyclical basis can be seen from Fig. 9-6. Here a program is assumed such that the reactor is on for 8 hr a day and turned off for 16 hr. It is assumed that the on time is at full power level and the off time is at 10 percent power level, possibly needed to supply the auxiliary system. The build-up of poison reactivity is given in Fig. 9-6 as a function of this operating schedule. It can be seen that at no time during the 24 hr does the reactivity remain constant.

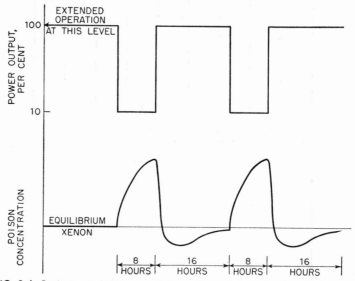

FIG. 9-6. Basic xenon build-up and decay for square wave on-off operation.

Flux Distribution Control. Fundamentally the limit on the power output from a reactor is the same as that of any other large piece of power-handling apparatus. That is, the limitation is apt to be a hot-spot temperature. Reactor flux distribution, hence temperature distribution, greatly depends upon the position of the control rods. It is possible to make a reactor critical with many combinations of control-rod configurations. However, there are certain configurations that lead to so-called flatter flux distributions, and these distributions permit higher power outputs in that the peak-to-average ratio of the flux is minimized. Figure 9-7 indicates some of the flux distributions that can be obtained with a fictitious three-rod slab type reactor. Figure 9-7a indicates the three rods inserted all the way into the reactor, and the flux distribution is examined at a cross section going through the middle of the slab. For this type of rod configuration the flux is apt to be reasonably flat. Figure 9-7b shows the shape of the flux distribution for all the rods out. The shape will be remembered as being roughly of the form of a squared cosine. Figure 9-7c illustrates a situation whereby the two outer rods are in and the center rod is part way out.   The flux distribution here indicates two peaks in the center of the reactor.   Figure 9-7d indicates a tipped flux type of distribution whereby a nonsymmetrical condition is set up.   This is the type of flux distribution which is usually avoided in power reactor operation, and whenever this sort of situation appears, control rods are usually moved to reflatten the flux.   The reactor, of course, can be operated with a tipped flux distribution.   Usually, however, it is necessary

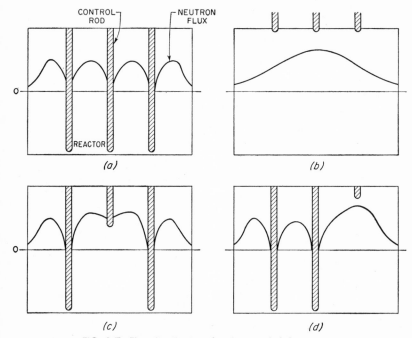

FIG. 9-7. Flux distributions for three-rod slab reactor.

to operate at a lower power output because of the limitation on the hotspot temperature caused at the tipped peak.   Obviously no speed requirement for changing the rods to compensate for flux distribution is involved. An alert operator will occasionally trim rod positions to keep his reactor always in the best possible flux configuration.

9-2. Automatic Control.   The required reactivity rates for power level operation will then be the sum of the six above-mentioned items.   It may seem possible to have all these items add up at the same time and require very large reactivity rates of change.   Actually, the time scales involved are usually quite different.   Programming, temperature, and pressure changes are likely to be on a minute-by-minute basis, whereas the xenon poisoning, which may be the largest reactivity change in a thermal power reactor, has been shown to be on an hour-by-hour basis. In any event, a summation of the above items calls for a maximum rate of change of reactivity to be designed into the control system. If the reactivity cannot be changed fast enough during the xenon burnout, the reactor could conceivably run away.

We have seen from Chaps. 4 and 6 that reactivity rates of change corresponding to given rod motion rates constitute a gain term in a servo loop. If this gain is too high, the system can conceivably oscillate. Therefore the designer is faced with the problem of first summing up all the reactivity rates required by the power-level changes and arriving at a maximum rod motion rate. He then designs a control system in accordance with the natural stability of his reactor and the required program and comes up with a permitted maximum rod motion rate for stability. He hopes that these two numbers overlap in the sense that his maximum permitted reactivity for stability will provide him with plenty of reactivity change rate for his operational and safety requirements. If he has a wide overlap, particularly one that is wide enough to take care of all his variables, including rod effectiveness, his problem is finished. If a suitable overlap does not exist, he has several choices. First, he may redesign the control system or provide proper compensation for this system to permit it to operate at a higher gain. Second, he may insist upon operational restrictions on the way the reactor will be run. For example, if the limiting rate of reactivity is at full power burnup of peak xenon, operational plans might be stipulated that the plant is not to be started up at peak xenon. Or full power burnup will not be permitted at peak xenon, but rather a slower burnup rate must be used. If these operational tactics are not sufficient, a third alternative is available, in that manual overrides in the negative reactivity direction may be permitted. Here, in the event that a combination of circumstances calls for it, rod motion at a faster rate than normal is permitted in the negative reactivity direction on a manual basis.

Regulator Rod. To accomplish automatic reactivity changes one control rod may be designated as a regulator rod. This rod is then tied to the automatic control system loop. The regulator rod is designated as such because it has special characteristics. First, the reactivity in this rod is likely to be limited. Usually under no set of circumstances may this rod be permitted to contain as much as prompt critical in reactivity. This step is taken on the assumption that if the automatic mechanism fails in some manner, prompt critical reactivity or greater cannot be inserted quickly into the reactor. A practical number for the reactivity of a regulator rod such as $0.006\delta k$ may be selected. That is, the maximum rod travel is held to $\pm 0.003\delta k$.

Rod effectiveness is very important in the case of a regulator rod, again because of the local control-loop gain.   Figure 9-8 illustrates a good regulator rod effectiveness setup in that here the regulator rod has a restricted travel to limit its reactivity and its effectiveness does not vary very much over its operating range.   Figure 9-9 illustrates a poor regulator rod setup.   Here the regulator rod is forced to travel above and below

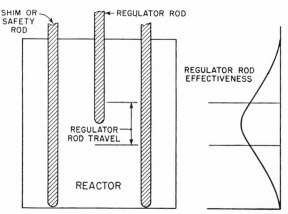

FIG. 9-8. Regulator-rod effectiveness for shim rods all the way in.

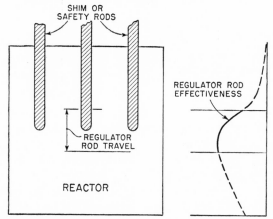

FIG. 9-9. Regulator-rod effectiveness for shim rods part way out.

the position of the adjacent shim rods.   Shadowing effects from one rod to another may be encountered, and the rod effectiveness pattern is apt to cause large variations in loop gain.

Automatic Shim-rod Follow-up.   For most minute-by-minute operations, reactivity in the regulator rod is sufficient to handle operational problems.   When the regulator rod does not have enough reactivity to accomplish a particular required operation, another rod or group of shim rods may be used to follow up the regulator rod. Figure 9-10 crudely illustrates this process. When the regulator rod approaches the end of its permitted travel, switches are closed which operate a control system to cause motion of the shim follow-up rods in the same direction as the regulator rod. In this way the regulator rod will ultimately be returned to its center position with the bulk of the reactivity being supplied by the shim rods. For this type of operation the regulator rod has by far the fastest motion in reactivity change per second. For stability purposes it is usually desirable that the shim-rod follow-up reactivity be at a rate between 10 and 100 times slower than that of the regulator rod.

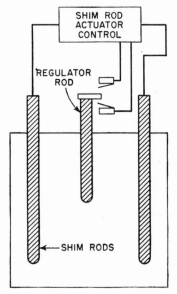

FIG. 9-10. Shim-rod follow-up of regulator-rod movement.

Under special design conditions a rate of only three to four times slower may be used if needed.

Shim rods themselves may be used individually or in banks to provide automatic control with or without a regulator rod. Or any one rod in a bank may be temporarily designated as a regulator rod. After this rod has been fully inserted or extracted, another rod can then take over and be designated as a regulator rod. The principal concern and danger in simultaneous multiple-rod operation are that too much reactivity change rate may be placed in any group or bank of rods. Many types of systems have been proposed to overcome this difficulty in multiple-rod reactors, but none of them has been completely foolproof or satisfactory. One of the safer system designs is shown in Fig. 9-11. Here in a 15-rod reactor, any or all of the rods may be used simultaneously. However, the rod motors are fed from a common power supply which has poor regulation. In this way, as more and more rods are thrown onto the line, the motor speeds become slower and the reactivity rate slows down, with the maximum reactivity rate obtainable being the maximum rate that permits the system to operate safely.

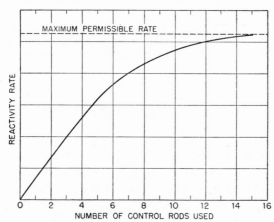

FIG. 9-11. Reactivity rate as a function of the number of rods moved.

REFERENCES

1. Harrer, J. M.: Controlling a Power Producing Reactor, *Nucleonics*, vol. 6, no. 3, p. 58, 1950.
2. Trimmer, J. D., and W. H. Jordon: Instrumentation and Control of Reactors, *Nucleonics*, vol. 9, no. 4, p. 60, 1951.
3. Schultz, M. A.: Automatic Control of Power Reactors, *AECD*-3163, 1950.
4. Cole, T. E.: Design of a Control System for a Low-cost Research Reactor, *Nucleonics*, vol. 11, no. 2, p. 32, 1953.
5. Commonwealth Edison et al.: "Reports to the United States Atomic Energy Commission on Nuclear Power Reactor Technology," Government Printing Office, Washington, May, 1953.
6. Moore, R. V.: The Control of a Thermal Neutron Reactor, *Proc. Inst. Elec. Engrs. (London)*, vol. 100, pt. 1, p. 90, 1953.
7. Glasstone, S., and M. C. Edlund: "The Elements of Nuclear Reactor Theory," D. Van Nostrand Company, Inc., New York, 1952.

CHAPTER 10

OPERATIONAL CONTROL PROBLEMS: SHUTDOWN

As has been pointed out, it is really impossible to shut off a reactor once it has operated at any power level. Shutdown does not mean removing the power to an amount that cannot be read by thermal instruments but rather means shutting down to some sort of neutron-source level. There are two types of shutdown that are of interest. One is the normal reactor shutdown; the second is a shutdown under duress, the so-called scram. Normal shutdown is a prosaic operation. The operator merely inserts the control rods at their usual rate, and the neutron-power level falls off reasonably fast at first and then ultimately settles down to falling off at the delayed neutron period of 80 sec. The problem which is of much more interest is that of enforced shutdown. A scram has been defined before as a violent insertion of control rods in an effort to cut down the neutron level as quickly as possible.

In this chapter only enforced types of shutdowns will be discussed. Shutdown philosophy and fundamentals of scram protection will be examined. Once these ground rules are laid down, there will be a brief discussion of possible accidents and finally some of the elementary circuit configurations used in scramming protection systems will be presented.

10-1. Shutdown Philosophy. There are two basic approaches that are used in the development of a shutdown philosophy. The most prevalent at this writing has been mentioned in Chap. 1 and is a semipolitical approach. It is based upon the need of protecting a reactor plant at all costs. Nuclear power plants differ from conventional power plants or chemical plants in that an accident in a nuclear power plant would have severe political repercussions as well as create local physical damage. Because of this fact, the designers of all reactors to date have been extremely safety conscious. As a matter of fact, this safety consciousness is actually required by law. The use of scramming systems stems directly from this all-pervading need to protect the plant, coupled with the additional factor that in early nuclear power plants many of the possible operational hazards were obscure. The scram therefore provides an excellent hedge in satisfying legal requirements and as a contingency against possible unknowns.

The second philosophy, with a diametrically opposed objective, is based on the need for providing continuous service. As with the case of a radio broadcasting station, the nuclear power plant must be kept "on the air" at all times. If the nuclear plant is being used to supply electric power to a consumer, the consumer expects to find voltage in the receptacle every time he plugs into it. The excuse that the reactor has just been scrammed because a pump failed would hardly satisfy him.

We have, then, the objectives of two philosophies. The first philosophy says that the reactor must be saved in all failure events. Any plant failure, any significant auxiliary component failure, or any item that could conceivably cause radioactivity to get out into the atmosphere must be so interconnected with the reactor control system that the reactor is always shut off as quickly as possible. The second philosophy is the one whereby each component in the plant system must be able to take care of itself. If the turbine fails, it must protect itself; if a pump fails, means must be provided for throwing another pump on the line. If a reactor fails, it either must be designed so as to be able to protect itself internally or it must have a local protective system. It is fairly apparent that as the nuclear industry progresses, the tendency will be away from the first philosophy and ultimately toward the more conventional second type.

In any event, a great deal of thought must be given to protecting the reactor regardless of whether the reactor sits alone or is a component of a complex plant. Three basic situations are involved, all of which can be related. The first type of incident that may require the shutting down of a reactor is that sort of incident which may be caused by catastrophe, sabotage, or military action. As the first large-scale nuclear power plants are to go aboard naval vessels, it is most conceivable that during the course of the operation of the vessel, naval action might rupture the plant system. In cases of this sort, where the primary loop may be violently torn apart, there really is not very much that can be done toward saving the reactor and a discussion of scramming systems is futile. Minor damage may possibly be relieved by scramming.

The second situation that may require a scram consists of a class of accidents which can be prevented by cutting down reactivity quickly. Accidents involving improper operation or malfunctioning of the control rods, accidents whereby malfunctioning of an auxiliary system might reflect back into the reactor, and any conceivable accident that creates a rapid neutron rise may be prevented by proper rod motions or scramming techniques. The distinctive fact about these accidents is that a neutron-power level is involved. If the neutron-power level can be shut down, the accident might be avoided.

A third set of conditions that may be hypothesized are incidents involving the reactor and its structure, but not the neutron level. A good example of this type of accident may be as follows: Let us assume that in a nuclear power plant the coolant through the reactor is suddenly lost for some reason. The reactor may be shut down neutronwise, either by the loss of the coolant or by scramming the rods, but the reactor might still be burned up by the excessive power coming from the beta-gamma radiation. This power has been indicated as $P_t \approx 0.07 P_0 / t^{0.2}$ where P_0 is the long-time power level in watts and P_t is the beta-gamma power t sec after shutdown.[12] A large power reactor might not be able to dissipate even a small fraction of its normal power output without designed coolant conditions, and thus the reactor might destroy itself even though the neutron level had been shut off most satisfactorily by a scramming system.

The large majority of conceivable accidents are of the second type, that is, the one in which the accident might be prevented by cutting down reactivity quickly. Philosophically, it can also be argued that it does no harm whatever to shut down the neutron level quickly in the event of any real accident. We shall therefore consider in some detail this situation of quickly lowering the neutron level.

We have the further choice of three subphilosophies to consider in preventing accidents: (1) fast insertion of control rods, (2) slow movement of reactivity, and (3) continuous monitoring of the neutron level. We shall discuss each of these types of operation below.

Fast Rod Insertion. Operating on the basis that a fast rod insertion is needed, we can examine the requirements of safety rods. We have previously considered the requirements for normal speed of travel of control rods and found that there was usually a direct basis for setting this speed. This basis was that each particular operating condition called for a given maximum and minimum rate of change of reactivity. In the case of safety rods, however, the approach historically has been a reverse one. Rather than asking: What are the requirements of a scramming system? the question is: How fast can one actually insert rods of a given type into a reactor? This rate being the best obtainable has then become the actual requirement. The time interval involved in starting the movement of the rods and the rate of motion of the control rods are severely restricted by mechanical considerations. Control rods are apt to be relatively heavy pieces of neutron-absorbing material. Insertion time limits in decades are likely to fit into the sort of pattern given below. To insert rods into a reactor in say 10^{-3} sec is likely to be impossible. To assure getting rods fully inserted in 10^{-2} sec would probably require explosives. To assure getting the rods into the reactor in 10^{-1} sec would require a very complicated mechanical design, but to get the rods into the reactor in 1 sec is relatively simple and probably would not require more than a gravity drop. It can be seen, therefore, that most practical scramming systems based on this reverse requirement will have an insertion time between 0.1 and 1 sec. Fast rod insertion requirements will gradually drift toward a more positive approach wherein the question is asked: What is actually needed by way of scramming speed to protect the plant adequately?

Slow Changes of Reactivity. Every reactor control designer has a mental plaque over his desk that reads: "If nothing is permitted to move fast, there can be no fast accidents." This statement refers to control rods, turbine controls, valve openings, or power-level changes. Any device that is inherently capable of quickly changing a plant loop parameter has the possibility of malfunctioning and causing a fast accident.

In Chaps. 4 and 6 it was emphasized that automatic controls should be made as slow as possible. In Chap. 8 it was pointed out that in the case of a startup accident, if reactivity were changed at a slow enough rate, the natural protection of a temperature coefficient was sufficient to safeguard a plant without the use of a scram. The simple corollary is that any reactivity rate of change should never be more than the protection system can safely shut down.

There are two reasons why the ideal safe-slow condition does not usually exist in a practical design. First, in order to be absolutely safe, operational maneuvers such as startup would take a very long time. If a plant required several hours to start up, its utility in a generating system or naval vessel might be questionable. Actually, from a safety point of view a plant that takes a long time to start up is not quite so safe as first appears. It has been shown that in startup operations which take longer than an hour or two, in which the operator sees effectively nothing happening, he sometimes feels compelled to do something about it. He examines his instruments and comes to a false conclusion that possibly the plant is far more subcritical than it actually is. If such a conclusion is drawn and the operator makes a mistake, severe accidents are possible. For this reason, unless the plant is fully automatic, the control designer sadly shakes his head at the realization that his plant may be safer if he makes its controls just a little faster.

The second reason for faster control, particularly in the negative reactivity direction, is that despite the fact that everything about the plant may be designed to move slowly, there are just some unknown accidents which conceivably could create a fast condition. The fear of the consequences of such an accident causes a scram or some other means of fast negative reactivity insertion to be designed into the system.

Continuous Monitoring and Correction. The third method of plant protection consists of always watching the neutron level with fast instrumentation and always having available fast means of taking corrective action.   If a period becomes too fast or any rapid movement is made in the plant, control rods are always available to initiate instantaneous corrective action.   Levels are not particularly involved.   It is period that is carefully watched.   Any fast rate of change involves a fast rate of change in the opposite direction.

This system suffers from the same difficulty as the previous ones; that is, the failure of a fast corrective circuit is apt in itself to create a fast accident.

10-2. Fundamentals of Scram Protection.   The environmental usage of fast safety rods will now be examined.   In an actual reactor plant some rods may be specifically designated as safety rods and others as control rods.   Another system which might be used is that all rods might be safety rods.   They are then withdrawn completely at startup, and the reactor obtains power-level variations through the negative temperature coefficient.   Still another more versatile setup exists whereby any rod may be either a safety rod or a control rod, depending upon its electrical circuit connections.

Let us examine a startup example involving a rod system of this third type.   Assume that a reactor has 16 rods and each rod is independently worth 2 percent in reactivity.   In a practical case the rods probably would not be independent in that the position of any one rod would affect the worth of the others.   The amount a reactor is shut off when all the rods are inserted is usually not known precisely because of the variations possible from temperature and poison.   Assume, for our example, that the shutoff reactivity range is from 10 to 30 percent in negative reactivity. Let us see what proper rod manipulations might be.   If it were known at all times exactly what the shutdown reactivity was, the problem would be a simple one.   Take the case of a 10 percent negative reactivity shutdown.   Here, if we desired to start up our reactor, the proper rod movement sequence might be that four rods would first be withdrawn and reconnected as a safety rod bank.   The rule to adopt is that the safety bank should always contain rods worth more in reactivity than those which are capable of being moved in the reactor at any one time.   To provide some safety overlap we would then be permitted to move only a maximum of three control rods when we have four of equivalent worth in the safety bank.   Practically, we might not wish to move three rods at a time, as it is recognized, for this example, that the reactor would go critical before three rods moved very far.   However, the electrical or mechanical interconnections should be such that with four rods out of the reactor, only three should be permitted to move.   As a matter of fact, conservative design dictates that possibly only two rods should be permitted to move, because the hypothesis may be made that the mechanism for one of the safety rods might have failed.

If it is known that the reactor in our example is subcritical by greater than 18 percent, a safer situation exists in that nine rods may be pulled out during startup to be used as the safety bank. Then, regardless of how many other rods are moved in the reactor, there is always more reactivity in the safety bank than can be taken out of the reactor by improperly maneuvering control rods.

Unfortunately, unknown reactivity, loading, control-rod worth, and poisoning usually exist. Proper instrumentation can give a feel for where the reactor is, but as has been shown in Chap. 7, there are so many variables which can affect the instruments that, at the present state of the art, only a very rough idea is available in most reactors as to the exact shutdown status. The only obvious safe type of startup operation then, of the sort attempted above, is where each rod is gingerly removed at a safe rate and committed to be a safety rod on the way up or as soon as it is withdrawn.

In some power reactors it may be possible to "load" the reactor so that it is always known that a given number of rods are capable of overriding the loading. Under these conditions, after a reactor has been shut down, the safest operating condition is to extract immediately sufficient rods to override the complete excess reactivity placed in the reactor by the loading. Where this step is possible, safety rods are then cocked and ready for any startup mishap. Startup accidents are likely to occur in getting ready for startup in the process of cocking safety rods, particularly if the safety rods are capable of moving fast. It is rather intriguing to realize that a reactor is probably safer with some of its rods out than with all its rods all the way in.

The question has not been discussed as to what constitutes a safe shutdown. There is, of course, no universal agreement for all reactors. Some number between 2 and 10 percent is generally agreed upon as being a minimum safe value. It will be remembered that 2 percent in negative reactivity represents a neutron multiplication of 50.

Scramming Parameters. In considering the type of scram protection system that should be set up for a given reactor plant, the first fundamental which is encountered is that manual scram is always permitted. That is, regardless of the condition of the plant or the status of its operating cycle, an operator seeing anything peculiar always has the choice of turning the reactor off. Large scram buttons are placed convenient to the operator at his control console, and in some installations scram buttons are placed around the control room, particularly close to exit doors.

The most common type of scramming system is the so-called overpower-level scram. Figure 10-1 indicates the operation that is involved. It is assumed that for some reason the reactor gets on a fast period, the curve of Fig. 10-1 being for a 0.1-sec period, and the power level of the reactor quickly goes through the power range up through rated full power to an arbitrary trip level. The trip level is indicated in this figure at 120 percent of full power, but this level may be set at any convenient point. When the power level hits the trip level, an electrical signal is given out which usually has to pass through such devices as a detecting instrument, an amplifier, and a relay. The relay closes a set of contacts, and rod motion is started. There is a time delay between when the power level hits the trip level and when the rods actually start to move. Figure 10-1 indicates that even when there is no time delay of this sort, there probably is some overshoot above the trip level because the power

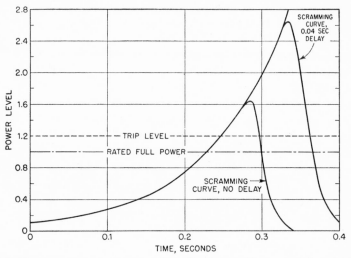

FIG. 10-1. Overpower scramming operation. Reactor on 0.1-sec period, and trip level at 120 percent full power.

level is moving fast, and a certain minimum amount of reactivity has to be inserted by the rods before the slope of the power curve is turned around. In other words, even with no delay time, the peak power level reached will overshoot the trip level and a direct proportionality is usually involved, that is,

$$P_{\text{peak}} = KP_{\text{trip}} \qquad (10\text{-}1)$$

where K is a function of the reactor period, the design of the scramming mechanism, and the rod worths. It will also be noted from Fig. 10-1 that even a small delay of a mere 40 msec is sufficient to cause a tremendous difference in peak power. Actually, however, it is not the peak power that is destructive but rather the energy that is involved. The energy in this case is the area under the curve in watt seconds. When the energy gets above a given amount, the plant is damaged. The energy is also usually directly related to the trip level.

$$E = K_1 P_{\text{trip}} \tag{10-2}$$

for a given reactor on a given period. Because energy and peak power are thus related, through Eqs. (10-1) and (10-2), it is usually simpler to describe accidents in terms of peak power rather than energy.

As far as limiting these peak excursions is concerned, it is most important, as can be seen in Fig. 10-1, to cut down on the time delay involved in the detection process and in the actuator mechanism. Having a large amount of negative reactivity available to insert into the reactor at a fast rate is also important. Figure 10-2 roughly indicates the effect of scramming speed upon peak power attained for a level trip operation similar to that of Fig. 10-1. Here a fixed small time delay is presupposed, and it

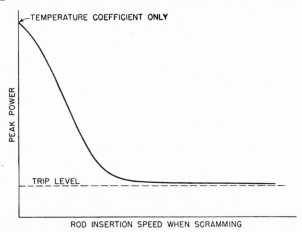

FIG. 10-2. Peak power attained versus rod speed when scramming. Level trip with fixed time delay. Reactor on fixed period at trip level.

can be seen that without any scramming speed whatever, the peak power reached by the reactor would ultimately be set by temperature coefficient considerations alone. This figure does not indicate whether or not this peak power would correspond to a destructive energy release. As rod insertion speed is increased, the peak is steadily brought down to a value very close to the trip level.

Figure 10-2 can also be interpreted as saying that in designing a scramming mechanism against a rising level accident of this sort, there is no point in designing the mechanism to move faster than a given amount. Above a given rod speed the peak power reached always is roughly the same. The major problem is usually one of taking every millisecond possible out of the delay time and starting the rods moving as quickly as possible. Rod speed is generally a secondary consideration. However, studies of this sort are needed for many types of accidents if one is to design a scramming mechanism on any basis other than as fast as possible.

Period Scram. We have seen that one of the difficulties with level scrams is that if they are fixed at a comparatively high level, they permit the power level to attain momentum and overshoot the trip point. A period scram, particularly in the source and period ranges, is more useful. If the reactor starts to change its power level at a too-fast rate, the reactor may be scrammed at a comparatively low level and the cause of the difficulty located. Period scrams are not too useful in the power range, as has been pointed out in Chap. 9. In this range the reactor is quite safe using a level scram, as short periods cannot usually be attained between levels that are close together.

The setting of the period scram trip point is not too important and depends upon the type of reactor. Period scram settings between 1- and 10-sec periods are in common usage.

Although period scram circuits are usually arranged to trip on positive periods, some reactor designers set their circuits to trip also on fast negative periods. The reasoning behind this setup is that if the reactor power level is moving fast in any direction, there must be something wrong with the reactor system and consequently it should be shut down and checked. The disadvantages of period circuits have been pointed out before.[1] These disadvantages exist because the period circuits are inherently subject to circuit noise and, because of the time constants involved, they are apt to give out erroneous answers in certain types of power-level changes. These disadvantages, coupled with complex circuitry, sometimes outweigh the advantages of period circuits, and consequently many attempts have been made to eliminate them.

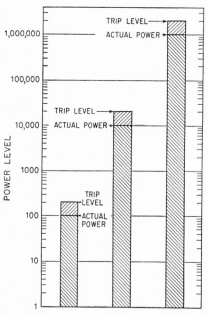

FIG. 10-3. Variable level scramming system operation. Trip level twice actual power level.

Variable Level Scrams. One system which at first appears to have the advantages of a period scram without being one is the so-called variable level scram. Its operation can be seen from Fig. 10-3 and is as follows: Regardless of the power level of a reactor, a scram level is automatically set up a given amount above this actual power level. This amount above the actual power level can be on a linear percentage or logarithmic basis.   Then if the level of the reactor were to move slowly, the variable level scram would move with it.   That is, let the power level be at 100 units and the variable level scram initially set to trip at 200 units.   If the power level were to move slowly to 1,000 units, the variable level scram would follow and automatically set itself up at 2,000 units.   On the other hand, if the power level were to change quickly, the variable level scram would be designed so as not to be capable of changing particularly fast, and consequently the power level would run into the tripping level for a fast operation.

A crude elementary circuit for performing this type of manipulation is indicated in Fig. 10-4.   Let us assume that the power signal, either linear or logarithmic, is converted into voltage and applied simultaneously to the grid and cathode of a vacuum-tube circuit.   In the plate circuit of the vacuum tube is a scramming re-

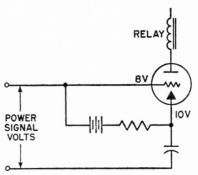

lay, and the current relationships are arranged so that the relay will close when the grid and cathode voltages are, for example, 1 volt apart.   A biasing battery is placed in the grid-cathode circuit so that normally the grid and cathode voltages differ by 2 volts.   In the example indicated in Fig. 10-4, the grid circuit is at an absolute level of 8 volts and the cathode circuit at 10 volts.   Conse-

FIG. 10-4. Elementary variable level scramming circuit.

quently, there is insufficient current available to close the relay and no scramming signal is given.   A time constant network is inserted in the cathode circuit, and in the event that power signal changes are very slow, the capacitor involved charges up to the signal level plus the battery voltage.   The grid and cathode voltages then effectively move together for slow changes.   In the event a fast voltage input change is involved, the grid circuit changes directly but, because of the time delay, the cathode circuit lags.   Consequently, a trip will occur when the grid voltage and cathode voltage are separated by the required 1 volt.

It can be seen that circuits of this type are not dependent upon the power level but rather are dependent upon the rate of change of power level.   This is exactly the condition of a period circuit.   As a matter of fact, when most continuously variable level trip circuits are analyzed, it turns out that they are really period circuits masquerading under another name.

Multiple Fixed Level Scrams.   Another useful type of scramming circuit of practical importance, particularly in startup problems where manual operation is involved, is the multiple fixed level scramming circuit. It will be recalled that the difficulty with fixed level scramming is that the reactor has the possibilities of attaining a short period by permitting its power level to rise unchecked over several decades. The multiple fixed level scram system is indicated in Fig. 10-5. Here fixed scram levels are placed at convenient intervals, in this figure at every decade. Manual operation of the reactor is presumed in startup. As

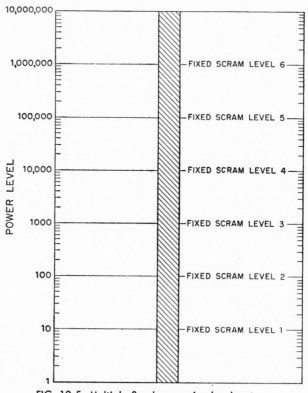

FIG. 10-5. Multiple fixed scramming level system.

the reactor power level is brought up and fixed scram level 1 approached, the operator checks to see that everything is under control and operating properly. He then manually switches off fixed scram level 1, permitting the reactor level to go up. As fixed scram level 2 is approached, a similar process is gone through, and so on. In the event that the reactor gets away, an early fixed scram level will catch it.

Other Types of Input Signals. Until now we have been discussing scrams created by neutron signals. As neutron level and power are directly related, this method provides an excellent means of keeping the reactor in check. However, if the philosophy is adopted that any major difficulty in the plant shuts off the reactor automatically, other types of input signals must be used. Some of these signals, such as a temperature signal in the primary loop, can usually be related to power level, but there may be a long time constant involved in the process. Some of the most frequently considered types of external scramming signals other than neutron-level, period, or manual signals are listed below.

1. Excessive core temperature
2. Excessive outlet coolant temperature
3. Excessive inlet coolant temperature
4. Low system pressure
5. High differential pressure across reactor
6. Pump failure
7. Electrical system power failure
8. Control-rod coolant system failure
9. Radioactivity level in secondary system too high
10. Radioactivity level in building too high

There are many other devices of this sort, all of which may be an indication that something is wrong in the plant. Generally, when a listing of devices that can shut off a reactor becomes too long, it is found that the cause of the shutoff is a malfunctioning of the device itself.

Rod Effectiveness. When examining reactor startup and reactor power-level operation, we found that rod effectiveness was a very important variable. For reactor shutdown problems as well, rod effectiveness plays an interesting role. The effectiveness of a shutoff rod enters in the following manner. Let us assume that we have a reactor situation in which the safety rods are fully withdrawn and their normal scram insertion method is by gravity drop. When the rods are fully withdrawn, we can further assume the situation given in Fig. 10-6. Here a reactor system is postulated in which the normal travel of the safety rods is 100 in. Figure 10-6a indicates rod position versus time for a simple gravity drop containing no friction. Of course, the rods start slowly and gradually increase speed. The rod effectiveness versus position will be assumed to vary as the simple $\int \sin^2 x\, dx$ as previously used and shown in Fig. 10-6b. Again the first several inches are useless as far as inserting much negative reactivity into the reactor is concerned. And when one combines these two effects of the initial slow rod movement rate and the low initial rod effectiveness, one obtains the curve of Fig. 10-6c. Here it is quite evident that the first 200 msec in time are practically worthless in bringing negative reactivity into the reactor. This type of rod ineffectiveness behaves very much like an additional delay in the scramming circuit, and in situations such as that of Fig. 10-1, for example, a delay of 200 msec would be disastrous.

There are two methods that may be used to combat this initial ineffectiveness of the scramming rods. A simple expedient would be not to pull the rods all the way out but to leave them partially inserted. In the situation of Fig. 10-6, if the rods were pulled out to within 20 in. of the top, a loss of only 10 percent of the total reactivity would be involved.

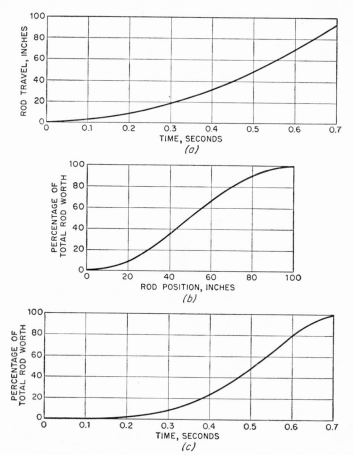

FIG. 10-6. Rod effectiveness in a gravity drop scramming situation. (a) Rod position versus time. (b) Rod worth versus position. (c) Rod worth versus time.

Unless the reactor in question had very little excess reactivity to spare, this would not be serious. However, in starting from 20 in. from the top, even on a gravity drop, substantial reactivity would be available quite quickly.

The second solution is not to use a simple gravity drop but instead to use some device such as a spring or pneumatic actuator, as shown in Sec. 5-4, to start the rods fast. For the first few inches the rods might be designed to attain a high initial velocity and then gravity permitted to take over. A curve of the resultant operation is indicated in Fig. 10-7. Here the reactivity, as a function of time, starts off in a satisfactory manner. It is not important that the reactivity insertion rate slows down from the initial rate because once the peak power has been contained, the slope of the power versus time curve in most accidents will remain negative.

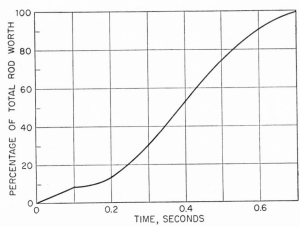

FIG. 10-7. Rod effectiveness versus time for initial motion accelerated.

10-3. Accidents. It has been pointed out previously that there are really three categories of accidents which can exist about a reactor plant. These categories are (1) catastrophes of sabotage or of a military nature from which there is no protection scheme whatever available—a scram was deemed advisable in this case merely because it could do no harm and might possibly do some good; (2) accidents involving means of protection other than scramming—loss of coolant was used as an example of this type of accident, whereby some form of additional reactor cooling, either in design or operation, had to be provided to prevent the accident; (3) accidents involving reactivity changes directly or reflected. Here neutron levels were involved and scramming would or would not be desirable, depending upon how fast the level was changing.

This third category breaks up into two classes: first, those classes of accidents which a large reactor negative temperature coefficient would limit and, second, those classes of accidents which a large negative temperature coefficient would assist. The example we have been using for an accident that a large negative temperature coefficient would limit is the startup accident or any similar type of accident whereby the neutron level is capable of rising quickly. The reactor negative temperature coefficient helps to limit this accident, because as the neutron level rises, the average temperature of the reactor system rises. Consequently, negative reactivity is inserted into the reactor, which is thus ultimately made subcritical and turned off.

The larger the temperature coefficient for this type of accident the better. The larger the temperature coefficient, the smaller will be the peak power level reached by the reactor, and conversely, for a given permitted peak power level, shorter periods may be used at any level or faster rod motions may be employed safely.

The new case that we wish to discuss is the one whereby the larger the temperature coefficient, the worse the situation. Let us examine an accident which we shall call the cold-coolant accident. Assume the following situation: A reactor plant is operating at its normal temperature when for some reason flow connections are made that would suddenly

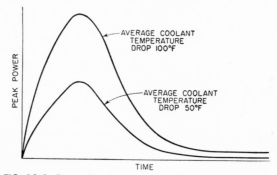

FIG. 10-8. Power level versus time, cold-coolant accident.

switch new coolant into the system from an external storage tank. If the new coolant is presumed to be at room temperature or at some temperature lower than the normal reactor operating temperature, the entrance of the new coolant into the reactor would cause the reactor average temperature to fall. This drop in average reactor-coolant temperature would now insert positive reactivity into the reactor, and the neutron level would rapidly rise. It is conceivable that this level would rise so fast and so far that even normal rod motions, plus the later action of the negative temperature coefficient as the coolant again is heated, would not be able to protect the reactor.

The amount of average temperature drop occurring and the rate of change of this temperature drop are both involved in the severity of the accident. The total temperature drop, however, is the most important parameter, as this represents the total amount of reactivity that must be overcome before the accident can be restrained. Figure 10-8 illustrates the relationship between power level and time for given average coolant temperature drops in which cold coolant is inserted at a fixed rate. These curves are very similar to those of Chap. 4, which showed various amounts of reactivity inserted into a reactor at specified rates. Obviously, the smaller the negative temperature coefficient, the less will be the reactivity change for a given temperature difference between the original average temperature and the final average temperature.

It can now be seen that if one again establishes a given protection power level above which the reactor will be damaged and below which it will be safe, for every value of the temperature coefficient there exists a corresponding reactor-coolant average temperature drop which a given type of protection system will safely handle. Figure 10-9 illustrates this situation. If one assumes that the protection level is a power level, as was

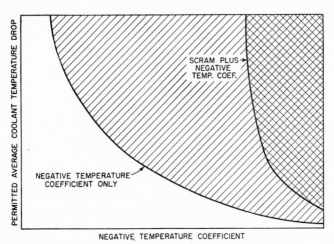

FIG. 10-9. Permitted changes in coolant temperature as a function of temperature coefficient and type of protection system.

done with the startup accident, then, at a constant rate of change of coolant temperature, the lower curve illustrates the area that may be used, as a function of permitted coolant temperature drop when the temperature coefficient is the sole means of protection against the accident. On the other hand, if a scram is also available as protection, far larger coolant temperature changes may be handled at any given temperature coefficient.

Figure 10-9 is similar to that of Fig. 8-15 on startup accident protection. However, for the startup accident the larger negative temperature coefficient gave better protection, but in the case of the cold-coolant accident, the smaller negative temperature coefficient gives better protection. It is evident, then, that an overlapping range of optimum values of negative temperature coefficient should exist for handling these two types of accidents. Figure 10-10 illustrates the area of permitted temperature coefficient variation to cover the startup accident and the cold-coolant accident for a given reactor plant. An optimum value very clearly exists.

It will be recalled that for automatic control purposes an optimum temperature coefficient situation also existed. A too high value of negative temperature coefficient would create instability and cause the system to oscillate. A too small value of negative temperature coefficient would create a poor transient response and possibly xenon-poisoning oscillations.

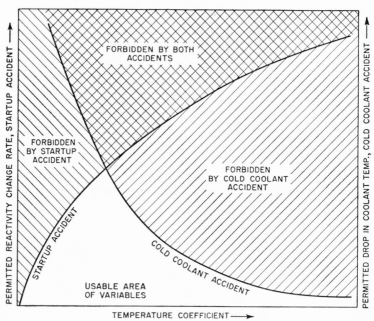

FIG. 10-10. Optimum range of temperature coefficient to prevent startup accident and cold-coolant accident.

10-4. Alarms and Cutbacks. Scramming is quite a severe operation. In fact, the act of scramming, because of the violence involved, might cause damage either to the control rods or to the surrounding structure if done too frequently. Therefore, whenever possible, it is desirable to limit or ward off accidents by means other than scramming. This generally is done by providing slower means of protection. Some of these slower protections are listed below in order of increasing effectiveness.

1. Sounding or lighting up an alarm. This means permits the operator to determine what has actually happened and then to perform a minor correction if he deems it necessary.

2. Stop all rod motion. It has been shown that in many cases the negative temperature coefficient is sufficient to handle certain classes of

accidents provided that additional complications are not introduced by rod motion. For a reactor with a high negative temperature coefficient, automatically stopping rod motion is usually a safe condition.

3. Permit rod motion in the negative reactivity direction only. Regardless of whether the automatic control or the operator wants to perform a given function, once this safety condition is switched in, only negative reactivity can be obtained.

4. Automatically cause rods to move into the reactor at their normal rate. This condition is sometimes called reverse.

5. Cause rods to move inward at a faster rate than normal. This condition is sometimes called cutback. It is not a scram situation, as the rods are driven inward either by the normal control motor with different excitation or by a separate motor with different gearing or clutching. Rod insertion rates of between two and ten times normal extraction rates can usually restrain most accidents.

6. Scram. As previously described, this is the condition of inserting the rods as quickly as possible.

Any given reactor system can use some or all of these devices, and they may be used in two ways. The first method is a parallel sort of operation whereby a given accident or a class of accidents can be assigned a given type of correction. For example, if an electrical interlock connection is broken, an alarm might be shown. If a pump fails, a slow inward rod motion might be called for, and so on.

The second system is a series operation in which the weakest type of correction in the system is always used first and then the corrective action progresses to more drastic types of protection if the severity of the accident continues to increase. For example, in the case of overpower protection, a sequence of the following type might be applied.

1. 105 percent power level—alarm

2. 110 percent power level—rod motion frozen

3. 120 percent power level—fast cutback—rods inserted above normal rate

4. 130 percent power level—scram

These two systems are generally used in combination. Examples of the systems presently employed are given in the literature.[2] The difference in performance between the various types of protection systems is indicated in Fig. 8-15 for the startup accident.

10-5. Last-ditch Emergency Shutoff Measures. Because of the destructive capabilities of a reactor plant, most power reactors have last-ditch backup safety devices which operate in the event that all of the above-mentioned types of protection fail. These failures are presumed to be from catastrophic causes such as explosions, earthquakes, or military action. The assumption is made that the reactor or control-rod mechanisms have been distorted or destroyed and that it is desirable to bring the reactor to the lowest possible state of subcriticality. It is conceivable, for example, that a control-rod passage might be blocked and the reactor otherwise be in reasonably good condition. Several methods have been mentioned as being used for last-ditch shutoff. The insertion of chemicals with high-absorption cross sections and the use of boron shot injected into control-rod passages are feasible. For reactors of the water boiler type, it is also possible to dump out the fuel into an auxiliary tank having a safe geometry. For reactors that have separate moderator and coolant, the moderator might also be dumped. The Oak Ridge graphite moderated reactor employs boron shot, whereas the Brookhaven reactor contains a means of injecting liquid trichlorobenzene into tubes in the reactor. The Canadian NRX reactor can have its moderator removed.

The speed of control required for a last-ditch emergency action usually is not fast. Presumably the damage has already been done. All the safety methods have been tried. These devices should not be triggered in without some thought because of the difficulty entailed in the reverse operation of cleaning the poison out of a system. Times in the order of 1 min to 1 hr could be used. The requirement for slow operation stipulates the use of manual devices. These devices are desirable because the catastrophe is likely also to have caused a power failure. Thus manual pumps or manually operated dump valves may be used.

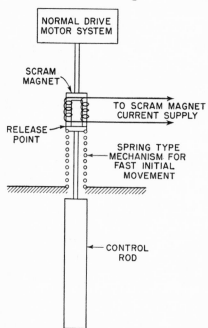

FIG. 10-11. Elementary scramming mechanism.

10-6. Scramming Circuits. Because of the emphasis placed upon scramming in many reactors, some of the elementary forms of circuits that are used to actuate a scram mechanism will now be examined. Some of the requirements of these scramming mechanisms have been presented in Chap. 5, and it is the feeding circuits driving these mechanisms that will now be examined.

Most scram actuators are schematically of the form of Fig. 10-11. The control rod is connected to the normal driving mechanism by means of a magnet. The scramming operation consists of releasing the control rod from the direct drive and causing the rod to be accelerated as quickly as possible into the reactor.   The point of release is the scram magnet, and this magnet is normally energized.   Either the current through such a magnet may be an on-or-off proposition, or in some circuits the condition is brought about that as the plant approaches an unsafe condition, the current through the release magnet is reduced toward the tripping point in some proportional manner.

Each control rod generally has its own magnet releasing system.   However, these rod magnets may be connected together on one or more common power supplies.   Three types of magnet feeding circuits will be described: the relay type, the magnetic-amplifier type, and the electronic type.

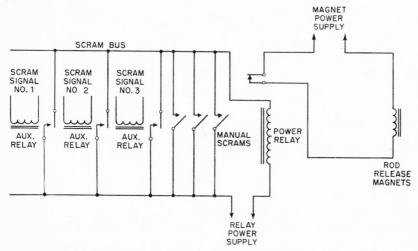

FIG. 10-12. Poor relay-type parallel feed scramming signal circuit.

Relay-type Scramming Feed Circuits.   One of the simplest types of rod release magnet feed circuits is the relay parallel feed arrangement.   This circuit is shown schematically in Fig. 10-12.   This is an on-off type feed and may be used with any number of rods or any number of input scramming signals.   Because of the fact that the rod release magnets will usually require considerable power, an auxiliary power relay may be necessary to disconnect the magnet circuit.   This type of power relay is generally quite slow.   A scramming bus is provided, to which any number of devices may be connected to close the power relay circuit, thus causing a scram.   Auxiliary relays would be used for most scramming signals except for manual scramming.   Those auxiliary relays shown in Fig. 10-12 normally have current through them and thus keep open a back-contact type of circuit.   Manual scrams may be placed in the auxiliary relay circuit or the power relay circuit, depending upon the power-handling capacity of the manual switches.

This is a poor type of circuit for several reasons.   From a safe failure point of view, the power relay circuits, requiring current to release the control-rod magnets, are backward.   Safe failure requires that when the power fails for any reason, the rods should scram.   In Fig. 10-12 the auxiliary relays are connected properly in that if their power supply fails, they close the scramming circuit.   Back contacts are used throughout this sort of circuit.   This is not considered good relay practice, as back contacts generally have less pressure available than front contacts.   The over-all circuit is quite slow because the auxiliary relays and the power relay are effectively in series.   The time delays in both relays add up,

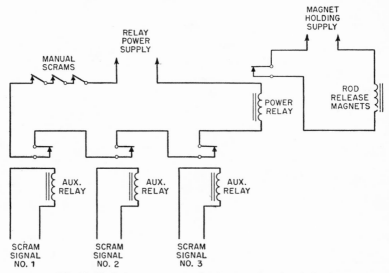

FIG. 10-13. Relay-type series feed scramming signal circuit.

and as has been pointed out in this chapter, time delays must be kept to a minimum.   The time-delay problem is accentuated by the fact that the power relay must be closed rather than opened to scram the circuit.   For usual relay design, opening a circuit is slightly faster than closing it.

A much better relay circuit is shown in Fig. 10-13.   Here all the auxiliary relay contacts are normally closed and are connected in series.   The power relay is normally operated with current through its coil, and a power failure of any sort releases the magnets.   Front contacts are used throughout, but two relays are still in series, which means that this is still a slow type of circuit.

Magnetic-amplifier-type Scramming Circuits.   In addition to the above difficulties, relays have other troubles.   Problems of contacts sticking, welding, or needing frequent cleaning make relays not too desirable. Vacuum-tube circuits are very fast and very versatile, but they are subject to occasional failures. Consequently, for utmost in reliability, magnetic-amplifier types of circuits are used. Magnetic-amplifier relays may replace electromagnetic relays on a one-to-one basis, or the unique

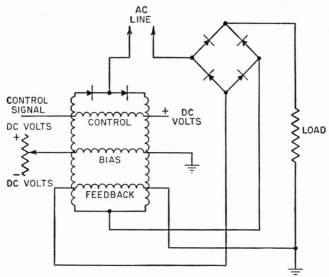

FIG. 10-14. Magnetic-amplifier relay circuit.

characteristics of magnetic-amplifier relays may be exploited to eliminate the equivalent of many relay contacts.

Figure 10-14 shows an elementary magnetic-amplifier relay circuit. Many more complex circuits are also available.[3] The circuit of Fig. 10-14 contains an input control winding fed by some d-c control signal such as the current from an ionization chamber. The output load current can be at either a very low or a very high value, depending upon the control-signal current. Figure 10-15 illustrates the load current as a function of the control-signal current. Feedback is applied to the magnetic amplifier in such a manner that its core operates either unsaturated or at complete

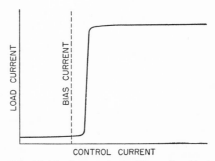

FIG. 10-15. Magnetic-amplifier relay load current versus signal current.

saturation. The load current is caused to shift abruptly from one condition to another as a function of signal current. A bias level is set up whereby the relay may be placed as close to the tripping point as desired.

The magnetic-amplifier relay, in common with other types of relays, has a hysteresis effect which is not shown in Fig. 10-15.

A scramming circuit employing a magnetic-amplifier power relay is indicated in Fig. 10-16. Here the current to the rod release magnets is either all on or nearly off, depending upon the state of the magnetic-amplifier power relay. The control winding of the power relay is fed from load windings of an auxiliary magnetic-amplifier relay, and the scramming signals are fed into a scramming bus via isolating diodes.

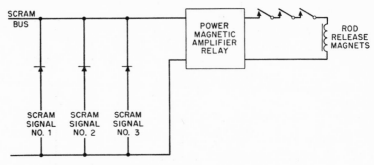

FIG. 10-16. Magnetic-amplifier relay scramming signal circuit.

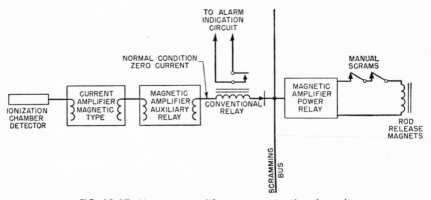

FIG. 10-17. Magnetic-amplifier scram protection channel.

These diodes are provided to prevent a scram in the event that any of the magnetic amplifiers feeding the scramming bus inadvertently shorts out.

The speed of operation of a magnetic-amplifier relay depends upon the frequency of its a-c power supply. Magnetic-amplifier relay closure times are measured in cycles of the primary excitation frequency. A closing time of 2 cycles or better can usually be obtained. This statement implies that for extremely fast-acting relays, high-frequency power supplies should be used and 400- and 800-cycle supplies are common.

Figure 10-17 shows a complete protection channel from an ionization chamber employing magnetic-amplifier relays. The current from the detector is amplified directly in a conventional magnetic-amplifier relay. The normal condition for the auxiliary relay is to supply minimum load current. The auxiliary relay feeds a scramming bus through the coil of a conventional electromagnetic relay, which is employed only to indicate which channel has caused the scram. The auxiliary relay is also isolated from the scramming bus by means of a rectifier. The scramming bus now feeds the power magnetic-amplifier relay which is biased so that its load current is normally on. This load current feeds the rod release magnet, and manual scrams are provided in the output circuit. A chan-

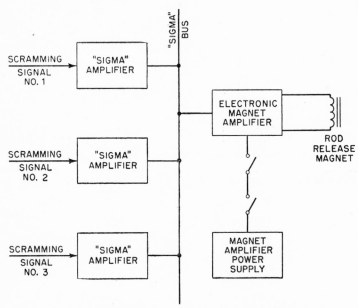

FIG. 10-18. Electronic scramming system block diagram.

nel of this sort may be constructed from conventional components operating at 400 cycles/sec and will have an over-all time delay from detector signal to rod motion of less than 60 msec.

Electronic Scram Circuits. When the utmost in scramming speed is desired, electronic circuits are generally used. To take advantage of the high speed obtainable from these circuits, special magnets with quick release times must also be designed. In the use of electronic circuits, problems concerned with safe failure are magnified. Direct-coupled tube circuits are generally used and so designed that a maximum amount of protection against tube failure is provided. The electronic type of relay circuit is usually of a proportional type rather than on-off. However, because of the versatility of these circuits, combinations of proportional and nonlinear operation can be easily provided.

Figure 10-18 shows a simplified block diagram of the basic type of circuit. Here, using the terminology originating at the Oak Ridge National Laboratories, a so-called sigma or summation bus is set up, which is fed from a group of summation amplifiers.[4,5] This summing bus in turn feeds a magnet holding amplifier of a vacuum-tube type. Because of the large current requirements, more than one magnet is usually not connected to a magnet amplifier. The current to the rod release magnet is a rectified alternating current, and the output tubes of the magnet amplifier are fed from a separate transformer. Manual scrams and other low-power interlocks may be inserted by controlling the primary voltage to this transformer. Obviously, if this primary voltage fails, the system scrams.

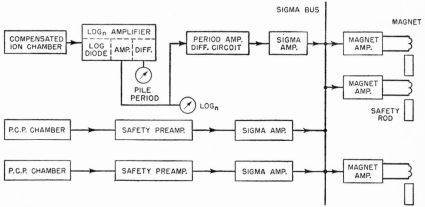

FIG. 10-19. Research reactor scramming system block diagram. (*Courtesy of Gilbert Goss, Radiation Counter Laboratories.*)

The amplifiers supplying the current to the magnets can be controlled from a mixing circuit. The output of the scramming signal detector is fed into the mixer which can accept signals from several sources. The mixer may operate in such a manner that a constant output signal is produced until the reactor approaches some dangerous condition. Then the output of the mixer becomes proportional to the largest signal applied to it. The current through the release magnet is set to release the rods at a given level. As a dangerous condition is approached, the magnet current will remain approximately constant until the tripping point is nearly reached. Then the current may be arranged to drop nonlinearly and sharply through the tripping point.

Figure 10-19 shows an elementary block diagram of a period and level safety circuit of this type for the Oak Ridge "swimming pool" research reactor. One period circuit and two level circuits are shown. The PCP chambers referred to in this diagram are parallel circular plate uncompensated ionization chambers. Channels of the sort indicated in Fig. 10-19 have been constructed with an over-all time delay from the detector to rod motion of less than 40 msec.

REFERENCES

1. Wade, E. J.: Instruments Used with Experimental Reactors, "Convention Record of the IRE 1954 National Convention," pt. 9, "Medical and Nuclear Electronics," Institute of Radio Engineers, New York, 1954.
2. Stephenson, R.: "Introduction to Nuclear Engineering," McGraw-Hill Book Company, Inc., New York, 1954.
3. Geyger, W. A.: "Magnetic Amplifier Circuits," McGraw-Hill Book Company, Inc., New York, 1954.
4. Cole, T. E.: Design of a Control System for a Low-cost Research Reactor, *Nucleonics*, vol. 11, no. 2, p. 32, 1953.
5. Trimmer, J. D., and W. H. Jordon: Instrumentation and Control of Reactors, *Nucleonics*, vol. 9, no. 4, p. 60, 1951.
6. Cochran, D., and C. A. Hansen, Jr.: Instrumentation for a Nuclear Reactor, *Nucleonics*, vol. 5, no. 21, p. 4, August, 1949.
7. Los Alamos Scientific Laboratory: An Enriched Homogeneous Reactor, *Rev. Sci. Instr.*, vol. 22, p. 489, 1951.
8. Dahl, A., and G. Randers: Heavy Water Reactor at Kjeller, Norway, *Nucleonics*, vol. 9, no. 5, p. 5, November, 1951.
9. Colmer, F. C. W., and D. G. Littler: Gleep: Design, Construction, and Use, *Nucleonics*, vol. 8, no. 1, p. 3, 1951.
10. Breazeale, W. M.: The "Swimming Pool," a Low-cost Research Reactor, *Nucleonics*, vol. 10, no. 11, p. 6, November, 1952.
11. Goss, Clinton G.: Reactor Control Instruments, "Proceedings of the 1953 Conference on Nuclear Engineering," University of California Press, Berkeley, Calif., 1953.
12. Lansing, N. F., (comp.): The Role of Engineering in Nuclear Energy Development, *AEC Report TID*-5031, p. 417.

CHAPTER 11

SIMULATORS

The transient response of nuclear reactors and their associated power plants cannot usually be obtained by direct analysis because of the numerical complexity involved. As we have seen in Chaps. 4 and 6, the solution of several simultaneous differential equations is needed, and the transient solution of these equations is most easily accomplished by means of analogue computing machinery. Special-purpose computing machines for the solution of reactor plant problems are called simulators because their performance approximates very closely that of an actual plant. Simulators are also useful to test the controls of a given plant in advance of its construction. That is, the simulator may be treated as though it were the plant and actual controls connected to it, sometimes by means of transducing elements. The complete control performance of a plant, its instrumentation, and its external feedbacks can thus be studied.

In this chapter we shall first briefly review elementary analogue computing techniques. Then we shall use these techniques to examine the forms of reactor and plant kinetic simulators. However, before the reader attempts the construction of any such device, it is recommended that a more detailed study be made of analogue computational methods.[1,2]

It must also be kept in mind that the simulators will be no better than the actual equations which they simulate. If the plant is treated kinetic-wise as a point source in a black box, the approximations in the equations will show up as approximate answers in the output of the simulator.

11-1. Elementary Analogue Computing Techniques. Kinetically many physical systems obey the same mathematical patterns. For example, exponential decay is exhibited by the decay of radioactive materials, the cooling of a thin metal sheet, the deceleration of mass in a viscous fluid, and the discharge of a capacitor through a resistor. The dimensionless equations of these actions exhibit the same form, and any one can be used to predict the performance of the others. Therefore any of these processes may be said to be the analogue of any one of the others.

Another definition of a simulator, then, might be that a simulator is a convenient system used to duplicate the action of an inconvenient system. The most convenient present-day type of simulator is the electrical or electronic simulator. Electrical quantities are easily and accurately measured. Electrical components are comparatively inexpensive and can be rapidly manipulated to simulate a great variety of natural phenomena. Electrical quantities can also induce mechanical motion and hence can be transformed into solenoid displacement or motor rotation. Conversely, mechanical motion can be transformed into an analogous electrical quantity through use of generators or other means. Or both mechanical and electrical systems can be used together in one simulator.

There are two types of electrical or electronic arrangements that are generally used. These are passive electrical networks and operational amplifier techniques.

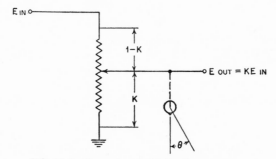

FIG. 11-1. Elementary multiplication process.

Linear Passive Elements. Electrical circuitry uses three basic linear passive elements: the resistor, the capacitor, and the inductor. The currents through these elements as a function of the voltage across them are given as $I = E/R$, $I = C(d/dt)E$, and $I = 1/L \int_t E \, dt$. The impedance of any of these elements or combination of them is defined as $Z = E/I$. Pure inductances are difficult to construct because of the finite amount of resistance and shunt capacitance in the windings. Large values of inductance also are nonlinear with current. Consequently, most analogue computing networks avoid the use of inductance and only resistive or capacitive passive circuit components are generally used.

Nonlinear passive elements when needed can generally be simulated by a diode or group of diodes. These devices are sometimes called function generators.

One other element, the coefficient potentiometer, is in common usage to provide simple multiplication. Figure 11-1 indicates the process of multiplication in an elementary potentiometer circuit. The potentiometer tapoff, which is usually proportional to an angular displacement of the potentiometer shaft, modifies directly the input voltage so that $E_{out} = KE_{in}$. Servomotors may be used to position the arm of a potentiometer. Multiplication of two or more changing variables is usually an inaccurate process, and the equations are rewritten whenever possible to avoid such multiplications.

Operational Amplifier Techniques. The basis of the design of most simulators depends upon the concept of the operational amplifier. In order to understand the operation of analogue computers properly, an understanding of operational amplifier technique is essential. Linear passive networks may be connected together in combination, and solutions to problems obtained. However, practical passive components unfortunately load each other in the interconnection process, and consequently the equations must be modified to take this loading into account. This loading usually creates extreme complications and inaccuracies. Therefore the operational amplifier is essentially a device designed to prevent loading effects, but because of its unique properties, other valuable computing features can also be obtained.

Ideally, an operational amplifier is a direct-coupled amplifier with a gain of 1,000 or more and a frequency response such that no instability occurs in the circuit when negative feedback networks are connected around the amplifier. In the design of an operational amplifier it is also customary that the amplifier have no zero offset; that is, the output for zero input is zero volts. The output is usually able to swing through a range of at least 100 volts centered around zero. For the purposes of unloading interconnecting elements and accurate computation, one of the most critical features is that the amplifier should have as high an input impedance as possible and a low output impedance.

Figure 11-2 indicates a typical nonstabilized type of operational amplifier. By "nonstabilized" is meant that the stability of the amplifier is obtained through the stability of all its components and power supplies alone. A stabilized operational amplifier has superimposed a-c circuitry for correcting amplifier drift and is used when higher precision is needed. In the amplifier of Fig. 11-2 the first stage is cathode coupled, giving the effect of a high-impedance cathode follower input. The grid of the second stage is used for two purposes. First, by applying a small voltage, usually $\frac{1}{2}$ volt or less, to this point, it is possible to compensate for any zero offset caused by variation in tubes and component tolerances. Second, since this point is separated from the output by an even number of inverting stages, positive feedback can be conveniently applied here to raise the effective gain of the amplifier to a very high value. This increased gain is used, as will be seen, to increase the accuracy of computation.

The third stage is coupled to the second stage directly by means of a voltage divider, and a similar network is inserted between the third stage and the output stage. Capacitors are used to compensate for the input capacitance of the tubes in order to extend the basic frequency response

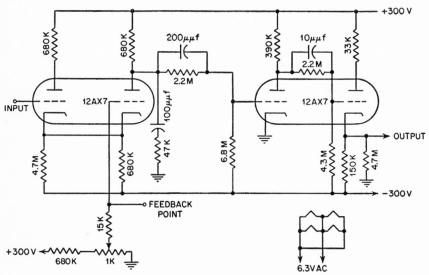

FIG. 11-2. Schematic diagram of nonstabilized operational amplifier.

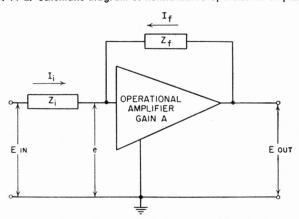

FIG. 11-3. Generalized operational amplifier circuit.

as far as possible. To prevent oscillations when feedback is connected around the amplifier, a network to attenuate the high-frequency response at the rate of 6 db per octave is used. The output stage is a cathode follower to give the necessary low-impedance output. The use of negative feedback in conjunction with this type amplifier will usually further reduce the output impedance.

Figure 11-3 shows a typical generalized operational amplifier circuit as it is used in computational work. Associated with the amplifier is an input impedance Z_i and a feedback impedance Z_f. Both of these terms may be functions of frequency and can be treated in Laplace notation as $Z_i(s)$ and $Z_f(s)$. Kirchhoff's law for Fig. 11-3 can be written as

$$E_{\text{in}}(s) = I_i(s)Z_i(s) + e(s) \tag{11-1}$$
$$E_{\text{out}}(s) = I_f(s)Z_f(s) + e(s) \tag{11-2}$$
$$E_{\text{out}}(s) = -Ae(s) \tag{11-3}$$

where the voltages are as indicated on the diagram.

The input impedance of the amplifier is considered to be infinite. Consequently, the current $-I_f(s)$ must equal $I_i(s)$. Rewriting and combining Eqs. (11-1), (11-2), and (11-3) result in

$$I_i(s) = -I_f(s) = \frac{E_{\text{in}}(s) + [E_{\text{out}}(s)/A]}{Z_i(s)}$$
$$= -\frac{E_{\text{out}}(s) + [E_{\text{out}}(s)/A]}{Z_f(s)} \tag{11-4}$$

$$\frac{E_{\text{out}}(s)}{E_{\text{in}}(s)} = -\frac{Z_f(s)}{Z_i(s)}\frac{1}{1 + \dfrac{1}{A}\left[1 + \dfrac{Z_f(s)}{Z_i(s)}\right]} \tag{11-5}$$

Equation (11-5) is the transfer function of the operational amplifier and its associated circuits, and usually the gain of the amplifier A is very high, so that the transfer function reduces to the simple form

$$\frac{E_{\text{out}}(s)}{E_{\text{in}}(s)} = -\frac{Z_f(s)}{Z_i(s)} \tag{11-6}$$

The operational amplifier can be used as a computing tool by the use of discrete networks for $Z_f(s)$, and $Z_i(s)$ and/or by using multiple inputs. When multiple inputs are used,

$$E_{\text{out}}(s) = -\sum_{k=1}^{n} E_{\text{in},k}(s)\frac{Z_f(s)}{Z_i(s)} \tag{11-7}$$

By proper use of Eqs. (11-6) and (11-7) many basic forms of computation can be accomplished. Figure 11-4 indicates some of the more common operations. Figure 11-4a indicates the process of summation. It will be noticed again that the gain and the characteristics of the amplifier have nothing to do with the process, and the accuracy of the computation depends only upon the accuracy of the individual resistances and input voltages. Because of the inverting action of the amplifier, a minus sign usually occurs for most output processes. The sign may be reversed quite simply by applying the output of one operational amplifier system to another operational amplifier which has equal input and feedback resistances. The output of the second amplifier will then give an inverted answer directly, on a one-to-one basis. Figure 11-4b indicates the process of integration. Integration is a very stable and accurate process, providing the drift of the amplifier and the leakage of the capacitor C_f are low.

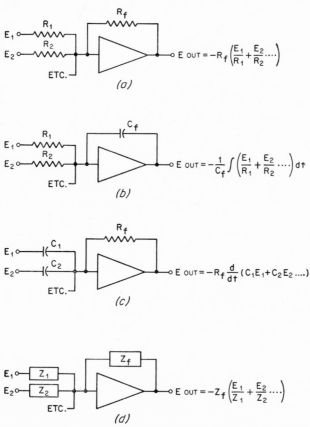

FIG. 11-4. Elementary forms of computation circuits using operational amplifier techniques. (a) Summation. (b) Integration. (c) Differentiation. (d) Generalized multiple input solution.

Care must be taken in selecting only the highest quality capacitors for this usage. Figure 11-4c indicates the process of differentiation. This process is not commonly used, particularly when the equations may be manipulated to place them in a form where integration can be used. Figure 11-4d shows the generalized multiple input solution.

For some of the servomechanism type analyses it is desirable to simulate directly elementary transfer functions. Figure 11-5 indicates some of these network simulations. In operational form Fig. 11-5a indicates a simple lag network in which

$$\frac{E_{\text{out}}(s)}{E_{\text{in}}(s)} = -\frac{R_f}{R_{\text{in}}}\frac{1}{1 + R_f C_f s}$$

Figure 11-5b, similarly, is the simulation of a lead network whereby

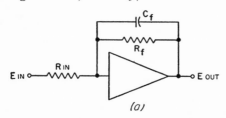

(a)

$$\frac{E_{\text{out}}(s)}{E_{\text{in}}(s)} = -\frac{R_f}{R_{\text{in}}}\frac{R_{\text{in}}C_{\text{in}}s}{1 + R_{\text{in}}C_{\text{in}}s}$$

Figure 11-5c indicates a combination network providing elementary lead and lag of the form

$$\frac{E_{\text{out}}(s)}{E_{\text{in}}(s)} = -\frac{R_f}{R_{\text{in}}}\frac{1 + R_{\text{in}}C_{\text{in}}s}{1 + R_f C_f s}$$

There are many other combinations available to the designer.[1]

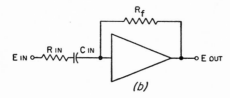

(b)

From these simple examples it can be seen that the transfer function of an operational amplifier circuit can be matched to the transfer function of most pieces of physical equipment and a voltage that follows the same equations as the input to the equipment may be applied to the input impedance. The output voltage then will follow the equations of the equipment output. This, then, is the basis of operational amplifier technique and circuitry to simulate given pieces of apparatus.

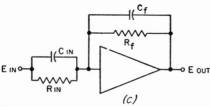

(c)

FIG. 11-5. Operational amplifier simulation of typical transfer functions. (a) Lag network. (b) Lead network. (c) Lag lead network.

11-2. Reactor Kinetic Simulators.† There are a number of reactor kinetic simulators mentioned in the literature.[3-6] These simulators vary in their complexity, depending upon the approximation to the physical reactor that is used. For servo transient problems it is usually not necessary to approximate the internal physical constants of a reactor in much detail. Instead, the basic reactor kinetic equations that we have been using in this text will usually prove to be sufficient. The manner in which the power level of a reactor will increase or decrease depends upon

† The derivations in the next three sections follow closely the original work of W. Pagels in Ref. 4 and other, unpublished, references.

the past history and the effective multiplication factor of the reactor. We may use the familiar reactor kinetic equations to describe this kinetic performance. However, the reactor kinetic equations must be rewritten and put into a more suitable form for computer operation as follows:

$$\frac{dn}{dt} = \frac{\delta k - \beta}{l^*}\, n + \sum_{i=1}^{6} \lambda_i C_i + S \tag{11-8}$$

$$\frac{dC_i}{dt} = \frac{\beta_i n}{l^*} - \lambda_i C_i \tag{11-9}$$

remembering that $\beta = \sum_{i=1}^{6} \beta_i$, combining the two equations, and multiplying by l^*, we have

$$l^* \frac{dn}{dt} = \delta k n - l^* \sum_{i=1}^{6} \frac{dC_i}{dt} + l^* S \tag{11-10}$$

Equation (11-10) is now much more convenient for a computer solution. In order, therefore, to have some idea as to the form of the networks

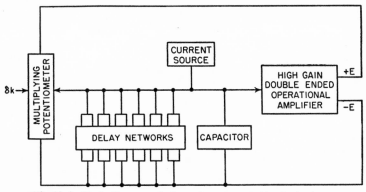

FIG. 11-6. Block diagram of elementary reactor kinetic simulator.

that will be used to simulate a reactor, Fig. 11-6 indicates in block form an elementary pile simulator. The potentiometer, delay networks, current source, and differentiating capacitor are the computing elements corresponding to the mathematical operations that are indicated in the kinetic equations. The voltage output of the operational amplifier is double ended, giving out two voltages which are equal in magnitude and opposite in sign. An adding bus is provided which is connected to the input grid of the amplifier. When the gain of the amplifier is very high, any voltage on the adding bus causes the output voltage to vary in such a manner as to reduce this input voltage to zero. All dependent voltages must then vary in accordance with the mathematical operations described by the feedback circuits as previously indicated. The system may be made regenerative or degenerative, depending upon the setting of the reactivity multiplying potentiometer.

Figure 11-7 indicates the elementary circuit networks that perform the operations mentioned above. The amplifier output voltage E represents ζn where ζ is a convenient proportionality constant which will be used to assist in setting the values of the electrical components. In this instance

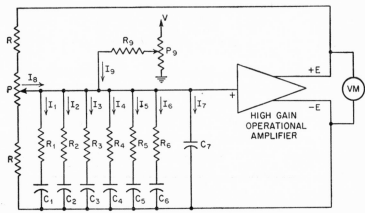

FIG. 11-7. Schematic diagram of elementary reactor kinetic simulator.

ζ has the dimensions of volts per neutron. From Fig. 11-7 we can simulate the performance of Eq. (11-10) by currents flowing into a junction point such that Kirchhoff's second law is obeyed. Then

$$I_7 = I_8 - \sum_{i=1}^{6} I_i + I_9 \tag{11-11}$$

We can now proceed to derive the simulator constants and scaling factors for each term of Eq. (11-10).

The left-hand term of Eq. (11-10) is represented by the capacitor c_7 which produces a current proportional to the time derivative across it. If the voltage E represents ζn, the current

$$I_7 = c_7 \frac{dE}{dt} = \left(\frac{\zeta c_7}{l^*}\right) l^* \frac{dn}{dt} \tag{11-12}$$

The symbol c will be used to denote capacitance in order not to confuse it with the symbol C, delayed-neutron concentration. The term enclosed in the parenthesis is a scaling factor having the dimensions amperes per neutron.

The first term on the right-hand side of Eq. (11-10) is the reactivity term and is simulated by the circuit involving R and P. The magnitude of the current I_8 is dependent upon the setting of the potentiometer tap on P, the voltage E, and the ohmic values of R and P.

Let D be the proportional distance of the potentiometer tap from the center of the potentiometer. D would then be zero at the center, $+1$ at the $+E$ end, and -1 at the $-E$ end. Because of the amplifier action, the tap remains at an essentially zero potential for any D.

By direct network analysis the current flowing from the potentiometer tap is

$$I_8 = \frac{DE}{R[1 + (R/P) + (P/4R)(1 - D^2)]} \tag{11-13}$$

When the tap is at either extreme end of the potentiometer, I_8 is a maximum for any given E. The maximum current in Eq. (11-13) is given when $D = 1$. We can then set the range of simulated reactivity variation of the simulator and the proper scaling factors by the following method: If we set the ratio $\delta k/\delta k_{max}$ equal to $I_8/I_{8,max}$ and note that

$$I_{8,max} = \frac{E}{R[1 + (R/P)]} \tag{11-14}$$

then
$$I_8 = \frac{E}{R[1 + (R/P)]} \frac{\delta k}{\delta k_{max}} \tag{11-15}$$

if again we represent the voltage E by ζn then

$$I_8 = \left\{ \frac{\zeta}{R[1 + (R/P)]\delta k_{max}} \right\} \delta k n \tag{11-16}$$

where the term in the braces is the scaling factor.

The summation terms in Eq. (11-10) are simulated by a group of six resistance-capacitance delay networks. The equation describing the voltage for any of the ith-type network is

$$E = \frac{Q_i}{c_i} + R_i \frac{dQ_i}{dt} \tag{11-17}$$

where Q_i is the capacitor charge in coulombs. This electrical charge is analogous to the storing of delayed neutrons in the fission fragments before they are emitted. The corresponding delayed-neutron equation that this circuit is to represent is Eq. (11-9) rearranged so that

$$n = \frac{l^*}{\beta_i} \lambda_i C_i + \frac{l^*}{\beta_i} \frac{dC_i}{dt} \tag{11-18}$$

Matching Eqs. (11-17) and (11-18) term for term and again introducing the proportionality constant $E = \zeta n$, we find that

$$Q_i = \frac{\zeta l^*}{\beta_i R_i} C_i \quad \text{and} \quad R_i c_i = \frac{1}{\lambda_i} \tag{11-19}$$

for Eq. (11-17) to be the same as Eq. (11-18).

The current contributed by each simulated group of delayed neutrons then becomes

$$I_i = \frac{dQ_i}{dt} = \left(\frac{\zeta}{\beta_i R_i}\right) l^* \frac{dC_i}{dt}$$

$$= \left(\frac{\zeta}{\beta_i R_i}\right) \beta n - \left(\frac{\zeta}{\beta_i R_i}\right) l^* \lambda_i C_i \tag{11-20}$$

In this way the quantity in the parenthesis is a scaling factor which can be made the same for all i species.

The sum of all the delayed currents is

$$I_1 + I_2 + I_3 + \cdots = \sum_{i=1}^{6} I_i \tag{11-21}$$

Then

$$\left(\frac{\zeta}{\beta_i R_i}\right) l^* \frac{dC_i}{dt} = \left(\frac{\zeta}{\beta_i R_i}\right) \beta n - \left(\frac{\zeta}{\beta_i R_i}\right) l^* \sum_{i=1}^{6} \lambda_i C_i \tag{11-22}$$

where $\beta_1 R_1 = \beta_2 R_2 = \beta_3 R_3 = \cdots = \beta_i R_i$.

The last term of Eq. (11-10), the source term, is simulated by introducing an independent current, I_9, into the adding bus. From Fig. 11-7, if R_9 is large compared with P_9, the current through R_9 is given as

$$I_9 = \frac{D_9 V}{R_9} \tag{11-23}$$

where D_9 is the fraction of P_9 tapped off and V is a constant voltage source. If D_9 is used to represent S/S_{max}, then

$$I_9 = \left(\frac{V}{R_9 S_{max} l^*}\right) l^* S \tag{11-24}$$

Now using Eq. (11-11) we can sum up the currents into the adding bus and find that

$$\left(\frac{\zeta c_7}{l^*}\right) l^* \frac{dn}{dt} = \left\{\frac{\zeta}{R[1 + (R/P)]\delta k_{max}}\right\} \delta k n - \left(\frac{\zeta}{\beta_i R_i}\right) l^* \sum_{i=1}^{6} \frac{dC_i}{dt}$$

$$+ \left(\frac{V}{R_9 S_{max} l^*}\right) l^* S \tag{11-25}$$

which now is of the same form as Eq. (11-10).

In order for the output current of each term to be of the correct magnitude the scaling factors of each term must equal each other. That is

$$\frac{\zeta c_7}{l^*} = \frac{\zeta}{R[1 + (R/P)]\delta k_{\max}} = \frac{\zeta}{\beta_i R_i} = \frac{V}{R_9 S_{\max} l^*} \qquad (11\text{-}26)$$

When these electrical quantities are set up, the scaling factors in Eq. (11-25) drop out and the equation of the simulator is the same as that of the reactor. The scaling factor, of course, can be set at any theoretical value, but limiting values are set to a large extent by such practical considerations as insulation leakage, stray capacity, and amplifier grid current. The currents caused by these effects must be small compared with the computing currents.

The above method outlines the design principles behind an elementary reactor kinetic simulator. Many such devices have been built, and complete circuits as well as the details of practical operation are given in the literature.[3-6]

These kinetic simulators may be operated by themselves in an open-loop condition, or they may be connected by means of control circuits into closed-loop configurations. From the open-loop operation one can obtain kinetic response curves such as those of Figs. 3-3 and 3-4. In the closed-loop situation, transient responses of a reactor control system can easily be obtained.

11-3. Subcritical Reactor Simulator. A simple variation on the reactor kinetic simulator just described is possible when problems involving negative reactivity only are being studied. For these cases a very wide range simulator may be designed which requires no active elements. This type of simulator is useful for shutdown problems, and the simulator of Sec. 11-2 may be quickly modified to this form by removing the operational amplifier and modifying the multiplying potentiometer. By eliminating the amplifier, only passive elements remain in the circuit, noise is minimized, and drift and extraneous source currents are eliminated.

Figure 11-8 shows the form of this simplified subcritical reactor simulator. The delay networks and prompt neutron capacitor are simulated as before, and a high-voltage power supply is used to feed these networks through a switch S_1. The equations of this circuit with the switch S_1 open are

$$\frac{E}{R_k} + c\frac{dE}{dt} + \sum_{i=1}^{6} \frac{1}{R_i}\left(E - \frac{Q_i}{c_i}\right) = 0 \qquad (11\text{-}27)$$

where

$$\frac{1}{R_i}\left(E - \frac{Q_i}{c_i}\right) = \frac{dQ_i}{dt} \qquad (11\text{-}28)$$

and the symbols have the same meaning as given in Sec. 11-2.

The values of the elements are given by

$$E = \zeta n \qquad R_k = \frac{1}{Y(-\delta k)} \qquad c = Yl^*$$

$$Q_i = Y\zeta l^* C_i \qquad R_i = \frac{1}{Y\beta_i} \qquad c_i = Y\frac{\beta_i}{\lambda_i} \tag{11-29}$$

The symbols Y and ζ are the arbitrary scaling factors. It will be noted that this particular simulation does not include a source term. If a source is desired, it is necessary merely to feed in a constant current into the adding bus. Substituting the relationships of Eq. (11-29) into Eq. (11-27) results in the original reactor kinetic equation (11-10). These equations obviously hold for negative value of δk, since the value of R_k, the reactivity potentiometer, must be a positive quantity. Without the operational amplifier present, regenerative feedback is not possible.

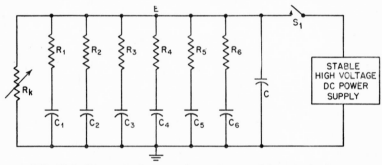

FIG. 11-8. Schematic diagram of negative-reactivity-only simulator.

The method of operation of this simulator is quite simple. For negative step changes in δk, R_k is first adjusted to the desired reactivity step value. The switch S_1 is closed, and all the capacitors are charged up from the high-voltage supply to some initial voltage. When the switch is opened, the voltage decay is analogous to the decay of the neutron population in the reactor after a negative step function of δk is introduced. From Figs. 3-5 and 3-6 neutron decay is rapid at first but decreases slowly after the first few decades. By using a sensitive stable d-c amplifier in a recorder system, this elementary simulator may be used to give accurate answers over a total range of 5 to 6 decades. It also can provide some flexibility in programming by varying R_k with time.

11-4. Xenon Simulator. To illustrate another form of useful simulator, a device for the computation of the xenon poisoning of a thermal reactor will now be discussed. It will be recalled that the effect of poisoning was to reduce the reactivity of the reactor but changes in poisoning occurred on a very-long-term basis. In Sec. 2-14 the equations for the build-up and decay of xenon were described, and these are the equations which will be simulated.

Where the parameters vary very slowly, mechanical analogues are sometimes more suitable than electronic ones. The electronic operational amplifier has good stable characteristics over periods of minutes, but for periods of many hours a mechanical device such as a gearbox may be more satisfactory. For these long-time situations a servo amplifier driving a servomotor can be substituted for the operational amplifier, and the feedback is provided around this amplifier by coupling devices onto the shaft of the servomotor. For example, differentiation is performed by coupling an electric tachometer onto the shaft of the servomotor and the output of the tachometer is proportional to the speed of mechanical rotation.

Again, using simple components we can proceed to design an elementary xenon simulator. The equations describing the number of xenon atoms in a thermal reactor at any time are now repeated in generalized form.

$$\frac{dI}{dt} = \gamma_I \phi - \lambda_I I \qquad (11\text{-}30)$$

$$\frac{dX}{dt} = \gamma_x \phi + \lambda_I I - \lambda_x X - \sigma_x X \phi \qquad (11\text{-}31)$$

The symbols have the meaning previously given in Chaps. 2 and 4. Equation (11-30) describes the rate of production of iodine and its subsequent decay into xenon. Equation (11-31) describes the production of xenon from nuclear fission and iodine decay and its subsequent elimination by natural radioactive decay and neutron absorption.

The schematic diagram for an electromechanical simulator that represents these equations is shown in Fig. 11-9. The action of the circuit is similar to one containing an operational amplifier in that the inputs to the servo amplifiers are held effectively at zero volts with respect to ground. Consequently, no current flows into the amplifiers. The output of each of the two servo amplifiers supplies the voltage for one phase of a two-phase low inertia servomotor. Each of these servomotors drives a tachometer directly and one or two potentiometers through step-down gear ratios N_1 and N_2.

A voltage representing thermal-neutron flux is given by E_1. The current flowing through R_1 is proportional to iodine build-up, while the current through R_2 is proportional to iodine decay. The resistance R_3 passes a current equivalent to the rate of change of iodine concentration.

Similarly, the current through R_4 represents the xenon build-up from the iodine decay while R_6 permits a current proportional to xenon production from the direct fission process. The currents representing xenon destruction by thermal neutrons and natural xenon decay flow through resistors R_5 and R_7, respectively. The resistor R_8 passes a current equivalent to the rate of change of xenon concentration.

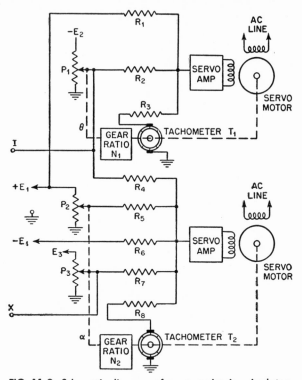

FIG. 11-9. Schematic diagram of xenon poisoning simulator.

Again using Kirchhoff's law for currents flowing into a junction the simulation of Eq. (11-30) is

$$\frac{E_1}{R_1} - \frac{\theta}{\theta_{max}} \frac{E_2}{R_2} - \frac{N_1 K_1}{R_3} \frac{d\theta}{dt} = 0 \qquad (11\text{-}32)$$

where θ = potentiometer rotation in revolutions from the grounded end of P_1

N_1 = gear reduction ratio between tachometer T_1 and potentiometer P_1

K_1 = voltage output per rpm of tachometer T_1

The selection of resistors is such that the effect of potentiometer loading by the resistors should be made negligible. The following additional conditions are imposed:

$E_1 = \zeta\phi$ = voltage representing neutron flux where ζ is a constant having the dimensions of volts per unit flux

$E_2 = K_3 I_{max}$ = voltage representing an arbitrary maximum density of iodine, where K_3 is a constant with the dimensions of volts per unit density of iodine and

$$\frac{\theta}{\theta_{max}} = \frac{I}{I_{max}} \qquad (11\text{-}33)$$

By substituting the above conditions into Eq. (11-32) and rearranging, we have

$$\left(\frac{N_1 K_1 \theta_{max}}{R_3 I_{max}}\right)\frac{dI}{dt} = \left(\frac{\zeta}{R_1 \gamma_I}\right)\gamma_I \phi - \left(\frac{K_3}{R_2 \lambda_I}\right)\lambda_I I \qquad (11\text{-}34)$$

Then adjusting R_1, R_2, R_3, and N_1 so that the quantities in the parentheses are equal to each other, Eq. (11-34) will be like Eq. (11-30). Similarly, the equation for xenon in the simulator is

$$-\frac{\theta}{\theta_{max}}\frac{E_2}{R_4} + \frac{\alpha}{\alpha_{max}}\frac{E_1}{R_5} - \frac{E_1}{R_6} + \frac{\alpha}{\alpha_{max}}\frac{E_3}{R_7} + \frac{N_2 K_2}{R_8}\frac{d\alpha}{dt} = 0 \quad (11\text{-}35)$$

where α = potentiometer rotation of P_2 and P_3 in revolutions from the grounded end

N_2 = gear reduction ratio between tachometer T_2, and P_2 and P_3

K_2 = voltage output per rpm of tachometer T_2

In addition we add the following conditions: $E_3 = K_4 X_{max}$ = voltage representing a maximum density of xenon, where K_4 is a constant with the dimensions of volts per unit concentration of xenon. Finally

$$\frac{\alpha}{\alpha_{max}} = \frac{X}{X_{max}} \qquad (11\text{-}36)$$

Substituting and rearranging, Eq. (11-35) now reads

$$\left(\frac{N_2 K_2 \alpha_{max}}{R_8 X_{max}}\right)\frac{dX}{dt} = \left(\frac{\zeta}{R_6 \gamma_x}\right)\gamma_x \phi + \left(\frac{K_3}{R_4 \lambda_I}\right)\lambda_I I - \left(\frac{K_4}{R_7 \lambda_x}\right)\lambda_x X$$
$$- \left(\frac{\zeta}{R_5 X_{max}\sigma_x}\right)\sigma_x \phi X \quad (11\text{-}37)$$

By adjusting R_4, R_5, R_6, R_8, and N_2 so that the quantities in the parentheses are equal, Eq. (11-37) becomes the same as Eq. (11-31).

From the above simulator equations it can be seen that the derivatives of X and I are proportional to motor speed. Because of the long time constants involved, rather large gearing ratios are required to make use of the full speed range of the motors. Once these gearing ratios are set, however, curves of X and I similar to those of Figs. 2-8, 2-9, and 8-16 can easily be obtained.

This type of xenon simulator may be combined with the reactor kinetic simulator just derived to give a combined thermal-reactor response under poisoning conditions. As the purpose of these simulators is usually to indicate transient response and not stability, the use of this combination is of interest only for problems of many hours duration. Short-term transients do not affect the xenon picture, and consequently the reactor simulator by itself may be used for these transient problems.

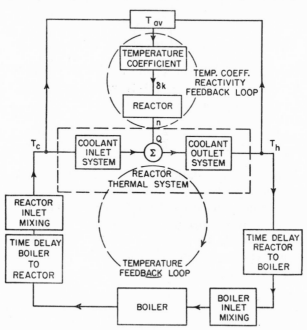

FIG. 11-10. Block diagram of components of nuclear-power-plant example.

11-5. Power-plant Simulators. Having seen what reactor kinetic simulators look like and having examined some of the principles behind their derivation, we can now attempt to set up a simulator describing the kinetic performance of an entire power plant. For simplicity we may use an example and attempt to simulate the fictitious power plant used in Chap. 6. Figure 11-10 indicates the plant we shall duplicate. It will be recalled from this figure that the plant consists of two basic feedback loops: first, a regenerative temperature feedback loop and, second, a degenerative temperature coefficient reactivity feedback loop. The reactor gives out a power level n which is changed into a thermal energy Q. This energy heats up a coolant, and the outlet coolant temperature T_h is warmer than the inlet coolant temperature T_c, with a constant-coolant flow being assumed. There is a time delay involved to transport the coolant from the reactor to the boiler and from the boiler to the reactor. Coolant mixing is assumed in both the boiler inlet and the reactor inlet. The average coolant temperature is formed simply as $(T_h + T_c)/2$. A change in the average temperature causes a change in reactivity of the reactor through the temperature coefficient. This is the system which has been previously described in Chap. 6 and shown to be exceedingly stable over large ranges of negative temperature coefficient.

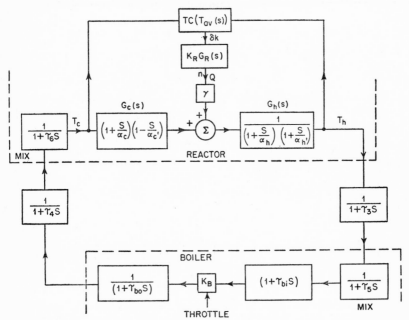

FIG. 11-11. Transfer functions of components of nuclear-power-plant example.

There are two methods of approach to simulating this system. The first method consists of writing the differential equations for all the processes involved. Then from these differential equations appropriate components can be put together to solve these equations, as was done in the case of the reactor kinetic simulator. The second method is to derive the transfer functions for each of the components shown in the block diagram and then to set up the corresponding operational amplifier circuits that match each of the transfer functions. For this example the second method will be used.

Figure 11-11 indicates the transfer functions as previously described in Chap. 6 for each of these blocks. It will be noted that a single point reactor thermal system representation is used. Also the approximate formula for the time delays between the boiler and the reactor are stipu-

lated.   That is, it will be recalled that these transport time delays were
a pure time lag having a transfer function of the form $e^{-\tau s}$.   Upon series
expansion of this function and by using only the first two terms of the
expansion, the transfer function becomes of the form $1/(1 + \tau s)$.

A block diagram of the simulator of the plant represented in Fig. 11-11
is indicated in Fig. 11-12.   In this simulation each section of the plant
is represented directly by its transfer function representation, no attempt
being made to combine transfer functions or components.   In a practical
design combinations of components are obvious and are usually made in

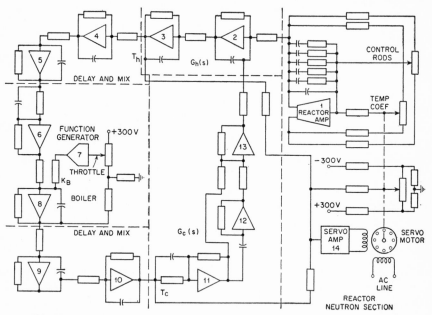

FIG. 11-12. Schematic diagram of simulator for nuclear-power-plant example.

order to minimize the number of operational amplifiers involved.   As
each amplifier has a small amount of drift, the cumulative effect of this
drift should be kept small.   In Fig. 11-12 each operational amplifier is
numbered, but the resistors and capacitor values are only indicated.
Their values, of course, are dependent upon the specific design of the
plant involved.

The simulation starts with the basic diagram of the reactor kinetic
neutron simulator.   The design for this section is similar to that set
forth in Sec. 11-2, with the exception that two resistance networks are
provided to change reactivity.   The first reactivity changing resistance
is labeled "Control rods," and the second one is a similar resistance network marked "Temperature coefficient."   The neutron output of the

reactor feeds the $G_h(s)$ reactor output thermal section which is represented in this diagram as two simple lag terms. These are shown as the circuits concerned with operational amplifiers 2 and 3. The transport delays and the mixing are also indicated as elementary resistance and capacitance time delays. These circuits are associated with amplifiers 4, 5, 9, and 10. The boiler is indicated as a lead network feeding a lag network in which the gain of the lag amplifier is modified by a function generator in its feedback loop. The purpose of this function generator is to change the gain K_B as a function of throttle position. This gain is nonlinear with throttle setting as indicated in Eq. (6-37).

The transfer function $G_c(s)$ is obtained in this representation by taking the term $[1 + (s/\alpha_c)][1 - (s/\alpha_{c'})]$ and converting it to the equivalent form $[1 + (s/\alpha_c)] - s\alpha_{c'}[1 + (s/\alpha_c)]$. The first term is simulated by a lead network shown at amplifier 11. The output of amplifier 11 is then differentiated in amplifier 12, and the output of amplifiers 11 and 12 added together in amplifier 13. This output is then tied back to $G_h(s)$. The form of computation just presented would rarely be used in practice because the direct differentiation involved tends toward less stable operation of the system. However, this is a good illustration of some of the operational amplifier techniques suggested in Sec. 11-1.

Finally T_h and T_c are picked off and averaged in a resistor network and a servo potentiometer arm moved to a position proportional to T_{av}. This potentiometer arm is then mechanically coupled to the temperature coefficient reactivity changing potentiometer.

Scaling factors are obtained in a similar manner to that indicated in Secs. 11-2, 11-3, and 11-4, and the simulated plant is then ready for operation. It is now apparent how one proceeds in nuclear power-plant simulation either from the direct differential equations or from the transfer function representation. The transfer function representation is most useful if measured transfer functions of actual physical components are available. If experimentally measured transfer functions can be used, great reliability can be placed on the accuracy of these simulators.

Transient-response curves of the form of Fig. 6-39 are very easily obtained by use of these devices. It will be noted that no controls have been placed upon the particular plant simulated. If it is desired to set up any form of programming or flow pattern, the components must be modified and suitable additions made to the circuit.

These simulators can be used extensively in synthesizing the control system for a power plant. It is easy to optimize the system simply by changing resistance coefficients. Another advantage accruing from the use of these simulators is the development of engineering judgment in connection with the power plant. While it is possible to design a power plant solely from the mathematical expressions describing its behavior, considerable time can be saved if the engineer can rely on intuitive judgment to some extent. This judgment is gained through experience in power-plant operation, and because of the present scarcity of nuclear power plants, the present way to obtain experience in nuclear power-plant control is by the use of these simulators.

REFERENCES

1. Korn, G. A., and T. M. Korn: "Electronic Analog Computers," McGraw-Hill Book Company, Inc., New York, 1948.
2. Svoboda, A.: "Computing Mechanisms and Linkages," M.I.T. Radiation Laboratories Series, McGraw-Hill Book Company, Inc., New York, 1948.
3. Bell, P., and H. Straus: Electronic Pile Simulator, *Rev. Sci. Instr.*, vol. 21, no. 8, August, 1950.
4. Pagels, Walter: A Portable Kinetic Simulator, *AIEE Trans.*, vol. 70, paper 51-262, 1951.
5. O'Meara, F. E.: Reactor Simulators, *J. Appl. Phys.*, vol. 24, no. 9, September, 1953.
6. Fischbeck, Kenneth H.: Nuclear Reactor Simulators, "Convention Record of the IRE National Convention," pt. 9, "Medical and Nuclear Electronics," Institute of Radio Engineers, New York, 1954.

PROBLEMS

Chap. 2

2-1. If a source is suddenly inserted into a subcritical reactor at $t = 0$, what is the kinetic equation of neutron level as a function of time?

2-2. If a source is suddenly inserted into a supercritical reactor operating initially at a level $n = n_0$, what is the kinetic equation of neutron level as a function of time?

2-3. Plot Eq. (2-20) for a reactor having a mean lifetime of 10^{-6} sec when a step of reactivity of 0.002 is inserted into the reactor. How far has the reactor level risen in one second?

2-4. Why is the transient period of a reactor longer for a negative change in reactivity than for a positive one?

2-5. What is the stable period of a reactor in which $l^* = 10^{-3}$ sec and $\delta k = 0.0012$?

2-6. Given a reactor with a negative temperature coefficient, indicate the position of the control rods as a function of power level assuming no coolant flow. How do these control-rod positions compare with those of the case of constant inlet temperature of Sec. 2-13? Assume conduction and radiation losses.

2-7. Derive the equations for the steady-state and peak poisoning after shutdown of samarium 149.

2-8. A given reactor has a designed excess reactivity of 5 percent and control rods worth 7 percent. When the reactor is hot, the negative temperature coefficient affects reactivity by 3 percent. If the peak xenon poisoning after a given shutdown is worth 9 percent, within what period of time after the shutdown can a hot startup be accomplished? If the reactor is not started during this time interval, how long a wait is involved before it can be started cold? Hot?

2-9. Derive the peak-to-average effectiveness of a control rod whose effectiveness varies as the sine cubed of the rod position.

Chap. 3

3-1. What is the equation for the response of a critical reactor having $l^* = 10^{-5}$ sec when a positive δk step of 0.003 is inserted into it?

3-2. How high does the level in the above problem reach at the end of one second?

3-3. Compare the response of Prob. 3-1 with the response obtained using the approximate method of Eq. (3-6).

3-4. Plot the response of a reactor having $l^* = 10^{-3}$ sec to a linear reactivity change of the form $-0.1 + 0.01t$ between 0 and 50 sec. Compare the levels obtained with the subcritical multiplication factor.

3-5. Plot the approximate response of a critical reactor having $l^* = 10^{-5}$ sec to a ramp function $\delta k = 0.012$ sec^{-1}.

3-6. Derive the equation of the transfer function of a reactor having $l^* = 10^{-3}$ sec.

Chap. 4

4-1. What are the values of the zero frequency gain and phase shift for a reactor having an elementary negative-temperature-coefficient feedback system in which $l^* = 10^{-4}$ sec, feedback time constant $\tau = 0.1$, and feedback gain factor $K_{TC} = 0.01$?

4-2. What is the zero frequency gain of the xenon poisoning feedback-factor transfer function $\delta X(s)/\delta\phi(s)$ at a flux level $\phi_0 = 3 \times 10^{11}$?

4-3. Develop an electronic circuit for a comparator which is the analogue of the magnetic-amplifier comparator of Sec. 4-6.

4-4. Develop an expression for the gain of an ionization chamber and compare this gain with that of a pentode vacuum tube.

4-5. Design a phase-compensating network to give a phase shift of 0° at zero frequency, 22° lead at 1 cycle, and 0° at an infinite frequency.

4-6. For the simulator example of Sec. 4-10, plot the peak power attained by the reactor as a function of the control-rod servo undamped resonant frequency for input disturbances in which $\tau = 0.5$ sec.

4-7. What is the transfer function of the samarium 149 poisoning effect?

Chap. 5

5-1. Given an elevated tank of water of 500-gal capacity, at what height must the tank be placed to equal the stored energy in a steel flywheel of diameter 2 ft and thickness 6 in. which is rotating at 3,600 rpm?

5-2. How many automobile-type storage batteries would be required to provide the same energy? Compare the weights of the three systems.

5-3. What is the power required to raise a 200-lb control rod at a rate of 1 ft/sec?

5-4. A reactor is 100 in. tall and has a 50-lb safety rod initially all the way out. Scramming is by gravity plus a 50-lb spring which acts over the first foot of rod travel. A steady frictional force of 10 lb is also present in the scramming system. How long does it take for the rod to be completely inserted? How fast is the rod going when it reaches the bottom of the reactor?

5-5. A given automatic-control system removes a transient disturbance from a reactor in 0.1 sec by moving a 25-lb regulator rod 6 in. How much horsepower is required from the regulator-rod drive motor?

Chap. 6

6-1. Indicate the temperature and pressure programs for a pressurized water-cooled reactor in which the reactor-inlet temperature is held constant, and there are three step changes in pump speed as a function of power level.

6-2. How much power can be transferred from the primary loop of a water-cooled reactor to the metal in the boiler tubes under the following conditions:

copper boiler tube area, 10 sq ft; boiler tubes, 1 in. inside diameter; water flow, 12 ft/sec; temperature difference between the water and metal, 50°F?

6-3. A plate-type uranium fuel element 0.125 in. thick is operating at an output of 1,000 cal/sec per square foot of surface. What is the rate of temperature rise of this element assuming no cooling?

6-4. Plot the response of the inlet temperature to a boiler as a function of time, using the approximate delay formula of Eq. (6-11), if the reactor outlet temperature is suddenly raised 500°F and the delay time between reactor and boiler is 3 sec. Compare this curve with the current rise through a coil when a sudden constant voltage is applied to it.

6-5. Indicate in block form the transfer function of a reactor thermal system for a four-region reactor in which the region closest to the coolant inlet puts out one-half as much power as each of the other regions.

6-6. Graphically determine $1/[1 - K_L G_L(s)]$ for the example used in Sec. 6-8 if the mixing time constants τ_5 and τ_6 are 1 sec each.

6-7. Derive the temperature-loop feedback transfer function $T_{av}(s)/n(s)$ of Fig. 6-19 in terms of the inlet-temperature transfer function $T_c(s)/n(s)$.

6-8. A pressurized water-reactor plant having a negative temperature coefficient and no external control system is operating at full power output with its control rods fixed. Suddenly the pumps fail and flow stops. Sketch the behavior of n, T_c, T_h, T_s, and p.

6-9. A pressurized water-reactor plant having a negative temperature coefficient and no external control system is operating at full power conditions with fixed coolant flow. Suddenly a control rod is dropped into the reactor. Sketch the behavior of n, T_c, T_h, T_s, and p.

Chap. 7

7-1. The sensitivity of a BF_3 counter using enriched B^{10} gas is 10 counts per unit of flux. What is its sensitivity if it is now filled with BF_3 made from naturally occurring B?

7-2. A cylindrical enriched fission counter and a B^{10}-lined counter have the same surface area and volume. Which tube has the highest sensitivity? Which one gives out the largest pulses?

7-3. A neutron has an energy of 4 ev. What is its effective velocity? With what temperature would you associate it?

7-4. What is the maximum counting rate that may be expected from a cylindrical BF_3 counter having a 2-in. diameter and a 12-in. length, operating in a neutron flux of 10^4 per square-centimeter-second at an energy of 5 ev? Assume 100 percent enriched B^{10}.

7-5. The thermal flux at the surface of a 2-ft-diameter reactor core is 10^{12} neutrons per square centimeter-second, and it drops off in accordance with $e^{-0.1r}/r$, where r is the distance into the reflector in centimeters. Where should a boron-lined chamber having a sensitivity of 2×10^{-14} amp per unit of flux be located to read 100 μa?

7-6. Derive a relationship between sensitivity and response time of a neutron thermopile.

Chap. 8

8-1. Assume that one out of every 10^5 alpha particles from radon will produce a disintegration in some surrounding beryllium.   How many neutrons are emitted per second from a mixture of 1 curie of radon and beryllium?

8-2. A nuclear power plant has a polonium^{210}-beryllium source.   The plant's most sensitive detector indicates 30 counts per second when the plant is shut down. How long will this instrument be able to function properly if the background counting rate is 2 counts per second?

8-3. The following table indicates an instrument counting rate as a function of control-rod position during a reactor startup.   At what rod withdrawal will the reactor go critical?

Rod position, in.	Counting rate, counts/min
0	924
4	1,990
5	2,600
6	3,540
7	7,580
7.5	16,660
7.74	48,130

8-4. A startup operation is begun from a negative reactivity of 30 percent.   A control rod is being removed from the reactor in such a manner as to produce a linear change of reactivity of $0.002\delta k$ sec^{-1}.   On what period is the reactor after one minute of rod pulling?

8-5. Show that the shortest period a reactor can be on is greater than

$$\sqrt{\frac{l^*}{2\gamma \ln (n_1/n_0)}}$$

where l^* = mean neutron lifetime
  γ = rate of increase of reactivity
  n_1 = neutron level at which safety devices operate
  n_0 = startup neutron level before rods are moved

8-6. Devise an electronic circuit which will take its inputs from three period meters and initiate a scram if any two of them indicate a shorter period than a demand reference.

Chap. 9

9-1. The boiler in a given reactor plant limits a change in reactor power level from 1 percent full power to full power to a time longer than 30 sec.   What is the fastest reactor period that can be used for this level change?

9-2. A thermal reactor has an excess reactivity of 5 percent.   At full power output at a neutron flux of 10^{13}, it burns up reactivity at the rate of 1 percent per year. How long can this reactor be operated continuously at full power output?

9-3. Draw a block diagram for a control system for a shim rod bank which follows a regulator rod in a pressurized reactor.   Indicate parameter values and gains.   Provide proof that the system does not oscillate.

Chap. 10

10-1. Given four safety rods whose reactivity values are 1, 2, 2, and 3, with one of the rods of value 2 initially out of the reactor, devise an interlocking system which prevents the other rods from being withdrawn unless there is more reactivity in the safety bank than in the rod being moved.

10-2. A power reactor has been operating at a steady output level of 100,000 kw for a long time. Suddenly the coolant flow stops, and the reactor scrams. The reactor and stagnant coolant can be considered to behave thermally like 1 ton of copper. Plot the average temperature of the reactor and local coolant as a function of time considering the effect of the beta-gamma power.

10-3. How large a spring is needed to assist gravity to drop a 100-lb rod into a 4-ft reactor in 0.1 sec neglecting friction?

10-4. An over-power-level scram system is so designed that if a reactor on a 0.1-sec period goes through a tripping level which is set at 120 percent of full power, the peak power reached is 180 percent. What peak power is reached if the tripping point is set at 150 percent?

10-5. For the plant of Fig. 6-2, propose a safety system of alarms, cutbacks, and scrams.

Chap. 11

11-1. Indicate in schematic diagram form how you would perform the following operations with an analogue computer: $3 + 5$, $ax - by$, $dx/xt + x = 3$.

11-2. Draw a schematic diagram and explain the operation of a contactor-stabilized operational amplifier.

11-3. The operational-amplifier setup of Fig. 11-5a is to be used to simulate a mixing process whose time constant is 1 sec. What is a suitable set of constants which might be used in this circuit?

11-4. Design a simulator to represent the decay of a polonium-beryllium source.

11-5. Design a simulator to represent samarium 149 poisoning.

INDEX